30·64

(THE UNIVERSITY OF) CHICAGO. *University.*

FIELD STUDY IN AMERICAN GEOGRAPHY

THE DEVELOPMENT OF THEORY AND METHOD
EXEMPLIFIED BY SELECTIONS

DEPARTMENT OF GEOGRAPHY.

Title: RESEARCH PAPER NO. 61

By

Robert S. Platt

Professor Emeritus of Geography
University of Chicago

CHICAGO · ILLINOIS

JULY, 1959

Table of Contents

                                                                            Pages

Introduction: A Search for Turning Points . . . .   1 - 9

PART I. BASIC TYPES.

Chapter 1. Journal of Exploratory Traverse . . . . . .   13 - 26

Journals of the Lewis and Clark Expedition, 1804 - 1806, by M. Lewis and
W. Clark.

Chapter 2. Report of Area Survey . . . .   27 - 34

Report upon Geographical Surveys West
of the 100th Meridian, by G. M. Wheeler,
1889.

Chapter 3. Explanatory Physical Geography . . . . . .   35 - 59

The Geography of Chicago and its
Environs, by R. D. Salisbury and W. C.
Alden, 1899.

Experiments in Geographical Description,
by W. M. Davis, 1910.

Chapter 4. Explanatory Human Geography . . . .   60 - 77

The Anglo-Saxons of the Kentucky
Mountains, by E. C. Semple, 1901.

Chapter 5. Analytical Economic Geography . . . . . .   78 - 95

An Analysis of the Apple Industry of the
Annapolis-Cornwallis Valley, by C. C.
Colby, 1925.

Chapter 6. Geography of Areal Uniformity and
Diversity . . . .   96 - 114

Detailed Field Mapping in the Study of the
Economic Geography of An Agricultural
Area, by W. D. Jones and V. C. Finch,
1925.

Geographic Surveying and Montfort: A
Study in Landscape Types in Southwestern
Wisconsin, by V. C. Finch, 1933.

Pages

Chapter 7. Geography of Areal Organization. . . . . .   115 - 139

A Detail of Regional Geography: Ellison
Bay Community as an Industrial Organism,
by R. S. Platt, 1928.

Chapter 8. Geography of Culture Origin and
Dispersal . . . .   140 - 160

Pueblo Sites in Southeastern Arizona, by
C. O. Sauer and D. Brand, 1930.

PART II. DERIVATIVES.

Chapter 9. Derivatives of Type 1 (Exploratory
Traverse). . . . .   163 - 177

The Railway Traverse as an Aid in Reconnaissance, by C. C. Colby, 1933.

An Air Traverse of Central America, by
R. S. Platt, 1934.

Chapter 10. Derivatives of Type 2 (Area Survey) . . .   178 - 183

Farmsteads and Land Types in Emmet
County, Michigan, by F. W. Foster, 1941.

Chapter 11. Derivatives of Type 3 (Explanatory
Physical) . . . .   184 - 199

Hurricanes into New England: Meteorology of the Storm of September 21, 1938,
by C. F. Brooks, 1939.

A Permanent Loss to New England: Soil
Erosion Resulting from the Hurricane, by
H. H. Bennett, 1939.

Chapter 12. Derivatives of Type 4 (Explanatory
Human).   200 - 216

The Kankakee "Marsh" of Northern
Indiana and Illinois, by A. H. Meyer, 1935.

Chapter 13. Derivatives of Type 5 (Analytical
Economic).   217 - 263

South Range, Keeweenaw Copper Country:
A Mining Pattern of Land Occupancy, by
R. S. Platt, 1932.

A Classification of Manufactures, Exemplified by Porto Rican Industries, by
R. S. Platt, 1927.

Summary Memorandum on the Bad River
Indian Reservation, by R. S. Platt, 1940.

Geographic and Political Boundaries in
Upper Silesia, by R. Hartshorne, 1933.

Chapter 14. Derivatives of Type 6 (Areal Uniformity)   264 - 301

Augusta County, Virginia - A Study of
Patterns, by G. D. Hudson, 1935.

A Method of Mapping Densities of Population: With Cape Cod as Example, by
J. K. Wright, 1936.

Field Mapping of Residential Areas in
Metropolitan Chicago, by W. D. Jones, 1931.

A Unit Area Method of Mapping Gross Land-
Use Associations in Urban Regions, by
A. K. Philbrick, 1952.

Chapter 15. Derivatives of Type 7 (Areal
Organization) . . . .   302 - 351

Field Approach to Regions, by R. S.
Platt, 1935.

An Urban Field Study; Marquette,
Michigan, by R. S. Platt, 1931.

Problems of Our Time, by R. S. Platt,
1946.

Principles of Areal Functional Organization in Regional Human Geography, by
A. K. Philbrick, 1957.

P 1932

Pages

Chapter 16. Derivatives of Type 8 (Culture Origin). .   352 - 397

Some Rural Settlement Forms in Japan,
by R. B. Hall, 1931.

The Log House in Georgia, by W.
Zelinsky, 1953.

Human Geography and Ecology in the Sinú
Country of Colombia, by B. L. Gordon,
1957.

Reconnaissance in Dynamic Regional
Geography: Tierra del Fuego, by R. S.
Platt, 1949.

Conclusion: Continuing Field Geography . . . .   398 - 405

List of Illustrations

Figure   Page

1. Part of a traverse map 18
2. Part of Atlas Sheet No. 75 30
3. Physiographic map of the Chicago Plain 40
4. Diagram of late mature coastal plain 57
5. Distribution of apple trees in Nova Scotia 81
6. Distribution of exports of apples 82
7. Types of land near Hennepin, Illinois 102
8. Fractional complex code map of the Montfort Area 107
9. Ellison Bay: Functional establishments 119
10. Ellison Bay: Lines & limits of movement. 120
11. Ellison Bay: Basic units of organization 121
12. Part of a map of culture affiliations. 156
13. Railway traverse map. 166
14. Air traverse map. 171
15. Complete occupance in a smooth plateau. 172
16. Sparse occupance in a valley. 173
17. Land Classification for occupance 180
18. Pressure map & track of hurricane 189
19. Severe erosion damage to crop land. 196
20. Part of a silhouette study in sequent occupance . . 203
21. Part of a map of Fundament. 204
22. Functional units of mining 221
23. Cross section of Keweenaw Peninsula 222
24. The four shafts of the Baltic Mine 223
25. Aerial view of mines & villages 224
26. Crossing places, German-Polish boundaries 261
27. Map of qualitative distinctions in areal uniformity . 272
28. Map of uniformity on a quantitative scale 273
29. Population maps of Cape Cod 283
30. Field map of a residential area 292
31. Part of a map of gross land use associations 299
32. Map indicating regional subdivisions 308
33. Sample of a basic unit in the fur region 309
34. A farm in the northern Clay Belt 310
35. Marquette, the Upper Peninsula of Michigan 318
36. The transportation pattern in Marquette. 319
37. The distribution of non-residential establishments. 320
38. The distribution of regional vs. local
       establishments. 321
39. Section 16. Chicago Municipal Airport 331
40. Extent of traffic control from Chicago 332
41. Traffic of domestic airlines in the United States . . 333
42. World air traffic before the war 334
43. A basic unit of organization & an area of
       uniformity. 339

Figure   Page
44. Functional establishments in Boswell, Indiana. . . .   340
45. Lines and limits of movement on Boswell.   341
46. Points of focus in a hierarchy of central places. . .   342
47. Lines of movement & points of focus of higher
        order central places.   343
48. Map of an area, Yamato Basin   357
49. Map of an area, Kagoshima Prefecture   358
50. Map of an area, Echigo Plain   359
51. Map of part of Tokachi Plain   360
52. Log house distribution.   372
53. Changing extent of savannas.   379
54. British ranchers & Chilean sheepherders in
        Tierra del Fuego   393
55. Neighboring ranches in Argentina & Chile   394
56. Political influence of Argentina & Chile   395

INTRODUCTION

A Search for Turning Points

Within the large loose field of knowledge known as geography, concerned with the Earth in one way or another, scholars have developed an academic discipline, marked by various concepts, theories, methods and techniques. In the discipline a major approach has been through field study, in which geographers go directly to the original source of all geographical knowledge and confront the raw and undisturbed phenomena with which they have to deal. Field study has been carried on under a succession of theories from various viewpoints with various methods and techniques at various times, in an endless effort to bridge the gap between raw data and penetrating comprehensive knowledge.

The project represented by this book is to analyze the development of American field study and recognize the stages through which it has come thus far, by means of representative substantive studies made by American geographers at different times and places. There is good evidence that field study has developed progressively, that results have been cumulative and when taken together show ways toward ever better geographic understanding. Clear channels have been opened through which we can advance with confidence. An intelligible course can be recognized and charted.

This opinion may seem at variance with a view expressed by Richard Hartshorne in "The Nature of Geography" in these words: "If we are to continue to experience violent shifts of the helm - formerly toward physiography, then toward environmentalism, now toward landscape studies, tomorrow to the topography of art and thereafter who knows whither - our ship will beat around with ever-changing aim, hence aimlessly, and will arrive nowhere."[1]

But perhaps our best recourse is to accept the need to come-about frequently as our ship beats slowly to windward, unable to lay a true course directly toward our goal by any simple dogmatic pronouncement and only hoping that each leg of our zigzag course will take us further in the desired direction. Hartshorne's view would be right if every shift of the helm were taken aimlessly and in ignorance of purposes and objectives in the whole series of directional changes. For this very reason it is proposed now to examine the successive stages by which we have reached our present position in geographic field study, in order to understand and take advantage of each and all of them for whatever they are worth.

The term "field study" is taken here in a broad sense to include any geographic work in which the author has familiarized himself directly with the area concerned. Ordinarily this

1. R. Hartshorne: "The Nature of Geography, A Critical Survey in the Light of the Past," in _Annals AAG_, vol. 29 (1939), p. 207 (31).

has involved systematic observation, inquiry and recording of data with technical equipment and procedure. But in some cases it has involved only casual acquaintance as a background and check on data otherwise gathered, and a few such studies seem worthy of consideration in the present inquiry. In all cases it seems apparent that ideas and viewpoints in field study are tied to and reflect those in geographic study in general.

The series of studies here reproduced begins early in the 19th Century and continues to the present decade. Geographic field work did not begin in the 19th Century and did not spring up independently in America. It is easily traceable back to the Age of Discovery and before that back to the Greeks, and from first to last American geography has had ties with European geography. But whatever contribution to knowledge is to be made in this project lies within the century and a half of this series and in American geography.

For this series the intention has been to select studies of special significance as mileposts in the development of field geography. However at many points there is not one conspicuous milepost but a whole grove of posts from which a suitable choice can be made almost at random to illustrate an advance in viewpoint or method. Obviously the series does not represent the only possible selection and not necessarily the best.

The choice of items is biased in favor of one author: nine studies by R. S. Platt in a total of 32 titles in the series. In extenuation it may be said that at an early stage in the project it was proposed to have the whole series compiled as an autobiographical collection from studies made in the period from 1916 to 1958 or (going back to boyhood travel writings) from 1904 to 1958. The change in this plan is probably an improvement. A student has justified the biased selection in these words: "I think the familiarity of R. S. Platt with his own work and the method or madness that goes along with it more than compensates for any weaknesses the articles themselves might have as examples."

Originally it was intended to reproduce all selections in their entirety. But when the total number of pages increased to excess and some examples were taken from books, it became necessary to select within selections and to omit irrelevant parts.[1]

A similar policy of selection has been followed in the case of illustrations. One or two maps have been needed in most cases, but not all the maps, to bring out or illustrate relevant

1. All omissions, whether of pages or phrases, are indicated similarly by a minimum symbol, in order to break up the text as little as possible. Footnotes have been omitted without indication. Where footnotes are added here wording from the original is indicated by quotation marks.

ideas or cartographic devices.[1] Most of the pictures have not been found necessary, either to reveal or supplement ideas of the text or to show progress in field-study photography.

There has been progress in map-making - at least in devices for expressing geographic ideas if not in cartographic skill. But apparently there has been little or no progress from stage to stage in pictorial illustration. There has been, in fact, a loss of skill in selective landscape sketching (Fig. 4) without a corresponding increase in skill in selective photography. Soon after field geographers were armed with cameras they gave up drawing in favor of the new equipment.[2] Then without delay they took the first short step of finding that ground photography cannot show widespread areal distributions as on a map (either singly or assembled in a panorama) but can show effectively individual features of nature and culture at the scale of human sight and occupance in their site associations (Fig. 25), or the texture at that same scale of landscape elements (Fig. 19), to illustrate types. A corollary followed as soon as air transport became available: that air photography can show widespread areal distributions (Figs. 15, 16 and 24). Photographs to illustrate these ideas are included here, but no others are included: the field studies seem to

1. *Captions have been reworded as needed, with quotation marks to indicate wording taken from the original.*
2. *With rare exceptions. Fig. 20 below.*

contain no evidence of further progress in the use of photography. [1]

In selecting the field studies little or no attention has been paid to the areas covered. By unintentional but natural choice there are 22 in the United States (13 in the Middle West, 6 in the East or Southeast, 3 in the Far West), 4 in Latin America, 3 in Canada, 2 in Europe, and 1 in Asia.

The order of arrangement in this series of studies is no less open to choice than the excerpts themselves. Several different ways have been tried. No one way is perfect because any linear arrangement is simple, and the real relations of the studies are much more complex. Chronological order is one possibility. Another possible arrangement is in relation to the sources from which new concepts take their start: geology, history, economics, anthropology. Another is in relation to objectives and objects toward which new concepts look: landscape, land occupance, resources, culture. Another is in branches of geography represented in "American Geography: Inventory and Prospect":[2] regional, historical, economic, etc.

1. Motion pictures are obviously unavailable for use in publication and have not proved otherwise useful in depicting either landscape or occupance features either stationary or moving in contrast with their evident usefulness in depicting dramatic action. Color photography has provided a step in advance as a means of depicting landscape and occupance, but only in lecturing and not yet in publication of field reports.
2. P.E. James and C.F. Jones (eds.): American Geography: Inventory and Prospect (Syracuse University Press, 1952).

Another is in the sequence of directional changes suggested by Hartshorne's fitful geographic voyage: physiography, environmentalism, landscape, topography of art, etc.

Chronological order serves in earlier stages, but not for interpretation of later complications. The other suggested ways show some correspondence to each other and this is easily seen in the course of discussion. The present arrangement has been adopted after consideration of these possibilities and a search for lines of thought and turning points in the geographic course of events.

Up to 1930 the lines and points in geographic field study are fairly simple. It is easy and convenient to recognize eight stages or types of work and to illustrate them by substantive studies. These stages are not mutually exclusive: the older types were not necessarily dropped when newer ones appeared; all were continued and several used in combination. The stages succeeded each other at irregular intervals - far between at first, and crowded together at the end, when the first generation of geographers trained professionally in geography in America had reached maturity and gone to work to build up the subject to which they were committed.

After 1930 the number of American geographers, working at different places and along different lines, is much greater, and most of them

have been conscious of several possibilities represented by several of the stages or types of
study. Geographical work has commonly made
use of more than one type of approach and is not
to be assigned exclusively to any one. Yet it is
likely to emphasize one type more than others
and in any case it is convenient to arrange all
the remaining studies in eight groups of derivatives corresponding to the eight types before
1930. These are therefore in topical order and
not all in chronological order - in fact, at least
one was made before 1930 but yet fits into place
topically.

A question may arise as to how the studies
in this series fit into the more systematically
subdivided branches of the subject in "American
Geography: Inventory and Prospect". First it
should be noted that there is no simple correlation between the arrangement of this series based
on turning points of emphasis, and the branches
of "American Geography", each followed through
in its separate history from beginning to end.
Moreover the selections in this series are substantive field studies, whereas the references in
"American Geography" are mainly methodological.

Considering these field studies individually
in relation to the topical divisions of "American
Geography" it is found that all of them fit in
appropriately under one heading or more than

one, and that a good many of them are included specifically in reference lists as methodological examples.[1]   Out of the 25 topical chapters in "American Geography" 21 are represented by at least one of the field studies.

There is no chapter in "American Geography" on cultural geography, and the concept of culture origin and dispersal (type 8 in the field study series) is included only incidentally in the chapters on Historical Geography and Settlement. Also there is no full expression in "American Geography" of areal organization (type 7 in the field study series) and this appears only incidentally in the chapter on Transportation and less clearly in a static form in the chapter on Regional Geography.

It should now be apparent that the list of studies in this series is a fairly conventional choice of work recognized in American Geography, not an odd lot of exotic items. A majority of the authors have been Presidents of the Association of American Geographers. But the arrangement of these studies is unorthodox and unprecedented and will have to be justified, if justifiable at all, in the chapters which follow.

1. 13 of the 32 plus some that doubtless would be referred to if there were a reference list in the Regional chapter.

PART I.

BASIC TYPES

CHAPTER 1

Journal of
Exploratory Traverse

Geographic knowledge in America at an early
stage grew casually from various sources, particularly from accounts written more or less
systematically by travellers returning to civilization from unknown regions. "Journals of
the Lewis and Clark Expedition, 1804–1806" are
taken as a source for the first item in this
series of field studies. Thomas Jefferson, then
President of the United States, was personally
responsible for the expedition and represented
American geographical knowledge and thought
as well as anyone of his time.

The President recommended the expedition to
Congress in 1803 with these words: "While
other civilized nations have encountered great
expense to enlarge the boundaries of knowledge
by undertaking voyages of discovery ...... our
own nation seems to owe to the same object,
as well as its own interests to explore this [the
Missouri River] the only line of easy communication across the continent, and so directly
traversing our own part of it. The interests
of commerce place the principal object within
the constitutional powers of Congress, and that
it should incidentally advance the geographical

knowledge of our own continent can not but be an additional gratification."[1]

Obviously there is nothing new or peculiarly American in the nature of the expedition or the reports of it. The tradition of such journeys and journals, as contributions to geographical knowledge, goes back beyond Marco Polo and beyond Xenophon.[2] Thomas Jefferson was not detached from European geographical ideas and even had some correspondence with Alexander von Humboldt. The whole enterprise follows the ancient objective in geography of providing accurate descriptive information on hitherto unknown parts of the world.

As leader of the expedition the President chose his private secretary, Meriwether Lewis, a young man of high intelligence, general knowledge and known reliability but with no professional or technical training in the field of geography or of any branch of science. The President had him provided with "instruments for ascertaining by celestial observations, the geography of the country through which you will pass",[3] and advised him to acquire readiness in their use. A prime essential, almost the only technical essential in geography, was taken to be the accurate location of the route and the features described.

1. R. G. Thwaites (ed.): _Original Journals of the Lewis and Clark Expedition, 1804-1806_ (8 vols.; N.Y.: Dodd, Mead & Co., 1904), vol. 7, p. 208.
2. Marco Polo: _Travels_ (N.Y.: E. P. Dutton & Co., 1914).
   Xenophon: _Anabasis_ (Boston: Ginn & Co., 1901).
3. R. G. Thwaites (ed.): _op. cit._, vol. 7, p. 247.

Lewis chose as his co-leader his friend, William Clark, whose elder brother, George Rogers Clark, already had a reputation for exploration in the Ohio country. William Clark had some skill in drafting and drew most of the maps. Lewis was better at literary expression and wrote more important parts of the journals.

Both Lewis and Clark wrote day by day descriptions of the country traversed and accounts of their experiences. The excerpts here included are the journal entries by Lewis of three full days and parts of three others, selected as illustrating daily progress by water and land, camping, hunting and gathering geographical information from observation and from Indians, and also as touching high spots in the journey: seeing the Rocky Mountains, discovering the Great Falls of the Missouri, and crossing the pass from headwaters of the Missouri to headwaters of the Columbia.

JOURNALS OF THE LEWIS & CLARK EXPEDITION, 1804-1806 [1]

by M. Lewis & W. Clark

Wednesday June 12th, 1805

This morning I felt myself quite revived, took another portion of my decoction and set out at sunrise. I now boar out from the river in order to avoid the steep ravines of the river which

1. R. G. Thwaites (ed.): op. cit., vol. 2, pp. 145–380.

usually make out in the plain to the distance of one or two miles;
after gaining the leavel plain my couse was a little to the West of
S. W. having traveled about 12 miles by 9 in the morning, the sun
became warm, and I boar a little to the south in order to gain the
river as well to obtain water to allay my thirst as to kill something
for breakfast; for the plain through which we had been passing
possesses no water and is so level that we cannot approach the buffaloe within shot before they discover us and take to flight. we arrived at the river about 10 A.M. having traveled about 15. M. at this
place there is a handsom open bottom with some cottonwood timber,
here we met with two large bear, and killed them boath at the first
fire, a circumstance which I beleive has never happened with the
party in killing the brown bear before. we dressed the bear,
breakfasted on a part of one of them and hung the meat and skins
on the trees out of the reach of the wolves. I left a note on a stick
near the river for Capt. Clark, informing him of my progress &c.
after refreshing ourselves about 2 hours we again ascended the
bluffs and gained the high plain; saw a great number of burrowing
squirrels in the plains today; also wolves Antelopes mule deer and
immence herds of buffaloe. we passed a ridge of land considerably
higher than the adjacent plain on either side, from this hight we
had a most beatifull and picturesk view of the Rocky mountains
which wer perfectly covered with Snow and reaching from S.E. to
N. of N.W. they appear to be formed of several ranges each succeeding range rising higher than the preceding one untill the most
distant appear to loose their snowey tops in the clouds; this was
an august spectacle and still rendered more formidable by the
recollection that we had them to pass. we traveled about twelve
miles when we agin struck the Missoury at a handsome little bottom of Cottonwood timber and altho' the sun had not yet set I felt
myself somewhat wary being weakened I presume by late disorder;
and therfore determined to remain here during the ballance of the
day and night, having marched about 27 miles today. on our way in
the evening we had killed a buffaloe, an Antelope and three mule
deer, and taken a sufficient quantity of the best of the flesh of these
anamals for three meals, which we had brought with us. This
evening I ate very heartily and after pening the transactions of the
day amused myself catching those white fish mentioned yesterday;
they are here in great abundance I caught upwards of a douzen in
a few minutes; they bit most freely at the melt of a deer which
goodrich had brought with him for the purpose of fishing.

The narrow leafed cottonwood grows here in common with
the other species of the same tree with a broad leaf or that which
has constituted the major part of the timber of the Missouri from
it's junction with the Mississippi to this place. The narrow-leafed
cottonwood differs only from the other in the shape of it's leaf and
greater thickness of it's bark. the leaf is a long oval acutely
pointed, about 2 & 1/2 or 3 inches long and from 3/4 to an inch in
width; it is thick, sometimes slightly grooved or channeled; margin
slightly serrate; the upper disk of a common green while the under
disk is of a whitish green; the leaf is smoth. the beaver appear to

be extremely fond of this tree and even seem to scelect it from among the other species of Cottonwood, probably from it's affording a deeper and softer bark than the other species. saw some sign of the Otter as well as beaver near our camp, also a great number of tracks of the brown bear; these fellows leave a formidable impression in the mud or sand. I measured one this evening which was eleven inches long exclusive of the tallons and seven and 1/4 in width.

Thursday June 13th, 1805.

This morning we set out about sunrise after taking breakfast off our venison and fish. we again ascended the hills of the river and gained the level country. the country through which we passed for the first six miles tho' more roling than that we had passed yesterday might still with propryety be deemed a level country; our course as yesterday was generally S.W. the river from the place we left it appeared to make a considerable bend to the South. from the extremity of this roling country I overlooked a most beatifull and level plain of great extent or at least 50 or sixty miles; in this there were infinitely more buffaloe than I had ever before witnessed at a view. nearly in the direction I had been travling or S.W. two curious mountains presented themselves of square figures, the sides rising perpendicularly to the hight of 250 feet and appeared to be formed of yellow clay; their tops appeared to be level plains; these inaccessible hights appeared like the ramparts of immence fortifications; I have no doubt but with very little assistance from art they might be rendered impregnable. fearing that the river boar to the South and that I might pass the falls if they existed between this an the snowey mountains I altered my course nealy to the South leaving those insulated hills to my wright and proceeded through the plain; I sent Feels on my right and Drewyer and Gibson on my left with orders to kill some meat and join me at the river where I should halt for dinner. I had proceded on this course about two miles with Goodrich at some distance behind me whin my ears were saluted with the agreeable sound of a fall of water and advancing a little further I saw the spray arrise above the plain like a collumn of smoke which would frequently dispear again in an instant caused I presume by the wind which blew pretty hard from the S.W. I did not however loose my direction to this point which soon began to make a roaring too tremendious to be mistaken for any cause short of the great falls of the Missouri. (Fig. 1.) here I arrived about 12OClock having traveled by estimate about 15. Miles. I hurryed down the hill which was about 200 feet high and difficult of access, to gaze on this sublimely grand specticle. I took my position on the top of some rocks about 20 feet high opposite the center of the falls. this chain of rocks appear once to have formed a part of those over which the waters tumbled, but in the course of time has been seperated from it to the distance of 150 yards lying prarrallel to it and a butment against which the water after falling over the precipice beats with great

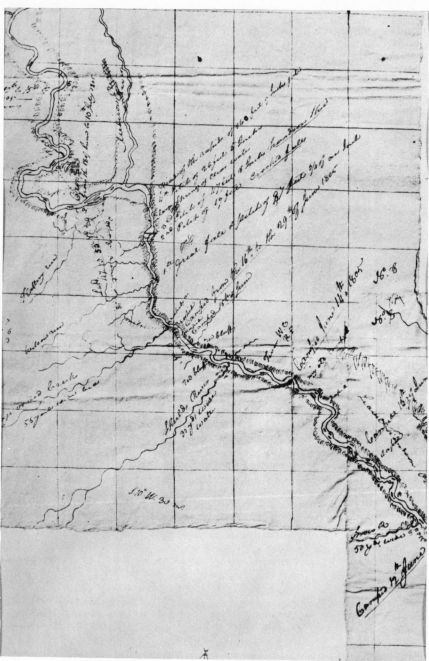

Fig. 1. Part of a traverse map, "A sketch of the Missouri from Fort Mandan to the
Rocky Mountains" by Wm. Clark, showing camping places from June 12 to
July 15, 1805, and the portage around the Great Falls of the Missouri.
Scale: 1 inch to 12.7 miles.

fury; this barrier extends on the right to the perpendicular clift which forms that board of the river, but to the distance of 120 yards next to the clift it is but a few feet above the level of the water, and here the water in very high tides appears to pass in a channel of 40 yds. next to the higher part of the ledg of rocks; on the left it extends within 80 or ninty yards of the land Clift which is also perpendicular; between this abrupt extremity of the ledge of rocks and the perpendicular bluff the whole body of water passes with incredible swiftness. immediately at the cascade the river is about 300 yds. wide; about ninty or a hundred yards of this next the Lard bluff is a smooth even sheet of water falling over a precipice of at least eighty feet, the remaining part of about 200 yards on my right formes the grandest sight I ever beheld, the hight of the fall is the same of the other but the irregular and somewhat projecting rocks below receives the water in it's passage down and brakes it into a perfect white foam which assumes a thousand forms in a moment sometimes flying up in jets of sparkling foam to the hight of fifteen or twenty feet and are scarcely formed before large roling bodies of the same beaten and foaming water is thrown over and conceals them. in short the rocks seem to be most happily fixed to present a sheet of the whitest beaten froath for 200 yards in length and about 80 feet perpendicular. the water after decending strikes against the butment before mentioned or that on which I stand and seems to reverberate and being met by the more impetuous courant they roll and swell into half formed billows of great hight which rise and again disappear in an instant. this butment of rock defends a handsome little bottom of about three acres which is deversified and agreeably shaded with some cottonwood trees; in the lower extremity of the bottom there is a very thick grove of the same kind of trees which are small, in this wood there are several Indian lodges formed of sticks. a few small cedar grow near the ledge of rocks where I rest. below the point of these rocks at a small distance the river is divided by a large rock which rises several feet above the water, and extends downwards with the stream for about 20 yards. about a mile before the water arrives at the pitch it decends very rappidly, and is confined on the Lard side by a perpendicular clift of about 100 feet, on the Stard. side it is also perpendicular for about three hundred yards above the pitch where it is then broken by the discharge of a small ravine, down which the buffaloe have a large beaten road to the water, for it is but in very few places that these anamals can obtain water near this place owing to the steep and inaccessible banks. I see several skelletons of the buffaloe lying in the edge of the water near the Stard bluff which I presume have been swept down by the current and precipitated over this tremendious fall. about 300 yards below me there is another butment of solid rock with a perpendicular face and abot 60 feet high which projects from the Stard. side at right angles to the distance of 134 yrds and terminates the lower part nearly of the bottom before mentioned; there being a passage arround the end of this butment between it and the river of about 20 yards; here the river again assumes it's usual width soon spreading to near 300 yards but still

continues it's rappidity. from the reflection of the sun on the sprey
or mist which arrises from these falls there is a beatifull rainbow
which adds not a little to the beauty of this majestically grand
senery. after wrighting this imperfect discription I again viewed
the falls and was so much disgusted with the imperfect idea which
it conveyed of the scene that I determined to draw my pen across
it and begin agin, but then reflected that I could not perhaps succeed
better than pening the first impressions of the mind; I wished for the
pencil of Salvator Rosa or the pen of Thompson, that I might be
enabled to give to the enlightened world some just idea of this truly
magnificent and sublimely grand object, which has from the com-
mencement of time been concealed from the view of civilized man;
but this was fruitless and vain. I most sincerely regreted that I had
not brought a crimee obscura with me by the assistance of which
even I could have hoped to have done better but alas this was also
out of my reach; I therefore with the assistance of my pen only in-
deavoured to trace some of the stronger features of this seen by the
assistance of which and my recollection aided by some able pencil
I hope still to give to the world some faint idea of an object which
at this moment fills me with such pleasure and astonishment; and
which of it's kind I will venture to ascert is second to but one in
the known world. I retired to the shade of a tree where I determined
to fix my camp for the present and dispatch a man in the morning
to inform Capt. C. and the party of my success in finding the falls
and settle in their minds all further doubts as to the Missouri. the
hunters now arrived loaded with excellent buffaloe meat and informed
me that they had killed three very fat cows about 3/4 of a mile from
hence. I directed them after tl ey had refreshed themselves to go
back and butcher them and bring another load of meat each to our
camp determining to employ those who remained with me in drying
meat for the party against their arrival. in about 2 hours or at 4
OClock P.M. they set out on this duty, and I walked down the river
about three miles to discover if possible some place to which the
canoes might arrive or at which they might be drawn on shore in
order to be taken by land above the falls (Fig. 1); but returned
without effecting either of these objects; the river was one continued sene of rapids and cascades which I readily perceived could
not be encountered with our canoes, and the Clifts still retained
their perpendicular structure and were from 150 to 200 feet high;
in short the river appears here to have woarn a channel in the
process of time through a solid rock. on my return I found the
party at camp; they had butchered the buffaloe and brought in some
more meat as I had directed. Goodrich had caught half a dozen
very fine trout and a number of both species of the white fish. these
trout are from sixteen to twenty three inches in length, precisely
resemble our mountain or speckled trout in form and the position
of their fins, but the specks on these are of a deep, black instead of
the red or goald colour of those common to the U'. States. these are
furnished long sharp teeth on the pallet and tongue and have generally a small dash of red on each side behind the front ventral fins;
the flesh is of a pale yellowish red, or when in good order, of a
rose red.

I am induced to believe that the Brown, the white and the Grizly bear of this country are the same species only differing in colour from age or more probably from the same natural cause that many other anamals of the same family differ in colour. one of those which we killed yesterday was of a creem-coloured white while the other in company with it was of the common bey or redish brown, which seems to be the most usual colour of them. the white one appeared from it's tallons and teath to be the youngest; it was smaller than the other, and although a monstrous beast we supposed that it had not yet attained it's growth and that it was a little upwards of two years old. the young cubs which we have killed have always been of a brownish white, but none of them as white as that we killed yesterday. one other that we killed sometime since which I mentioned sunk under some driftwood and was lost, had a white stripe or list of about eleven inches wide entirely arround his body just behind the shoalders, and was much darker than these bear usually are. the grizly bear we have never yet seen. I have seen their tallons in possession of the Indians and from their form I am perswaded if there is any difference between this species and the brown or white bear it is very inconsiderable. There is no such anamal as a black bear in this open country or of that species generally denominated the black bear.

My fare is really sumptuous this evening; buffaloe's humps, tongues and marrowbones, fine trout parched meal pepper and salt, and a good appetite; the last is not considered the least of the luxuries.

[The expedition portaged around the falls and continued up the river in the following weeks].

Saturday July 27th, 1805.

We set out at an early hour and proceeded on but slowly the current still so rapid that the men are in a continual state of their utmost exertion to get on, and they begin to weaken fast from this continual state of violent exertion. at the distance of 1 3/4 miles the river was again closely hemned in by high Clifts of a solid limestone rock which appear to have tumbled or sunk in the same manner of those I discribed yesterday. the limestone appears to be of an excellent quality of deep blue colour when fractured and of a light led colour where exposed to the weather. it appears to be of a very fine grin the fracture like that of marble. we saw a great number of the bighorn on those Clifts. at the distance of 3 3/4 Ms. further we arrived at 9 A.M. at the junction of the S.E. fork of the Missouri and the country opens suddonly to extensive and beatifull plains and meadows which appear to be surrounded in every direction with distant and lofty mountains; supposing this to be the three forks of the Missouri I halted the party on the Lard. shore for breakfast. and walked up the S.E. fork about 1/2 mile and ascended the point of a high limestone clift from whence I commanded a most perfect view of the neighbouring country. from this point I could see the S.E. fork at about 7 miles. it is rapid and about 70 Yards wide. throughout the distance I saw it, it passes through a smoth extensive green meadow of fine grass in it's course meandering in several streams, the largest of which passes near the Lard. hills, of which, the one I stand on is the extremity in this direction. a high wide and extensive plain succeeds the meadow and extends back several miles from the river on the Stard. side and with the range of mountains up the Lard. side of the middle fork. a large spring arrises in this meadow about 1/4 of a mile from the S.E. fork into which it discharges itself on the Stard. side about 400 paces above me. from E. to S. between the S.E. and middle forks a distant range of lofty mountains ran their snow-clad tops above the irregular and broken mountains which lie adjacent to this beautifull spot. the extreme point to which I could see the S.E. fork boar S. 65º E. distant 7 M. as before observed. between the middle and S.E. forks near their junction with the S.W. fork there is a handsom site for a fortification. it consists of a limestone rock of an oblong form; it's sides perpendicular and about 25 feet high except at the extremity towards the middle fork where it ascends gradually and like the top is covered with a fine terf of green-swoard. the top is level and contains about 2 Acres. the rock ises from the level plain as if it had been designed for some such purpose. the extreme point to which I can see the bottom and meandering of the Middle fork bears S. 15. E. distant about 14 Miles. here it turns to the right around a point of a high plain and disappears to my view. it's bottoms are several miles in width and like that of the S.E. fork form one smoth and beautifull green meadow. it is also divided into several streams. between this and the S.W. fork there is an extensive plain which appears to extend up both those rivers many miles and back to the mountains. the extreme point to which I can see the S.W. fork bears S. 30. W. distant about 12 Miles. this stream passes through a similar country with the other two and is more divided and serpentine in it's course than either of the others; it aso possesses abundanly more timber in it's bottoms. the timber here consists of the narrowleafed cottonwood almost entirely. but little box alder or sweet willow the underbrush thick and as heretofore discribed in the quarter of the missouri. a range of high mountains at a considerable distance appear to reach from South to West and are partially covered with snow the country to the right of the S.W. fork like that to the left of the S.E. fork is high broken and mountainous, as is that also down the missouri behind us, through which, these three rivers after assembling their united force at this point seem to have forced a passage. these bottom lands tho' not more than 8 or 9 feet above the water seem never to overflow. after making a draught of the connection and meanders of these streams I decended the hill and returned to the party, took breakfast and ascended the S.W. fork 1 3/4 miles and encamped at a Lard. bend in a handsome level smooth plain just below a bayou, having passed the entrance of the middle fork at 1/2 mile. here I encamped to wait the return of Capt. Clark and to give the men a little rest which seemed absolutely necessary to

them. at the junction of the S.W. and Middle forks I found a note
which had been left by Capt. Clark informing me of his intended
rout, and that he would rejoin me at this place provided he did not
fall in with any fresh sighn of Indians, in which case he intended to
pursue untill he overtook them calculating on my taking the S.W.
fork, which I most certainly prefer as it's direction is much more
promising than any other. beleiving this to be an essential point
in the geography of this western part of the Continent I determined
to remain at all events untill I obtained the necessary data for fixing it's latitude Longitude &c. after fixing my camp I had the
canoes all unloaded and the baggage stoed away and securely covered on shore,and then permitted several men to hunt. I walked
down to the middle fork and examined and compared it with the S.
W. fork but could not satisfy myself which was the largest stream
of the two, in fact they appeared as if they had been cast in the same
mould there being no difference in character or size, therefore to
call either of these streams the Missouri would be giving it a
preference wich it's size does not warrant as it is not larger than
the other. they are each 90 yds. wide. in these meadows I saw a
number of duckanmallad with their young which are now nearly
grown. Currants of every species as well as goosberries are
found her in great abundance and perfection. a large black goosberry which grows to the hight of five or six feet is also found here.
this is the growth of the bottom lands and is found also near the
little rivulets which make down from the hills and mountains it
puts up many stems from the same root, some of which, are partially branched and all reclining. the berry is attatched separately
by a long peduncle to the stem from which they hang pendant un-
derneath. the berry is of an ovate form smooth as large as the
common garden goosberry when arrived at maturity and is as
black as jet, tho' the pulp is of a cimson colour. this fruit is ex-
treemly asced. the leaf resembles the common goosberry in form
but is reather larger and somewhat proportioned to the superior
size of it's stem when compared with the common goosberry. the
stem is covered with very sharp thorns or bryers. below the tree
forks as we passed this morning I observed many collections of the
mud nests of small martin attatched to the smooth face of the
limestone rocks sheltered by projections of the same rock above.
Our hunters returned this evening with 6 deer 3 Otter and a Muskrat. they informed me that they had seen great numbers of
Antelopes, and much sign of beaver otter deer Elk, &c.

Monday, August 12th, 1805.

. . . I now determined to pursue the base of the mountains
which form this cove to the S.W. in the expectation of finding some
Indian road which lead over the Mountains, accordingly I sent
Drewyer to my right and Shields to my left with orders to look out
for a road or the fresh tracks of horses either of which we should
first meet with I had determined to pursue. at the distance of
about 4 miles we passed 4 small rivulets near each other on which

we saw som resent bowers or small conic lodges formed with willow
brush. near them the indians had geathered a number of roots from
the manner in which they had toarn up the ground; but I could not
discover the root which they seemed to be in surch of. I several
large hawks that were nearly black. near this place we fell in with
a large and plainIndian road which came into the cove from the N.E.
and led along the foot of the mountains to the S.W. oliquely approaching
the main stream which we had left yesterday. this road we now pursued to the S.W. at 5 miles it passed a stout stream which is a principal fork of the man stream and falls into it just above the narrow
pass between the two clifts before mentioned and which we now saw
below us. here we halted and breakfasted on the last of our venison,
having yet a small peice of pork in reserve. after eating we continued our rout through the low bottom of the main stream along the
foot of the mountains on our right the valley for 5 Mls. further in a
S.W. direction was from 2 to 3 miles wide the main stream now after
discarding two stream on the left in this valley turns abruptly to the
West through a narrow bottom between the mountains the road was
still plain, I therefore did not dispair of shortly finding a passage
over the mountains and of taisting the waters of the great Columbia
this evening. we saw an animal which we took to be of the fox kind
as large or reather larger than the small wolf of the plains. it's
colours were a curious mixture of black, redis brown and yellow.
Drewyer shot at him about 130 yards and knocked him dow bet he
recovered and got out of our reach. it is certainly a different
animal from any that we have yet seen. we also saw several of the
heath cock with a long pointed tail and an uniform dark brown
colour but could not kill one of them. they are much larger than
the common dunghill fowls, and in their abits and manner of flying
resemble the growse or prarie hen. at the distance of 4 miles further the road took us to the most distant fountain of the waters of
the Mighty Missouri in surch of which we have spent so many toil-
some days and wristless nights. thus far I had accomplished one
of those great objects on which my mind has been unalterably fixed
for many years, judge then of the pleasure I felt in allying my thirst
with this pure and ice-cold water which issues from the base of a
low mountain or hill of a gentle ascent for 1/2 a mile. the mountains are high on either hand leave this gap at the head of this
rivulet through which the road passes. here I halted a few minutes
and rested myself. two miles below McNeal had exultingly stood
with a foot on each side of this little rivulet and thanked his god
that he had lived to bestride the mighty & heretofore deemed endless Missouri. after refreshing ourselves we proceeded on to the
top of the dividing ridge from which I discovered immence ranges
of high mountains still to the west of us with their tops partially
covered with snow. I now decended the mountain about 3/4 of a
mile which I found much steeper than on the opposite side, to a
handsome bold running Creek of cold Clear water. here I first
tasted the water of the great Columbia river. after a short halt of
a few minutes we continued our march along the Indian road which
lead us over steep hills and deep hollows to a spring on the side of

a mountain where we found a sufficient quantity of dry willow
brush for fuel, here we encamped for the night having traveled
about 20 Miles. as we had killed nothing during the day we now
boiled and eat the remainder of our pork, having yet a little flour
and parched meal. ...

Tuesday August 13th, 1805.

... we had not continued our rout more than a mile when we
were so fortunate as to meet with three female savages. the short
and steep ravines which we passed concealed us from each other
untill we arrived within 30 paces. a young woman immediately
took to flight, an Elderly woman and a girl of about 12 years old
remained. I instantly laid by my gun and advanced towards them.
they appeared much allarmed but saw that we were to near for
them to escape by flight they therefore seated themselves on the
ground, holding down their heads as if reconciled to die which the
expected no doubt would be their fate; I took the elderly woman by
the hand and raised her up repeated the word tab-ba-bone and
strip up my shirt sleve to sew her my skin; to prove to her the
truth of the ascertion that I was a white man for my face and hads
which have been constantly exposed to the sun were quite as dark
as their own. they appeared instantly reconciled, and the men
coming up I gave these women some beads a few mockerson awls
some pewter looking-glasses and a little paint. I directed Drewyer
to request the old woman to recall the young woman who had run off
to some distance by this time fearing she might allarm the camp
before we approached and might so exasperate the natives that they
would perhaps attack us without enquiring who we were. the old
woman did as she was requested and the fugitive soon returned almost out of breath. I bestoed an equvolent portion of trinket on her
with the others. I now painted their tawny cheeks with some vermillion which with this nation is emblematic of peace. after they had
become composed I enformed them by signs that I wished them to
conduct us to their camp that we wer anxious to become ac-
quainted with the chiefs and warriors of their nation. they readily
obeyed and we set out, still pursuing the road down the river. we
had marched about 2 miles when we met a party of about 60 warriors mounted on excellent horses who came in nearly full speed,
when they arrived I advanced towards them with the flag leaving
my gun with the party about 50 paces behid me. the chief and two
others who were a little in advance of the main body spoke to the
women, and they informed them who we were and exultingly showed
the presents which had been given them these men then advanced
and embraced me very affectionately in their way which is by putting
their left arm over you wright sholder clasping your back, while
they apply their left cheek to yours and frequently vociforate the
word ah-hi-e, ah-hi-e that is, I am much pleased, I am much re-
joiced. bothe parties now advanced and we wer all carresed and
besmeared with their grease and paint till I was heartily tired of
the national hug. I now had the pipe lit and gave them smoke; they
seated themselves in a circle around us and pulled of their

mockersons before they would receive or smoke the pipe. this is
a custom among them as I afterwards learned indicative of a
sacred obligation of sincerity in their profession of friendship
given by the act of receiving and smoking the pipe of a stranger.
or which is as much as to say that they wish they may always go
bearfoot if they are not sincere; a pretty heavy penalty if they are
to march through the plains of their country. after smoking a few
pipes with them I distributed some trifles among them, with which
they seemed much pleased particularly with the blue beads and
vermillion. I now informed the chief that the object of our visit
was a friendly one, that after we should reach his camp I would
undertake to explain to him fully those objects, who we wer, from
whence we had come and wither we were going; that in the mean
time I did not care how soon we were in motion, as the sun was
very warm and no water at hand. ...

Tuesday August 20th, 1805.

... I now prevailed on the Chief to instruct me with rispect
to the geography of his country. this he undertook very cheer-
fully, by delienating the rivers on the ground. but I soon found
that his information fell far short of my expectation or wishes.
he drew the river on which we now are to which he placed two
branches just above us, which he shewed me from the openings of
the mountains were in view; he next made it discharge itself into
a large river which flowed from the S.W. about ten miles below us,
then continued this joint stream in the same direction of this
valley or N.W. for one days march and then enclined it to the
West for 2 more days march. here he placed a number of heaps
of sand on each side which he informed me represented the vast
mountains of rock eternally covered with snow through which the
river passed. that the perpendicular and even juting rocks so
closely hemned in the river that there was no possibily of passing
along the shore; that the bed of the river was obstructed by sharp
pointed rocks and the rapidity of the stream such that the whole
surface of the river was beat into perfect foam as far as he said
that this being the state of the country in that direction that himself
nor none of his nation had ever been further down the river than
these mountains. I then enquired the state of the country on either
side of the river but he could not inform me. he said there was an
old man of his nation a days march below who could probably give
me some information of the country to the N. W. and refered me to
an old man then present for that to the S. W. the Chief further
informed me that he had understood from the persed nosed Indians
who inhabit this river below the rocky mountains that it ran a great
way toward the setting sun and finally lost itself in a great lake of
water which was illy taisted, and where the white men lived ...

CHAPTER 2

Report of Area Survey

In the latter half of the 19th Century American geographic field work had progressed to a stage beyond that of exploratory traverses: to filling in the blank spaces between traverses, to the topographic mapping of areas and systematic description of their features. The general objectives were about the same as before: the term "geography" still referred to the major features of land and water, and "geographical work" referred to the locating and mapping of the features. But field methodology had developed and workers were specialists trained in surveying and in various branches of natural science.

Following the Gold Rush to California, the War between the States, and the opening of the first trans-continental railroad, waves of settlement spread westward to fill the habitable areas still left vacant and available. To provide the geographical information needed as a basis for successful settlement, government surveys were carried on during a memorable period beginning in the late 1860's and ending in the 1880's.

The project involved mapping and describing areas, especially land forms but also climate, vegetation, people and resources. Apparently the designation "geographer" was applied to a field worker concerned with major measurements in triangulation and the designation "topographer" to one concerned with details of mapping. Others were "geologist", "naturalist" and "botanist".[1] Great names connected with the period are those of F. V. Hayden, J. W. Powell, G. M. Wheeler, C. King, and H. Gannett.

From voluminous reports an excerpt has been chosen to represent a second type in this series. It is a generalized description by G. M. Wheeler of an area surveyed by him and his field party in Arizona. Wheeler more than any of the others is responsible for the introduction and development of a system of land classification, begun in 1872, looking toward potential land use, in four types: (1) agricultural, (2) timber, (3) grazing, (4) arid and barren.

Some of the maps show the land classified in four colors. In the area of central and western Arizona the classification is applied and used in the description, and types may be inferred in part from features on the map, but no colors are used on the map as originally published and none could be used anyway in reproduction here.

The U.S. Geographical Surveys west of the 100th Meridian came to an end without completely covering the West, and only more recently have the geographical purposes of regional descrip-

1. *U. S. Geological and Geographical Survey of the Territories*, (Washington), vol. 7, 1873, pp. 627-677; vol. 8, 1874, p. 413.

tion and land classification for settlement been
taken up anew.

REPORT UPON GEOGRAPHICAL SURVEYS
WEST OF THE 100th MERIDIAN[1]
by G. M. Wheeler

ATLAS SHEET 75.

Locality - Parts of central and western Arizona.
Scale - One inch to 8 miles, or 1:506880. Boundaries, 34°
to 35° 40' north latitude, and 111° to 113° 45' longitude west from
Greenwich. Area, 17,952 square miles. Adjacent published
sheets: NW. 66, N. 67, E. 76, SE. 83.

GENERAL PHYSICAL FEATURES

This sheet shows, in part, the geographic relations of two
great orographic systems (the Colorado Plateaus and the Basin
Range), together with the border land between them (Fig. 2). The
line of separation happens here to be well marked by the topographic distinction of table and ridge, so that part of the southwestern border of the great plateau can be traced by drawing a
line from Music Mountain in the northeast toward the southeast
corner of the area, passing north of the Black Hills. The area
north of this line is part of the great southern bench of the plateau.
It is capped by the upper limestone of the Carboniferous, and
upon it stand the volcanic peaks called Floyd, Picacho, Bill
Williams, Sitgreaves, Kendrick, Agassiz, and Humphreys. The
latter four belong to the San Francisco group, which is briefly a
series of massive trachytic eruptions, surrounded by small ba-
saltic cones, which have thrown out a great lava mantle extending
far to the south and east, covering the somewhat indefinitely
named Black Mesa and part of the Mogollon.
To the southwest of the line of demarkation lies the Basin
Range country, characteristically broken by a succession of
ranges having approximately the same trend, and inclosing trough-
like alluvial valleys. The sheet contains four ranges and six
groups of mountains, three plateaus and two mesas, one small
lake, twenty-four principal peaks (seven above 10,000 feet), two
main passes, and four cañons   of magnitude.

1. *Engineer Dept., U. S. Army, vol. 1, Geographical Report (Washington, 1889), pp. 294–300.*

Fig. 2. Part of "Atlas Sheet No. 75; U. S. Geographical Surveys West of the 100th Meridian, Lt. Geo. M. Wheeler, Commanding." The Colorado Plateaus in the northeast, Basin Range area in the southwestern corner. Scale: 1 inch to 10.1 miles.

DIVIDES AND DRAINAGE SYSTEMS

The entire area, so far as its surface drainage is concerned, belongs to the Colorado Basin. The most important divide is that running from Music Mountain to Floyd's Peak, of the San Francisco Group, and southward over the crest of the Mogollon Mesa, separating the area into a northern and southern watershed. The waters of the north pass off to the Colorado through the heads of Cataract Creek and the Colorado Chiquito and its tributaries. Those of the south are tributary to Bill Williams Fork on the west and the Gila on the east. The divide of these secondary basins passes from Floyd's Peak over the crest of the Juniper Range, Aztec Pass, Santa Maria, Granite, Weaver, and Date Creek Mountains to the Cactus Plain.

The only stream of importance is the Rio Verde, the drainage of the entire area being confined to small streams and dry arroyos, sometimes filled with water from melting snows gathered in the high plateau.

The highest point in the area (and in Arizona) is Humphrey's Peak in the San Francisco Mountains, 12,562 feet above sea (Fig. 2) and the lowest is the Canyon of Bill Williams Fork, about 800 feet above sea.

The lava-capped San Francisco Plateau varies in altitude from 5,526 feet at Lockwood Spring to 6,857 and to 7,108 feet along its most elevated portions, trending to the southeast from the San Francisco Mountains.

The soil immediately adjacent to the lava in situ is black and often meager, while that found in the valleys and glades is dark, deep, rich, and of most positive fertility.

Climate - The prevailing climate is dry, although this section of Arizona is unusually favored as regards rain-fall. The summer climate of the uplands and higher valleys (5,500 feet) is delightful, and the winters mild though variable. The highest peaks of the San Francisco Group carry snow during the winter months, and upon the higher plateaus heavy snows sometimes occur, rarely lying long enough, however, to seriously impede travel. There is a well-marked rainy season during the months of July, August, and September, when showers are frequent. Series of observations at typical points over the whole area are not at hand, but the following meterological data from the Signal Office records at Forts Verde and Whipple and for Wickenburgh give an idea of what might be expected at similar localities:

At Fort Whipple (altitude 5,340 feet, latitude 34° 33' north, longitude 112° 28' west), from November, 1873, to July, 1883, the mean annual temperature was 52° Fahr.; the mean relative humidity 43.2; average precipitation 13.86 inches (maximum in August); prevailing wind south; highest temperature in July (maximum of 103° Fahr., in July, 1878), lowest temperature in January (lowest minimum of -18° Fahr., in December, 1879).

At Fort Verde (latitude 34° 33', longitude 112° 52' west, altitude 3,100 feet) from November, 1874 to July, 1883, the mean annual temperature was 60.9° Fahr. (maximum in July, highest 114° in July, 1881 -- minimum in January, lowest -- 6° Fahr., in December, 1879, and January, 1882); the mean relative humidity was 42.4, with an average precipitation of 13.46 inches (greatest in August), with south as the prevailing wind.

At Wickenburgh (latitude 34°, longitude 112° 44', altitude 1,400 feet) from January, 1874, to April, 1882, the mean annual temperature was 62.9° Fahr., maximum in July, highest 111° Fahr., in July and August, 1877; minimum in January with lowest - 12°, in 1878); the mean relative humidity was 46.1; the average precipitation 8.6 inches (greatest in August), with south for prevailing wind.[1]

The Colorado Plateau consists of Silurian, Carboniferous, and Triassic formations, with a large exposure of Basalt.

The ranges in the western and southwestern parts of the sheet are of Archaean, with large Trachyte and Rhyolite areas, while the valleys are all of Quaternary. The Cretaceous and Tertiary of the Plateau series (see sheet 67) are wanting.

GENERAL ECONOMIC FEATURES

Timber - The Mogollon Mesa and the San Francisco Mountains, which have extensive forests, produce the finest timber in this section, the best being the yellow pine (pinus ponderosa), which in large growth clothe the higher altitudes, and Douglass spruce. The lower ranges, as a rule, have a fair growth of full timber; piñon, cedar, or juniper (J. occidentalis), ash, oak, and cottonwood, and sycamore grow in the bottom lands of the principal streams and fringe the glades and openings of the subordinate basins.

Agriculture and Grazing - Good gramma and bunch grass is to be found throughout the mountains and mountain slopes, affording ranges for large herds of cattle and sheep.

Building material --Good stone for building purposes may be found in the magnesian limestone of Cañon Diablo, the lava rock of the Mogollon Mesa, and the sandstone in the vicinity of Chino Valley.

1. *"The Signal Service gives the following for rain-fall: Old Camp Willow Grove, one year seven months, between February, 1868, and September, 1869: Average 9 inches: Old Camp Hualapais, two years eleven months, between April, 1870, and June, 1873: Average, 20.89 inches. Camp Verde, seventeen years eight months, between December, 1868, and November, 1887: Average, 11.44 inches; maximum, 17.22 inches, 1884, and minimum, 4.80 inches, 1871. Fort Whipple, twenty years seven months, between June, 1865, and December, 1887: Average, 16.83 inches; maximum, 27.13 inches, 1874, and minimum, 10.02 inches, 1880. Old Camp Date Creek, six years three months between May, 1867, and July, 1873. Average, 13.76 inches; maximum 27.84 inches, 1868, and minimum, 13.60 inches, 1870. Wickenburgh, eight years five months, between November, 1875, and January, 1886: average, 9.83 inches; maximum, 17.17 inches, 1884, and minimum, 6.35 inches, 1877."*

The principal agricultural lands occur in Chino and Williamson's Valleys, between the Aztec and Cactus Passes; in the vicinity
of Prescott (Fort Whipple) and Fort Verde and in the bottom lands
of Bill Williams Fork. South of the San Francisco Mountains along
the Prescott and Santa Fe road are little valleys and open glades
suitable for farming homes (Fig. 2). The deep depression in the
southeast corner is the area called the Tonto Basin, containing
forest meadows and fine valleys suitable for stock-raising. The
soil in the localities mentioned is fertile, and favorable for corn
and grain, but as a rule irrigation is necessary to make agriculture here remunerative, as droughts are frequent.

A rough estimate of the classes of lands in this area of
17,952 square miles is: Agricultural with irrigation, 796 square
miles, or 4.4 per cent.; grazing, 7,154 square miles, or 39.9 per
cent.; timber, 2,614 square miles, or 14.6 per cent.; arid or
barren, 7,388 square miles, or 41.1 per cent.

Considerable spaces now covered with a sage-brush growth
can probably never be made productive for lack of water; these
notably are the Cactus and Prescott Plains, the flat country in the
northwestern part of the area, that north and south of the Cactus
Pass, the plains between the Kendrick and Aquarius Ranges, and
parts of the basin of Aqua Fria Creek. Of the lands included
under the head of agricultural with irrigation probably not over
one-fifth is actually under cultivation.

The principal crops grown are barley, Indian corn, potatoes,
and some wheat. The ordinary vegetables and fruits can be raised.

Game - The San Francisco Mountains and Mogollon Mesa
include the best game country in this area. In 1871-'73, grizzly,
black, and cinnamon bear, deer, and antelope were all noted.

Routes of communication - The Atlantic and Pacific Rail-
road crosses the area from east to west; entering at Cañon
Diablo, it traverses the forest-clad plateau south of Humphrey's
Peak, where it reaches its greatest altitude, 7,355 feet above sea,
passes north of Bill Williams Peak and between Mounts Floyd and
Picacho, crosses Aubrey Valley, and leaves the area by way of
Truxton Springs. From Ash Fork Station on Partridge Creek it is
about 50 miles by stage to Prescott.[1]

The main wagon routes to the westward are the Fort Mohave
(Colorado River) and Prescott Road and the Ehrenburg (Colorado
River) and Prescott Road; to the south the Prescott and Fort
McDowell Road; and to the east the Prescott and Apache Road and
Verde and Apache Road, and the Old Prescott and Santa Fe Road,
striking the Little Colorado at the mouth of Cañon Diablo.

Since this area was surveyed in 1873 the Atlantic and Pacific
Railroad has been built, and numerous settlements not shown on
the map have sprung up.[2]

1. *"In 1884 a railroad was in course of construction along this route."*
2. *"The only town of importance is Prescott, seat of Yavapai County and capital of
   Arizona; population in 1880, 2,074. Wickenburgh, on the Hassyampa, is a village of
   about 200. Two miles northeast of Prescott is the post of Fort Whipple, and about
   40 miles further east, by road on the Rio Verde, is Fort Verde. According to the
   census of 1880 the population of this entire area was about 4,800 (or .27 to the
   square mile), and thus nearly one-half was centered at Prescott and Forts Whipple
   and Verde."*

A number of mining camps have been established in the
Bradshaw or Silver Mountains and the hills east of Prescott, known
as the Lynx Creek, Hassyampa, Big Bug, Turkey Creek, Walnut
Grove, Pine Grove, Tiger, and Humbug districts. There is also
the Weaver district in the range of the same name, the Martinez
in the Date Creek Mountains, and the Greenwood in the Aquarius
Range and the flat country east of it.[1]

Wickenburgh, on Hassyampa Creek, and Bradshaw, in the
Bradshaw Mountains, are (1880) mining camps of about 200 and
100 inhabitants, respectively. There are other mining settlements in the Bradshaw Mountains. In the Cañon of Beaver Creek,
north of Fort Verde, are many interesting ruins of the buildings
of extinct aboriginals (Fig. 2).

No.	Name	Approximate geographical position				Remarks
		Long.	west.	Lat.	north	
		o	'	o	'	
1	Maynard	113	50	35	10	. . . .
2	Tiger	112	15	34	05	Bradshaw Range. . .
3	Pine Grove	112	20	34	10	. . . . do . . . .
4	Bradshaw	112	20	34	13	. . . . do . . . .
5	Turkey Creek	112	20	34	18	. . . . do . . . .
6	Weaver	112	20	34	05	. . . . do . . . .
7	Walnut Grove	112	22	34	20	. . . . do . . . .
8	Hassyampa	112	25	34	18	. . . . do . . . .
9	Martinez	113	00	34	06	Date Creek Mountains
10	Santa Maria	113	00	34	30	Kendrick Mountains

1. "The following were post-offices in July, 1883, on the Atlantic and Pacific Railroad:
Flagstaff, south of Agassiz Peak, near Antelope Spring; Williams, northeast of Bill
Williams Peak, near New Year Spring; Ash Fork, about 50 miles north of Prescott,
on north branch of Partridge Creek, and Hackberry, near Truxton Springs. From Ash
Fork there is a daily mail to Prescott and Whipple Barracks. Other post-offices are
Aqua Fria Valley, Cienega, Stoddard, and Fort Verde, on the Prescott and Verde
Road; Big Bug, Bumble Bee, and Gillett, on the Prescott and Phoenix Road; Skull
Valley, Antelope Valley, Stanton, and Wickenburgh, on the Prescott and Wicken-
burgh Road; Cox, Walnut Grove, and Kirby, on the Hassyampa Creek, Simmons, on
Mint Creek, Juniper, in Williamson's Valley; Hassyampa, Meesville, Bueno,
Alexandria, Bradshaw, Walker, Howell, and Tip-Top, in the Bradshaw Mountains.
There are also settlements east from the Mazatzal Range in the Tonto Basin, at
present without direct mail communication. This area embraces the southern and
most populous part of Yavapai County and the Southeastern part of Mohave County."

CHAPTER 3

Explanatory Physical Geography

At the end of the 19th Century a desire for explanation began to exceed that for pure description of the land. Ideas of evolution had permeated and stimulated the natural sciences. Geology and Paleontology grew and flourished, with physiography on their geographical side absorbing a good share of interest.

"The Geography of Chicago and its Environs" by R. D. Salisbury and W. C. Alden, 1899, has been selected as representing a third type in this series of field studies. Salisbury was Professor of Geographic Geology at the University of Chicago, and Alden was field assistant. Salisbury was the first President of the Geographic Society of Chicago, for which this study was prepared as Bulletin #1. Shortly thereafter (1903) he organized at Chicago the first full-fledged department of geography in an American University and was head of it for sixteen years.

The study is called "The Geography of Chicago", but the city itself does not appear in it. The purpose is to explain the origin of the site, to set the stage for the works of man. The field method is that of topographic survey, observation and inference based on knowledge of geologic processes.

The style of writing is clear and elementary, as of a teacher addressing the Geographic Society of Chicago audience of people interested in geography but not academically trained in the subject.

A second edition published twenty-one years later (1920) bears the same name, ''The Geography of Chicago and its Environs''. By that time there may have been some question about the name, and if later editions had been published, the text could have remained the same, but the name might have been changed, possibly to ''Physical Geography''.

The text of the second edition differs only slightly from the first, except for the addition of paragraphs on the Indiana Dunes (which are added in this reprinting also). These new paragraphs represent the recognition, in the meanwhile, of plant ecology as another explanatory evolutionary subject, on the geographical side of botany. Evidently the inspiration for these paragraphs came from H. C. Cowles, Professor Botany at the University of Chicago, who served as President of the Association of American Geographers (1910) as well as of the Ecological Society of America (1918). Cowles' ideas were exemplified with particular felicity in field study of the ecology of plants in the Indiana dunes, and were expressed in ''The Plant Societies of Chicago and Vicinity'', written by Cowles and published by the Geographic Society of Chicago as Bulletin #2, 1901.

An excerpt from another source is here added for further illustration of explanatory physical geography: "Experiments in Geographical Description" by W. M. Davis, 1910. The author, Professor of Geology at Harvard, first exerted major influence in the development of physiography into an explanatory evolutionary science, and then exerted influence in geography as founder and thrice President of the Association of American Geographers, and as recommending the development of geography into an explanatory evolutionary science of life in relation to physical environment[1].

In this advise to geographers Davis drew a line between inorganic environment as cause and organic creatures (plants, animals & human beings) as effect. However, a different division was adopted elsewhere in geography, drawing a line between natural environment (inorganic matter, plants and animals) on the one hand and human beings on the other. In accordance with this alternative division, Cowles' plant ecology belongs with Salisbury's physiography in "The Geography of Chicago." So in this volume physical geography includes biological non-human as distinguished from human geography.

It is noticeable that in "Experiments in Geographical Description," addressed to an audience of geographers as his third Presidential Address

1. W. M. Davis: "An Inductive Study of the Content of Geography", second Presidential Address, AAG. in Bull.Am. Geog. Soc., vol. 38, (1906), pp. 67-84.

before the Association of American Geographers, Davis does not follow his recommendation to geographers to undertake the causal explanation of life in relation to physical environment, but does follow his well established practice of explaining land forms in terms of the physical processes of their origin. In this his "Geographical Description" does not differ basically from Salisbury's "Geography of Chicago." A minor difference is that in his description of the landscape Davis does include the elements of human settlement in addition to the land forms themselves. However, he does not launch out here into evolutionary explanation and so is shown in this study at his geographical best, dealing with the phenomena of land forms and their evolution, which he knew so well.

THE GEOGRAPHY OF CHICAGO AND ITS ENVIRONS[1]
by R. D. Salisbury and W. C. Alden

PREFATORY NOTE

It is the purpose of this essay to present an outline of the geography of Chicago and its immediate surroundings, and especially to sketch in as simple a manner as possible the course of events by which that geography was developed. The essay is not intended to take the place of the detailed descriptions of special localities heretofore published or yet to be published. Rather it is meant to give such an account of the region about the city that the interpretation of local phenomena may be more easily and more generally understood. ...

---

1. _Bull. # 1, Geographic Society of Chicago_ (Univ. of Chicago Press, 1899).

I. THE CHICAGO PLAIN

Topography

General topographic relations. - The topography of a region is always significant of its history. The City of Chicago is situated on a low, strikingly flat plain, bordering the west side of the head of Lake Michigan. The limits of the plain for a tract about the city are shown in Fig. 3, from which it will be seen that the plain is roughly crescentic. Its inner border is formed by the shore of Lake Michigan, while its outer margin, marked by higher land (shaded in Fig. 3), extends from Winnetka on the north, through Galewood and La Grange on the west, to Glenwood and Dyer (Indiana) on the southwest and south. Its greatest width is about 15 miles in a direction southwest from the city.

From the shore of the lake, the level of which is about 581 feet above mean tide level in New York Harbor, the Chicago plain rises very gradually to a nearly uniform height about 60 feet above the lake. At this level, the flatness of the plain is interrupted, and to the west and south the surface rises promptly, and its topography is rolling. The rise is continued until the rolling surface reaches an extreme altitude of 200 feet above the lake. From this considerable elevation there is a decline toward the west, southwest and south. In other words, the Chicago plain is shut in by a broad, ridge-like belt of gently rolling topography. Observations beyond the immediate vicinity of Chicago show that this ridge-belt comes down from the north and swings about the head of the lake basin. It is in reality a glacial moraine, and has been called the Valparaiso moraine from the city of Valparaiso (Indiana), which is situated upon it. ...

Cutting directly across this low broad ridge in a southwesterly direction, from Summit to Lemont, is the valley now traversed by the Des Plaines river, the Illinois-Michigan canal, and the new Drainage Canal. This valley has abrupt slopes, varies in width from one-half mile to one and one-fourth miles, and is 30 to 100 feet deep. From side to side, the floor of this valley is nearly flat. At its lakeward end, the bottom is continuous with the Chicago plain, and is less than 15 feet above the level of the water in the lake. These relations are shown in Fig. 3. From Summit to Lemont, the fall is so slight as to be spoken of as the "twelve-mile level."

Tributary to this valley at Sag Station, about three and one-half miles above Lemont, is a second valley of like dimensions known as "the Sag". This valley runs nearly due west from the village of Worth on the Wabash Railway, to Sag Station on the Chicago & Alton Railway. It is traversed by a small creek known as the Canal Feeder. These valleys converge and unite at Sag Station, including between them a triangular tract of elevated land of undulating topography. This isolated area, known as Mount Forest, has a length of six miles and a width of four.

The floor of the Sag, as well as that of the Des Plaines

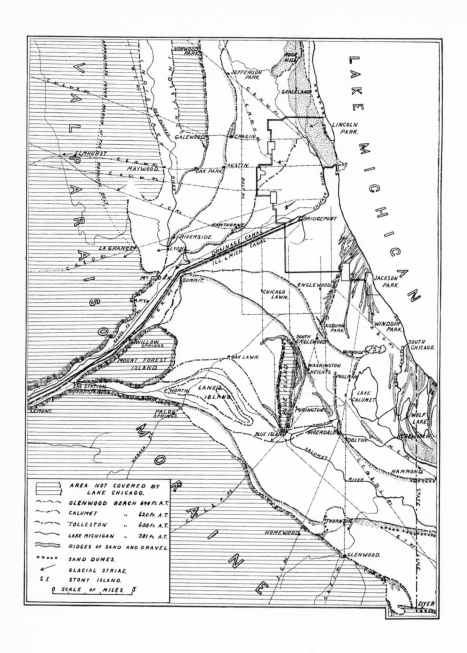

Fig. 3. Physiographic map showing part of the Chicago Plain and its surroundings.

valley, is continuous with the Chicago plain. These two valleys, therefore, give ample outlet for drainage from the Chicago plain southwestward across the moraine belt, and thence by way of the Illinois and Mississippi rivers to the Gulf of Mexico. Following the line of the canal, there is a rise of less than 15 feet from the present level of the lake to the divide which separates it from the Des Plaines river. The lake, therefore, barely escapes drainage into the Mississippi river system, even without the new canal.

Topography of the plain. - Apart from the Mount Forest island already mentioned, the most prominent topographic feature of the plain is the Blue Island ridge,(Fig. 3) seven miles west of the lake at South Chicago. This ridge runs nearly due north and south, having a length of six miles, a width of about one mile, and an elevation of 25 to 50 feet above the surrounding flat.

Just west of South Chicago, between the Blue Island ridge and the lake, is a minor elevation of rock known as Stony Island (Fig. 3). Its longer axis has an east-west direction. The length of the "island" is one and one-fourth miles, its width about half a mile, and its height about 20 feet above its marshy surroundings.

Traversing the plain and converging to the two southwestward valley-extensions of the plain on either side of Mount Forest, are a series of low ridges of sand and gravel so related to the lake, to the valleys on either side of Mount Forest, and to one another, both in elevation and arrangement, as to be most significant in working out the geographic history of the region. In many parts of the city where the natural surface has not been destroyed by grading, as well as at many points outside the city, these low ridges are brought into prominence by the trees which grow upon them, while their surroundings are treeless. Some of these inconspicuous ridges are shown in Fig. 3.

Apart from these features, some of which are not pronounced, the notable characteristic of the topography of the plain is its flatness.

STRUCTURE OF THE PLAIN

Relations of rock and drift. - The sub-structure of the Chicago plain is solid rock. This may be seen in the several quarries about the city, and is made known by deep borings and excavations of other sorts at many points where the rock is not exposed at the surface.

Overlying the bed-rock is a mantle of unconsolidated material composed of bowlders, clay and sand, and known as drift. Borings for wells, excavations for the foundations of buildings, and the exposures of rock in the quarries, show that the thickness of the drift mantle is extremely variable, and since the surface of the plain is nearly flat, it follows that the surface of the rock on which the drift rests must be very uneven. If the drift mantle were to be stripped off, there would remain, instead of the flat plain on which the city now stands, a markedly uneven surface. The present rock outcrops, where the drift is thin or absent, would be the tops of hills rising above their surroundings, that is, above the plain where the drift is now thick. The slopes from the hilltops to the valleys about them would be sometimes steep and sometimes gentle. ...

The rock. - The rock which underlies the plain about Chicago is limestone. At the various quarries, and wherever the rock is exposed, it may be seen to contain bits, or sometimes even large masses of coral, fragments of crinoid stems, and fragmentary or perfect shells of various forms of shell-bearing life. Locally, the limestone may almost be said to be made of such fragments. These fossils give positive evidence of the origin of the limestone, for all of them are the relics of life which lived in sea water. In the ocean today similar accumulations of coral and shells are making, where the conditions are favorable. Geologists are therefore confident that the limestone of this region was accumulated beneath the sea, and this means that the ocean covered the site of our city when the limestone was formed.

By means of its fossils, and by other means less readily explained, the age of the limestone, in terms of geological chronology, is known. It belongs to the later part of the Silurian period, and the Silurian is the third of the six or seven long periods which make up the Paleozoic era, the first era when, so far as now known, there was abundant marine life. The local rock is known as the Niagara limestone, because it is believed to be of the same age as the limestone at Niagara Falls, and the limestone at that point was long since named Niagara. ...

THE DRIFT

Unstratified drift. - The drift at various points presents various characteristics. In most of the localities where the more permanent exposures occur, the drift consists of a matrix of dense blue (in places buffish) clay, in which are imbedded many stones. In size the stones range from pebbles to bowlders several feet in diameter. The material is in general without arrangement; that is, the fine and the coarse are intimately mingled. To put the matter in another way, the drift does not show the assortment and stratification characteristic of deposits made by water. Much of the stony material is too coarse to have been handled by waves or currents of any ordinary strength.

The greater part of the stony material of the drift was derived from the Niagara limestone which underlies the drift, not only about Chicago, but throughout northeastern Illinois and eastern Wisconsin as well. Another, but smaller portion of the stones of the drift are fragments of sedimentary rock from other formations, while still another part are fragments of metamorphic and igneous rocks. More commonly than otherwise the larger bowlders belong to this last class, and the formations from which they came are found about Lakes Superior and Huron, and other points to the north and northeast.

If the stones imbedded in the clay be examined, they are found

-42-

to be partly angular and partly rounded, but largely sub-angular with numerous flat surfaces or facets. They show neither the rounding of shore pebbles nor the angularity of freshly broken rock. The facets often show polishing, parallel grooving and scratching, as though smoothed and striated while being held in a firm position and moved over a hard surface beneath.

The fine material of the unstratified drift, that is, the blue clay (which is sometimes yellowish at the surface), is found on examination to be made up of minute particles of rock. It is, in fact, nothing more than finely pulverized rock. Particles from many sorts of rock enter into its composition, though some are abundant and some rare. About Chicago, particles of limestone are by far the most abundant. ...

The surface portion of the clayey drift to the depth of two or three feet, is often buffish or yellowish in color. This portion does not usually effervesce when acid is applied, showing that it does not contain much lime carbonate. The reason of the buff, non-calcerous surface portion, will appear later. ...

In some places about the city, and at numerous points throughout the drift-covered area, bits of timber, and even large logs are found in the drift. Vegetable mould and beds of peat, which represent buried swamps, are also found both about Chicago, and throughout the broader area of which this forms a part. These logs, beds of peat, etc., record the fact that as the glacier ice advanced over the region it found forests, soils and swamps. Trees from the forests were buried where they grew, or more commonly detached and carried away by the ice and incorporated with its stony and earthly debris. The soils and the peat of the swamps sometimes suffered a similar fate, but since they offered no resistance to the ice, they were overridden and buried without being carried forward, more commonly than trees. It is manifest that if the species of the plants could be determined, they would give some clue as to the climate preceding the advent of the ice.

Stratified drift. - In many parts of the City of Chicago, and at many points outside the city on the Chicago plain, the shallow excavations which are frequently to be seen show the upper part of the drift to be stratified, and to consist of sand and gravel, instead of clay and stones. If the excavations be deep, the blue clay with its content of stones is often exposed beneath the sand and gravel. The stones of the stratified drift are usually rounded, and almost never striated. This superficial mantle of stratified drift is wanting in many parts of the plain. The stratified drift is, however, not strictly confined to the plain. At the south end of the Blue Island ridge, for example, there is a considerable body of stratified drift running well up to the summit of the elevation. Nor is the stratified drift all at the surface, though this is where it is most commonly seen. Deep excavations sometimes show thin beds of stratified drift below thick or thin bodies of unstratified. A complete explanation of the drift must of course take account not only of the unstratified drift, but of the stratified drift in all its positions and relations. ...

Surface of the rock beneath the drift. - These various characteristics of the drift, stratified and unstratified, are hardly less
significant, in the explanation of the phenomena about Chicago,
than the surface of the limestone beneath. In general it may be
said that the surface of the limestone where it is accessible is
relatively smooth. This statement is not to be confused with the
idea already distinctly stated, that the surface of the limestone is
very uneven. What is here meant is that the surface of the limestone
over an elevation or in a depression is, for any small area, essentially smooth. When the limestone is uncovered, its surface
frequently looks as if it had just been smoothed or polished. It
has not the numerous little irregularities which characterize the
surface of limestone which has decayed under the influence of
atmospheric changes. In such cases the surface of the limestone
is irregularly etched, and often so soft and crumbling that an
exact line marking the distinction between the earthy matter above
and the rock below cannot be drawn; but here beneath the drift,
the surface of the limestone is in general hard as well as smooth,
and the demarkation between it and the drift is perfectly definite. ...

Not only is the surface of the rock beneath the drift hard and
in general smooth, but it is also marked by numerous lines and
grooves comparable to the lines and grooves on the surfaces of the
stones of the drift. So striking is the correspondence between
these marks on the bed-rock and those on the stones of the drift,
that there can be no doubt that they owe their origin to a common
cause. Furthermore, the striae which are to be seen on the surface of the limestone beneath the drift are, in any locality, essentially parallel to one another.

The characteristics which have been mentioned as affecting
the surface of the limestone, as well as many other phenomena
which need not be here detailed, indicate that the limestone was
worn in such a way as to smooth and striate its surface at the
time the drift was deposited. ...

The drift is of glacial origin. - The characteristics of the
unstratified drift, together with the characteristics of the surface
of the rock on which it lies, point in no uncertain way to the origin
of the drift and its accompanying phenomena. The drift is identical
in kind with the deposits now being made by glaciers in various
parts of the world, and the characteristics of the surface of the
rock beneath the drift are identical with those of the surface of
rock over which glacier ice is known to have recently passed.
These points are easily demonstrable. ...

So unique and so distinctive are the results of the work of
glacier ice that they cannot be mistaken for the work of any other
agency; and so many and so striking are the points of correspondence between the work of existing glaciers and the work of the
agencies which produced the drift about Chicago (and the large
drift-covered area about it), that there is no escape from the
conclusion that the latter, with all its accompanying phenomena,
is the work of glacier ice.

In the valleys and on the plains beyond the existing glaciers

there are frequently deposits of stratified sand and gravel, borne
out beyond the ice by waters which came from its melting. Water
action necessarily accompanies glacier action, and the deposits
made by water are stratified. Every glacier, therefore, gives rise
to water, which is sure to stratify more or less of the material
which the ice had deposited, or which it was carrying. It is through
the agency of water, therefore, that the stratified drift accompanying the unstratified is to be explained. It will be seen in the sequel
that the water which stratifies the drift may be lake or sea water,
as well as that of streams.

II. DEVELOPMENT OF THE PRESENT GEOGRAPHY

The preceding pages should have made it clear that two formations determine the geography of Chicago. These are the rock,
and the drift which overlies it.

THE GEOGRAPHY OF THE ROCK SURFACE

After the Niagara limestone was deposited, and after such
younger beds as once covered it had been laid down on it, the sea
retired from this region, either because it waters were drawn off
by the sinking of the deeper parts of the ocean bottom elsewhere,
or because this section of the earth's crust was warped upward
sufficiently to bring it above the level of the sea. So soon as it
became land, its surface was exposed to the action of heat and cold
of rain and wind, of plants and animals. Of primary importance
was the rain, and the streams to which the rain gave rise. These
streams, working as streams have always worked, began to cut
valleys in the surface of the land, and ultimately wore away much
of the rock, carrying the eroded material back to the sea. During
the long period which followed the deposition of the youngest
marine beds, almost all of the formations down to the Niagara
were carried away by erosion. Not only were the formations above
the Niagara destroyed, but the surface of the Niagara limestone
itself was deeply eroded by the same processes which had carried
away the overlying beds. The cutting of valleys in the surface of
the limestone left ridges and hills between them, and the surface,
at the close of the long period of erosion, was even rougher than
that which now affects the limestone beneath the drift.

In northwestern Indiana, the Niagara limestone is overlain by
Devonian formations. At the junction of the Des Plaines and Kankakee rivers is found the northeast margin of the formations of the
Carboniferous system (next younger than the Devonian), which
covers most of the State, while farther west, in Iowa and beyond,
the systems of the Mesozoic and early Cenozoic eras overlie the
Carboniferous. The mantle of drift which covers the Niagara
limestone of Chicago, covers all these systems of strata. It is
therefore evident that all the vast geologic periods represented by
these several systems of rock must have intervened between the
deposition of the Niagara limestone, and that of the mantle of

bowlder clay which rests on its surface. These relations show that the period of erosion following the deposition of the Devonian beds and preceding the deposition of the drift, was very long.

THE GLACIAL PERIOD

The long period during which the rock beds of this region were exposed to the ordinary agencies of rock disintegration and erosion was brought to a close by climatic changes the like of which had never occurred in this latitude, so far as now known, in all the earth's history. This change consisted in the development of arctic conditions, not only about Chicago, but over a wide area in the northern and northeastern parts of the United States, as well as over a still larger area farther north. Under the influence of these conditions, a vast continental ice-sheet, comparable to that which now covers Greenland, though many times larger, came into existence. ... The cause of the climatic change which brought about the glacial conditions is not here discussed. Conjecture has attributed it now to great changes in the orbit or axis of the earth, now to changes in the elevation or distribution of the land, and now to changes in the constitution of the atmosphere, as well as to many other changes, real or speculative. Suffice it to say, that scientists are by no means agreed as to the hypothesis which best explains the facts. Whatever the cause, the fact that a great ice-sheet, about 4,000,000 square miles in area, came into existence in the northern part of the continent, is no longer open to question. As already pointed out, the proof is found in the character of the drift, and in the peculiar and distinctive features of the rock surface beneath it.

The results of careful and extensive study of the drift in North America have led those geologists who have concerned themselves especially with the drift, to the confident conclusion that the glacial period consisted of several more or less distinct glacial epochs, separated by epochs which have been called inter-glacial. During the glacial epochs, the climate was severe, and the ice-sheets were being enlarged; during the interglacial epochs the climate was less severe, and the ice-sheets diminished in area and thickness, if indeed they did not altogether disappear. During these mild intervals, plants and animals returned to latitudes from which they had been driven by the cold and ice, only to be driven southward again with the advent of the next epoch of rigorous climate. ...

The ice-sheets of several of the glacial epochs passed over northeastern Illinois, and each contributed to the aggregate effects of glaciation. In the paragraphs which follow, it is the effects of glaciation, rather than the effects of the ice of any one glacial epoch, which are referred to; yet the effects of the last glacial epoch on the geography of Chicago are of so much more importance than those of the others, that the chief emphasis is laid on its results. It should be noted, however, that some of the great geographic features of the region, such as the basin of Lake

Michigan, may have been formed before the latest advance of the ice and, perhaps, much before.

Development of the ice-sheet. - The especial feature of the glacial period was an ice-sheet of continental dimensions. The climate which preceded and caused the development of this ice-sheet, probably came gradually, and the growth of the ice-sheet was probably slow. ...

When the ice covered the region about Chicago, its surface was probably essentially smooth, and not notably affected by the topography of the rock beneath. Its surface must have been many hundred feet above the surface of the highest rock hills of the region. Though the irregularities of the rock surface probably caused deflections of movement in the lower part of the ice, its movement as a whole seems not to have been much affected by any topographic feature immediately about Chicago, unless by the lake basin itself.

The erosion work of the ice. - When the ice invaded this region, the surface was probably covered with a mantle of soil and decayed rock, and vegetation was probably growing upon it. In its movement, the ice soon incorporated in its lower part much of the vegetation, soil and decayed rock. So soon as these loose materials were removed, the surface of the rock beneath was exposed to wear, and the advancing ice polished, scratched and grooved it by means of the earthy matter and rock fragments which it slowly but steadily carried forward. The rock fragments in the ice were themselves ground, striated and polished at the same time, and perhaps crowded farther up into the ice and borne onward with the load of debris. ...

The erosive effect of the ice was therefore to grind down the elevations and to make rough surfaces smooth. The rock surface beneath Chicago and its environs still remains about as it was left by the ice. Could it be seen, it would be found to be wanting in the many little rugosities which affect surfaces eroded subaerially.

At the same time that the hills of rock were worn down by the ice, depressions in the rock were in some cases made deeper. This is especially true where the ice moved through a valley lengthwise. Where it crossed a valley, its effect was to wear down it borders, rather than its bottom.

The moving ice must have covered the site of Chicago for long periods of time. During that glacial epoch when the advance of the ice was greatest, its stay in this region began when, coming down from the north, it reached this latitude. Glacier ice remained over this locality while the edge of the ice was advancing some 150 miles farther south, during such time as the edge remained stationary in this advanced position, and during the time occupied in melting its edge back again to this region. If the edge of the ice advanced and retreated at the rate of but a few feet per day, it will be seen that a very long period of time, several thousands of years at least would be needed. During other ice epochs, when the ice advanced less far to the south, its stay may not have been so long.

Deposits made by the ice. - On melting, glacier ice leaves it former bed covered with the debris which it carried, chiefly in its lower part. Were this material equally distributed in the ice during its motion, and were the conditions of its deposition everywhere the same, the drift would constitute a mantle of uniform thickness over the underlying rock. Such a mantle of drift would not greatly alter the topography. It would simply raise the surface by an amount equal to the thickness of the drift, leaving elevations and depressions of the same magnitude as before, and sustaining the same relations to one another. But the drift carried by the ice, in whatever position, was not equally distributed during the process of transportation, and the conditions under which it was deposited were not constant in the same area, much less in different ones. Because of the unequal amounts of material carried by different parts of the ice, and because of the unequal and inconstant conditions of deposition under the body of the ice and its edge, the mantle of drift has a very variable thickness; and a mantle of drift of variable thickness cannot fail to modify the topography of the region it covers. The extent of the modification will depend on the extent of the variation in thickness. This amounts, in our region, to 150 feet or more, and on our continent to upwards of 500 feet. The continental ice-sheet therefore modified the topography of the region it covered, not only by the wear it effected, but also by the deposits it made.

About Chicago the average thickness of the drift on the highlands is greater than on the low. From this it might be inferred that the relief of the present surface about Chicago is greater than it would have been without the drift. But this is probably not the fact, for there are somewhat deep valleys in the surface of the rock beneath the Chicago plain, and they increase the relief of the rock surface notably. At any rate, the angles of slopes of the present surface are probably notably less than some of the angles of slope of the rock beneath the drift. Reference has already been made to the belt of thick drift which skirts the Chicago plain. The greater thickness of drift along this belt seems to have resulted from the halting of the ice edge in this position, during its final retreat. If the edge of the ice had melted back at a constant rate, its position at one stage would not be marked by notably more drift than its position at another; but if its edge remained in a given position for a time, drift was being continually brought to that position by the forward motion of the ice, and not carried beyond. Under the stationary edge, therefore, a belt of drift, thicker than on either side, might be accumulated. This is the explanation of the Valparaiso moraine (Fig. 3) and of submarginal moraines in general. In its greater thickness only does it differ from the ground moraine which the great body of the drift constitutes.

Not only did the deposition of the drift affect the topography about the city by diminishing (probably) the relief and by obliterating the more striking depressions in the surface of the rock, but its surface had a topography of its own. Like glacial deposits in general, its surface, as left by the ice, was undulatory, being marked by many minor and gentle elevations and depressions, the latter often without outlets. In our own region this rolling topography, marked by low swells and basin-like or saucer-like depressions, is common outside the Chicago plain. The same topography is wide-spread throughout the whole area affected by drift. In the depressions lie many of the ponds and lakes which abound in the glaciated part of our country.

The topography of the region as left by the ice was then the result of the superposition of an unequally thick mantle of drift, on an uneven surface of rock.

LAKE CHICAGO

Origin. - Every ice-sheet has a period of advance followed by a period of decline. In the former, the growth of the ice-field exceeds its waste, and in the latter the waste exceeds the growth. The duration of the last ice-sheet in the region is unknown, but it is probably to be reckoned in thousands of years. When the conditions became such that the ice front was melted back faster than it advanced, the final retreat of the ice began. While the edge of the ice was being melted back to the Valparaiso moraine, and while it stood in that position, the water which arose from its melting flowed off to the south. That from Northern Illinois found its way by various valleys to the Mississippi, and thence to the sea. One line of drainage was down the Des Plaines valley to the Illinois. When the ice retreated northeast of the Valparaiso moraine, the depression between the ice front on the one side, and the moraine ridge on the other, was flooded with glacial water, and a lake, marginal to the ice, came into existence. As the edge of the ice which formed one shore of the lake retreated northward the lake enlarged. Its water rose until it reached a level about 60 feet above the present surface of Lake Michigan, when it overflowed to the west along the line of the present Des Plaines river valley and through the Sag (see Fig. 3).

The accumulation of water between the moraine and the ice was the beginning of what has been called Lake Chicago, in some sense the ancestor of the present Lake Michigan. This lake is the third great factor to be considered in studying the geography of this region. The lines of drainage which developed into the present Des Plaines valley and the Sag tributary to it, have long been known as the Chicago outlet.

The Chicago outlet. - The general features of the outlet have already been given. Near Lemont, the valley is largely cut in rock, the limestone beds rising 40 to 60 feet above the valley bottom on either side. This valley is probably not preglacial, though it may have antedated the last glacial epoch. If so, it was largely filled with drift during that epoch. The top of the rock in the bluffs has about the same elevation as that of the waters of Lake Chicago at its highest stage.

At its maximum, the discharge of water through this outlet must have been comparable to that now discharged through the Niagara river. Below Lemont, the bed of the outlet declines 90 feet in 25 miles. Of this fall 76 feet is made in less than 10 miles, between Romeo and Joliet pool. The nature of the rock is such that it is not probable that a waterfall was established, but the high gradient must have caused strong rapids.

Stages. - There were several more or less distinct stages in the history of Lake Chicago. During the first stage, which has been recognized (the Glenwood stage), its water seems to have stood about 60 feet above the level of Lake Michigan. This stage lasted for a considerable period of time, during which the waves and currents did their appropriate work. Where they cut into the shores they developed cliffs; where they were depositing instead of eroding, they made beaches and spits of sand and gravel. All this time the ice may have been melting back, so that the ice-shore of the lake was receding to the northeastward, and the area of the lake increasing.

Following this maximum stand of Lake Chicago, when its waters were 60 feet higher than those of Lake Michigan, there was a stage during which the waters are thought to have been too low to discharge through the outlet to the west, or even to cover all of the Chicago plain. On this plain, so far as not covered with water, vegetation gained a foothold, and where marshy conditions pre-vailed, distinct deposits of peat were formed. This was the second stage of the lake. The reason for the lowering of the lake level at this stage is not known. Probably the ice had retreated so far to the north as to open an outlet in that direction, lower than that via the Des Plaines and Illinois.

Later, the water of the lake rose again, though not so high as before, covering the plain and burying the peat and other vegetal deposits under accumulations of sand and gravel. This rise of the lake was the beginning of its third stage (the Calumet stage). The cause of the rise of the water may have been an advance of the ice from the north, blocking the outlet of the preceding stage, or a rise of the land to the north, raising the outlet in that direction, and with it the level of the lake. As the waters rose the discharge through the southwestern outlet was again resumed. ...

The outflow lowered the outlet, and with this lowering the level of the lake was gradually drawn down. About 20 feet above the present lake its level remained nearly constant long enough to allow a third series of beaches to be developed. This may be called the fourth stage (the Tolleston stage) of the lake.

Still later, an outlet was opened to the north, probably as the result of the recession of the ice. This outlet was lower than that via Lemont, and the level of the lake was drawn down sufficiently to cut off the flow via the outlet. When this was done, the present conditions were inaugurated, and the history of Lake Chicago was at an end.

THE BEACHES OF LAKE CHICAGO

The Upper or Glenwood beach. - The different levels at which the waters of Lake Chicago stood for any considerable length of time are marked by a series of well-defined shore-lines, whose ridges of beach sand and gravel have been mentioned as significant features of the Chicago plain. The positions of the various shore-lines are indicated in Fig. 3. As before stated, the water at first rose to a level about 60 feet above that of Lake Michigan, or 640 feet above sea level, before it found an outlet, and at this level was formed the first and highest beach. ...

Life. - No satisfactory evidence of life has been found in the waters of the lake at the Glenwood stage. This is as would be expected in the waters mostly derived from the melting of the great ice-sheet.

Blue Island. - Within the area of the Chicago plain shown in Fig. 3, the only emerging land was Blue Island, the ridge of drift already mentioned. That this is a ridge of drift and not of rock covered with a mantle of drift, is shown by well borings. ...

There seems to be no assignable reason why excessive deposition should have occurred at this point. It is probable that as left by the ice, this elevation of drift spread out to the east, north and south somewhat more than now, with more gentle slopes, such as now occur on the west. If this be true, it originally formed a broader and less abrupt swell than now.

At the Glenwood stage of the lake, this drift ridge was an island rising 10 to 35 feet above the waters of Lake Chicago. On its eastern side the waters developed a cliff, and the debris resulting from the erosion was carried out some slight distance from the shore. The currents toward the outlet from the east and southeast appear to have been divided by the ridge, one part of the water sweeping about the north end, and the other part about the south. These currents gathered up the debris which the waves developed, and swept it out to the leeward of the island in a pair of spits, one at the north end and one at the south (Fig. 3). ...

The deposits of sand and gravel seen just east of the till ridge at Morgan Park, Washington Heights and elsewhere, were probably built in the form of barrier ridges by the action of the waves and currents. The beach gravels along the west side of the island are buried beneath an accumulation of dune sand which was blown up later, when the sandy flat to the west emerged from the waters. This well-defined dune sand deposit gives evidence of prevailing west and southwest winds, as at present.

Interval of emergence. - After the Glenwood beach was formed, a northern outlet for the lake seems to have been opened, and its level was lowered until the waters of the lake receded to or beyond the present shore-line of Lake Michigan. ...

The Calumet beach. - Following the period of emergence, the waters of Lake Chicago again rose and flooded the Chicago plain. ... The height to which the water rose in the second submergence of the Chicago plain is marked by the second or Calumet beach, about 35 to 40 feet above the present lake, and about 20 feet below the beach of the Glenwood stage. ...

At the Calumet stage of the lake, the Mount Forest and Blue Island islands of the Glenwood stage were no longer separate, for the plain between them was above water. These islands of the Glenwood stage, and the area between them now formed one large island between the two outlets. Sag Station marks its western extremity, Summit the northern, and Blue Island village the southeastern (Fig. 3).

From Summit, the shore-line of the Calumet stage swung in a broad curve southeastward about the north end of the Blue Island ridge, through Washington Heights. Throughout this distance of eleven and one-half miles, the Calumet beach is marked by a continuous, well-developed ridge of sand and gravel, five to ten feet high, and 50 to 100 yards wide. From Washington Heights to the town of Blue Island, the outer of the barrier ridges marks the shore-line of this stage. ...

The Third or Tolleston beach. - Following the Calumet stage of the lake was a stage during which the waters stood at a level but 20 feet above the present lake. ... The change of level may have been less sudden than the position of the two shorelines might lead us to infer.

At this stage of the lake a third beach was developed, called the Tolleston beach, from the village of Tolleston in northwestern Indiana. ...

At the Tolleston stage of the lake, Stony Island had begun to emerge as an island or a reef (Fig. 3), and its position gave it a controlling influence on the currents. ...

Stony Island. - Stony Island is an elevation of rock. Its strata have quaquaversal or perclinal dips, i.e., the strata, on all sides of the ridge, dip outward. The angle of dip ranges from 30° to 42°. At first thought, the "island" appears not to be an erosion remnant, but due to a local elevation of the rock strata. Gentle undulations of the rock-beds are seen at other exposures, but none so abrupt as this. No very satisfactory evidence is at hand by which the date of the uplift which deformed the beds can be fixed. If it preceded the later part of the erosion which affected the limestone before the glacial period, the erosion remnant (that is, the island) happened to correspond in position with the center of the uplift. There is some evidence in the rock itself that its deformation took place while the layers which are now exposed were under great weight. If this be so, the great weight was probably the weight of other beds since eroded away. ...

Evidences of life at the Tolleston stage. - In striking contrast with the Glenwood and Calumet beaches, the Tolleston beach contains abundant traces of life closely related to the life of Lake Michigan, if not identical with it. ...

RECENT CHANGES

Lake Michigan beach. - With the diversion of the waters of the lake from the outlet to the north, the history of Lake Chicago may be considered as passing into the history of Lake Michigan, so that the series of beaches and bars lying between the Tolleston shoreline of Lake Chicago and the present shore of Lake Michigan, mark the closing stages of the history of Lake Chicago, and the earliest stages of Lake Michigan. During this stage, so much of the Chicago plain as was still submerged was being built up by deposits of sand and gravel brought to the head of the lake by the southward drift of the littoral currents. In the northern part of the city, as far south as Lincoln Park, there is a close-set series of sand and gravel ridges 10 to 15 feet high, between the Tolleston beach and the present shore of the lake. These ridges are often capped with a little dune sand. ... Northeast and east of Washington Park, there is a series of 10 to 12 low ridges. These were built as subaqueous ridges by drift from the north. They have a generally parallel direction, sometimes branch, and vary in length from one to six miles, running out into the sandy plain. Their southern ends are usually turned slightly to the west, as in hook formations. The longest and most prominent of these ridges is that passing through the campus of the University of Chicago, where its structure was well seen before destroyed by grading. It continues southward through the western part of Oakwood cemetery, terminating one mile north of Burnside (Fig. 3.).

The existence of the basin of Lake Calumet is probably due, in part, to the influence of Stony Island which deflected the currents about its eastern end, whence they continued southward, depositing sand and gravel along their course, and leaving the area of the shallow lake unfilled. Like ridges enclosed Hyde Lake, Wolf Lake and Lake George, as well as the adjacent marshy areas.

Between these lakes and the Tolleston beach to the south is a remarkable series of parallel ridges, so closely set that they cannot all be separately represented on the map. Including those indicated on the map (Fig. 3) as belonging to the Tolleston stage, there are, from Hammond north to the south end of Lake George, 90 of these ridges, ranging from three to ten feet in height. They are separated, in many cases, by narrow marshy belts. The ridges running southward between these lakes break up into several narrow ridges, and curve to the eastward to form a part of the whole series. These ridges are composed of sand with little gravel, and taken together have the form of a great depositional terrace. This extensive filling, together with a slight lowering of the water level, brought the lake shore to its present position. The drift of the sand at the head of the lake and its accumulation there is still in progress.

Shore erosion. - The opposite phase of lake shore work, namely, wave erosion, is also well shown near the city. From Evanston northward, the waves of the lake are cutting into the bluffs, and driving the shore-line farther and farther west. Locally and very recently this advance of the water on the land has been stayed by various human devices, but the process by which cliffs and wave-cut terraces are developed is still clearly shown. ...

The material eroded by the waves from the bluffs has been shifted southward. The fact of this southerly transportation may be seen on the north side of every pier extending into the lake,

and in the spits wrapping around the ends of these piers from
north to south below the water surface.

As at earlier stages in the history of the lake, so now, bars
are constantly forming across the river mouths, and must be repeatedly removed by dredging to keep the harbors open. Before
the improvement of the present harbor at Chicago there was a bar
across the outlet of the Chicago river, which shifted the debouchure
southward nearly one-half mile from its present position, or opposite the foot of Madison street. The Calumet river has undergone
similar changes. That part of the stream east of Hegewisch has
been reversed by the dredging of a channel from Hegewisch to the
outlet of Lake Calumet. ...

The dunes. - The formation of sand dunes by the blowing up
of the fine sand from the beach into ridges and hills has been going
on, perhaps since the birth of Lake Chicago; but the most striking
results have been accomplished since the shore of the lake reached
approximately its present position. ... At Dune Park and Millers,
dunes are to be seen in all stages of development, from the little
drifts of sand in the lee of stumps or shrubs, to great shifting
hills of sand 100 to 200 feet in height. ...

The formation of the dunes is easily understood. As the brisk
wind which is carrying sand passes an obstructing object, such as
a tree, a shrub, or a tuft of grass, its current is interrupted, and
in the quieter area in the lee of the obstruction some of the sand
is dropped. A little pile or drift of sand accumulating in such a
position is the beginning of a dune. Hundreds of them may be seen
along the shore at the present time. Where a drift of sand becomes
appreciable, it itself becomes an obstruction, against and beyond
which more sand lodges. Thus the dune grows, and under favorable conditions may attain great dimensions.

But destruction goes hand in hand with construction. The
wind takes up sand not only from the beach, but from the surface
of the dunes. It is gathered up from the windward side, and carried up over the crest only to be dropped on the leeward slope. So
the dune may be shifted, inch by inch, from windward to leeward.
This movement, which in the course of time may be great, is
known as the migration of dunes. In places dunes have moved inland great distances, burying vegetation and devastating fields.
Some of the dunes about the head of the lake are now far from
shore, but it is not always possible to say how far their position
is due to their migration inland, and how far to the recession of
the shore from them, as the result of shore-filling. Dunes are
likely to be migratory until vegetation gets a foot-hold on them.
When this is done the sand ceases to be blown, and the dune
ceases its travels. ...

After a dune has become clothed with vegetation, sand may
accumulate upon it, being lodged by the shrubs and trees. If the
sand accumulates more rapidly than the trees grow upward, they
will be buried. ... If the sand which buries the forests be blown
on again before vegetation gets a foot-hold on it, the dead forest
may be again discovered,--resurrected, but not to life. This also

is to be seen about the head of the lake at various points near
Millers. ...

Weathering. - Since the glacial drift was deposited, perhaps
6,000 to 10,000 years ago, it has been changed to some slight extent by weathering. The change is most obvious in the alteration
of color which its surface has undergone. While the body of the
unstratified drift is gray, the upper part just beneath the soil is
buffish or brownish. This change in color is primarily the result
of oxidation of the iron compounds originally in the drift.

The formation of the soil. - So soon as the ice melted from
the region, weathering began to prepare the surface for the support
of plant life. When vegetation began to grow and die and decay,
organic matter was contributed to the mineral matter which supported the first vegetation, and the carbonacous matter made the
soil black. The same changes affected the area temporarily occupied by the lake, so soon as the water was drawn off. The
growth of the vegetation has, in turn, furthered the surface
changes in the drift.

[The following paragraphs on Plant Ecology of the Dunes added in
Second Edition, 1920]:

Vegetation on the dunes. - Plants get their first foothold on
the lower slopes of the dunes, especially on their lee sides. The
sand in this position is less dry than elsewhere. The earliest
plants to gain a foothold are xerophitic, i.e., have adaptations for
preventing ready transpiration of moisture. This is not so much
because moisture is scarce, for the sand is almost always moist
a short distance below the surface, as because the air above the
sand gets very warm and dry in the sunshine and wind. The air
conditions, therefore, are those of arid regions.

The succession of plant life which takes possession of the
dunes has been worked out with much care by Professor Cowles.
He has shown that the plants which first get a foothold on the dune
sand are herbaceous perennials, such as some species of grasses,
milkweed, etc. A little later shrubs appear, such as certain
species of willows, the sand cherry, and one of the dogwoods. As
the shrubs get a foothold, they drive out their herbaceous predecessors, which will not thrive in the shade. The bass (linden) is
one of the first trees to appear. It is soon followed by the cottonwood, and later by hardwoods, such as the oak, the elm, and certain maples. Many lianas (vines), such as the grape, appear with
the trees. The falling leaves of the trees and vines give rise to
humus, and once the soil has abundant humus the range of plants
which may grow is greatly enlarged. The sugar maple, the beech,
and the hemlock are late comers. Plant formations of this advanced type are not well developed in any region easily accessible
from Chicago.

On windward slopes and crests, conifers, such as the juniper,
which will stand greater drought than many other plants, get a
foothold. The juniper may be accompanied by such plants as the

bearberry, the sand cherry, certain willows, and some herbaceous plants. Many of the established (fixed) dunes are covered with scrubby xerophitic types of oaks. Pines appear both above and below the oaks on some dunes. Where oaks establish themselves, they appear to drive out the pines. In some places cacti, similar to those of deserts, flourish.

The study of the successions of plant life on dunes is a very interesting and instructive one, and is illustrated better in few places than about the head of the lake. Adding to the interest of the study of the plant life on the dunes is the fact that the depressions between the hills and ridges afford the proper habitat for a group of plants wholly different from those which grow on the drier dunes above. The destruction of so fine a field for the study of plants and plant adaptation would be a great loss.

The fauna of the dunes, though perhaps less extensive than the flora, also is interesting and well worth preservation. Lizards, characteristic of warm and arid regions, are one of the interesting members of the dune fauna.

EXPERIMENTS IN GEOGRAPHICAL DESCRIPTION[1]

by W. M. Davis

THE DISSECTED COASTAL PLAIN NEAR ANCONA

... The northeastern Apennines serve as the oldland to a dissected coastal plain, some 20 or 30 kilometers in breadth, composed of unconsolidated strata of clay and sand. The dissection has been carried to a stage of late maturity by prevailingly consequent streams with short insequent branches, the largest consequents being those which have been extended across the plain from the Apennine oldland to the sea. The oldland, although not sharply separated from the coastal plain, has a more deformed structure, a great altitude, and a tendency to a longitudinal rather than to a transverse arrangement of its ridges. The relief of the district is moderate or small, with altitudes of 200 or 250 meters along its inner border, and of from 50 to 120 meters near the coast, where the sea has developed a fully mature line of cliffs which truncate all the sea-board hills in even alignment. The texture of dissection is rather coarse. In consequence of a slight and recent elevation, increasing from zero at the coast to 10 or 20 meters at the inland border of the district, the larger consequent

1. *Bull. Am. Geog. Soc.*, vol. 42 (1910), pp. 412-430.

streams have excavated mature floods plains below the terraced remnants of their earlier valley floors; and during about the same recent period the sea has withdrawn from the maturely aligned cliffs of its former attack and prograded a strand-plain from 200 to 300 meters in breadth, which at the river mouths is broadened in faintly convex deltas of about double this measure. Hence it seems as if the recently revived rivers had rapidly washed so much waste to the sea, that the waves could not immediately dispose of all of it, and therefore deposited a part of it along the shore, thus prograding the strand plain. These features are graphically summarized in Figure 4, an imagined bird's-eye view, looking northwest.

The essentials of the above description are, first, that it begins with a general statement from which the reader may immediately infer the total initial structure and form of the district concerned; second, that it proceeds, tacitly implying the action of normal and of marine processes of erosion, to state the stage that each of these processes has reached in the regular progress of its

Fig. 4. "Diagram of the Late Mature Coastal Plain, South of Ancona, Italy; looking West".

work; and third, that it adds in closing a brief account of the result of a slight interruption of the first cycle of erosion due to a slanting uplift of small amount, and with the cautionary words, as if, provisionally suggests the correlated origin of two new features, the terraced valley floors, and the prograded strand plain, concerning which our brief excursions did not suffice to provide full proof.

Let us consider these points in more detail. From the term, coastal plain, which is given in the first sentence of the description, the initiated reader immediately understands a simple structural mass chiefly composed of stratified sediments, deposited on a sea floor when the region formerly stood lower than now, and when the sea had its shore on the flanks of the Apennine oldland; but now revealed as a land area, sloping gently seaward, in virtue of a broad uplift without significant deformation. Even if all this had been explicitly stated, instead of having been only implied in the term, coastal plain, the description would not have been too geological, for every point of the expanded statement bears helpfully on the appreciative understanding of the existing landscape, and hence on its proper description. Nothing is introduced simply for the sake of its geological interest, however great that may be; even the geological date of the strata concerned is left unmentioned, because this is geographically irrelevant.

It may be noted in passing that the terms, coastal plain and coast plain, have been used by some geographers to designate platforms of marine abrasion, now uplifted so as to form a littoral lowland. Geographical terminology is so little developed and systematized that no agreement as to the limitation of these and various other terms has yet been reached. ...

The technical terms here employed are few; most of them are almost self explanatory, but they are all highly significant. Consequent and insequent streams and valleys present elementary and fundamental conceptions in rational physiography. Retrogradation and progradation of a shore line by marine action correspond to degradation and aggradation of a valley floor by a stream; in both cases, the steady action of balanced forces is implied. Surely there can be no sufficient reason that the newly recognized ideas represented by these newly introduced terms should be neglected by modern geographers who employ, whenever they can, such innovations as motor cars, film cameras and daylight developers. Nor need there be any fear that the mere use of such technical terms as are here suggested will necessarily result in enforcing an unattractive, non-literary style upon geographical descriptions. Attractiveness of style is a matter to be cultivated for and by itself; it is as well worth cultivating in geography as in history; but in neither subject should it involve a sacrifice of truth and efficiency to form and sound. The degree of technicality appropriate in a geographical description will depend largely on the condition of the readers for whom it is written. As the description here in discussion is intended for mature geographers, it does not seem to be either unduly technical or unattractively awkward.

It is assumed at the beginning of the description that Apennines and Adriatic are names that every mature geographical reader will know without explanation. No other local names are used in the general physiographic description. But now that the general features of the district have been presented, local names and all sorts of details may be conveniently added, and ontographic relations may be effectively introduced. For example, agricultural villages are found on the broader hills of the dissected interfluves, one of these being Loreto with its famous shrine, standing on a full-bodied spur crest some four kilometers back from the coast; here pilgrims would appear to yield a larger revenue than farms. Fishing villages lie on the harborless strandplain, especially near the mouths of the larger valleys; in bad weather their boats are hauled up on the beach or towed into the little rivers. An important trunk railroad and a main wagon road follow the level strandplain for a long distance; branch railroads enter some of the larger valleys, and wagon roads turn up all of them; while roads of less importance enter certain smaller valleys and sidle in zigzags up the spurs to the farming villages on the interfluve hills, or follow the hill crests in passing from one upland village to another. It may be pointed out that Ancona does not belong to the coastal plain; it lies on the northern side of a cliffed promonotory of altogether different constitution. ...

GEOLOGY, AS SUCH, TO BE AVOIDED IN GEOGRAPHICAL DESCRIPTIONS

The influence of geology upon geography has indeed been so great that it has come to be a common practice to introduce some statement of geological history, as if in explanation of the origin of land forms, so as to aid in their description; but if geological history is introduced in a more or less haphazard way, it often goes too far in taking the attention away from the geographical present and holding it too long on the irrelevant past; and it often does not go far enough in the way of emphasizing the origin of visible forms. The accidental geological explanation is moreover especially deficient in not developing a carefully extended series of deductive types, in terms of which existing forms may be presented. In some way or other such a series of types certainly ought to be developed and carried in the mind as an indispensable equipment for outdoor observation and description. The way that has been most convenient, effective and helpful in my experience is the one embodied in the method to which I have given the name "structure, process and stage," and of which some illustration has been afforded by the examples presented above from my Italian excursion.

GRAPHIC AIDS IN GEOGRAPHICAL DESCRIPTION

... In the fancy view of the dissected coastal plain south of Ancona, here given in Figure 4, the hill shading is very rough; all the slopes are drawn convex, and hence fail to show the graceful concave lower sweep down to the valley floors. The terraces in the main valleys and the narrow belt of oldland included in the background are too definite and distinct. The absence of all indications of forests and fields, of villages and roads, gives an impression of barrenness and vacancy that does no justice to the pleasing reality. Moreover, the dissected hills and the broad valleys of two extended consequent streams from the oldland do not correspond to any particular hills and valleys of the district concerned; they merely show the observer's generalized idea of the kinds of hills and valleys that characterize the district. Nevertheless the drawing has a value in immediately presenting the essential features of a late maturely dissected plain, in which the streams and valleys are prevailing consequent, with some insequent branches; in which the hill sides are all reduced to gently graded slopes; and in which the spurs in the foregound are all evenly truncated by the former sea cliff, in front of which the strand plain is now prograded.

C H A P T E R 4

Explanatory Human Geography

From explanatory physical geography it was a short and logical step to explanatory human geography in an effort to account for the inhabitants of the Earth as well as for the Earth itself in evolutionary natural science. The logic of it appealed to W. M. Davis and other natural scientists and was expressed in Davis' recommendation to geographers to make such an effort.[1] Meanwhile Ellen C. Semple, as a student of Friedrich Ratzel, had caught a kindred idea in Germany and brought it to America as Anthropogeography.

"Anglo-Saxons of the Kentucky Mountains" by Miss Semple, 1901, is taken to represent a fourth type in this series. It is an explanatory description of a group of people and their way of life particularly in terms of their natural environment. The author was not a natural scientist but a student of history, and her ideas were cast in a mould of historical evolution rather than of physical process. On this account perhaps her work escapes the determinism of scientific cause and effect explanation but on the other hand may overlook opportunities for exact analytical findings in an array of broad generalizations. In any case it is evident that the study has had its strong appeal not from

1. *p. 37 above.*

scientific explanation nor from broad generalization but from eloquent and colorful local description of people in their habitat and way of
life. In this respect it is more like the "Journals of the Lewis and Clark Expedition"[1] than
like anything else in this series.

The field method is that of casual observation
and inquiry and of inference from postulated
theory. Precise locations, orientations or areal
associations are not involved, and the one map
included originally is not essential. The study
is intended for an audience of students and others
interested in geography.

Miss Semple was accompanied and followed by
many other enthusiasts in the field of environmentalism, rightly convinced that there are relations of a cause and effect character between
natural environment and human life, and wrongly
convinced that a simple and direct way of determining those relations is immediately available.

The range of ideas is represented in the variety
of terms expressing environmental relations in
a scale from strong to weak: environmental
determinism implying absolute cause and effect;
environmental control implying less than absolute determinism; environmental influence implying active if not determinative natural force;
environmental response implying that nature
speaks and man answers; possibilism implying

1. pp. 15 - 26 above.

certain inherent possibilities from which to
choose; and environmental adjustment implying
that man may choose from what he understands
to be available. Miss Semple's approach in this
study and others, commonly called geographic
influence[1], is near the middle of the scale.

THE ANGLO-SAXONS OF THE KENTUCKY MOUNTAINS:
A STUDY IN ANTHROPOGEOGRAPHY[2]
by Ellen C. Semple

In one of the most progressive and productive countries
of the world, and in that section of the country which has had its
civilization and its wealth longest, we find a large area where
the people are still living the frontier life of the backwoods, where
the civilization is that of the eighteenth century, where the people
speak the English of Shakespeare's time, where the large majority
of the inhabitants have never seen a steamboat or a railroad,
where money is as scarce as in colonial days, and all trade is
barter. It is the great upheaved mass of the Southern Appalachians
which, with the conserving power of the mountains, has caused
these conditions to survive, carrying a bit of the eighteenth century intact over into this strongly contrasted twentieth century,
and presenting an anachronism all the more marked because
found in the heart of the bustling, money-making, novelty-loving
United States. These conditions are to be found throughout the
broad belt of the Southern Appalachians, but nowhere in such
purity or covering so large an area as in the mountain region of
Kentucky.
A mountain system is usually marked by a central crest,
but the Appalachians are distinguished by a central zone of depression, flanked on the east by the Appalachian Mountains proper, and on the west by the Alleghany and the Cumberland Plateaus. This central trough is generally designated as the Great
Appalachian Valley. It is depressed several hundred feet below

---

1. E. C. Semple: *Influences of Geographic Environment*, (New York: Henry Holt
& Co., 1911).
2. *Geog. Jour.*, vol. 17 (1901), pp. 588-623. Reprinted in *Bull. Am. Geog. Soc.*,
vol. 42, (1910), pp 1-34.

the highlands on either side, but its surface is relieved by intermittent series of even-crested ridges which rise 1000 feet or
more above the general level, running parallel to each other, and
conforming at the same time to the structural axis of the whole
system. The valleys between them owe neither width nor form
to the streams which drain them. The Cumberland Plateau forms
the western highland of the Great Valley in Eastern Kentucky,
Tennessee, and Northern Alabama. This plateau belt reaches its
greatest height in Kentucky, and slopes gradually from this section to the south and west. Its eastern escarpment rises abruptly
800 to 1500 feet from the Great Valley, and shows everywhere an
almost perfectly straight skyline. The western escarpment is
very irregular, for the streams, flowing westward from the plateau, have carved out their valleys far back into the elevated district, leaving narrow spurs running out into the low plains beyond.
The surface is highly dissected, presenting a maze of gorge-like
valleys separating the steep, regular slopes of the sharp or rounded hills. The level of the originally upheaved mass of the plateau
is now represented by the altitude of the existing summits, which
show a remarkable uniformity in the north-east-south-west line,
and a slight rise in elevation from the western margin towards
the interior.

About 10,000 square miles of the Cumberland Plateau fall
within the confines of the State of Kentucky, and form the eastern section of the State. A glance at the topographical map of
the region shows the country to be devoted by nature to isolation
and poverty. The eastern rim of the plateau is formed by Pine
Mountain, which raises its solid wall with level top in silhouette
against the sky, and shows only one water-gap in a distance of
150 miles. And just beyond is the twin range of the Cumberland. Hence no railroads have attempted to cross this double
border-barrier, except at the north-east and south-east corners
of the State, where the Big Sandy and Cumberland Rivers have
carved their way through the mountains to the west. Railroads,
therefore, skirt this upland region, but nowhere penetrate it.
The whole area is a coalfield, the mineral being chiefly bitu-
minous, with several thousand square miles of superior cannel
coal. The obstructions growing out of the topography of the
country, and the cheap river transportation afforded by the Ohio
for the Kanawha and Monogahela River coal have tended to re-
tard the construction of railroads within the mountains, and even
those on the margin of this upland region have been built since
1880.

Man has done so little to render this district accessible because nature has done so little. There are here no large streams
penetrating the heart of the mountains, as in Tennessee, where
the Tennessee River, drawing its tributaries from the easternmost
ranges of the Appalachians, cuts westward by flaring water-gaps
through chain after chain and opens a highway from the interior
of the system to the plains of the Mississippi. The Kentucky
streams are navigable only to the margin of the plateau, and

therefore leave this great area without natural means of communication with the outside world to the west, while to the east the mountain wall has acted as an effective barrier to communication with the Atlantic seaboard. Consequently, all commerce has been kept at arms' length, and the lack of a market has occasioned the poverty of the people, which, in turn, has prohibited the construction of highroads over the mountains of the Cumberland plateau.

It is what the mountaineers themselves call a rough country. The steep hills rise from 700 to 1200 feet above their valleys. The valleys are nothing more than gorges. Level land there is none, and roads there are almost none. Valley and road and mountain stream coincide. In the summer the dry or half-dry beds of the streams serve as highways; and in the winter, when the torrents are pouring a full tide down the hollows, foot trails cut through the dense forest that mantles the slopes are the only means of communication. Then intercourse is practically cut off. Even in the best season transportation is in the main limited to what a horse can carry on its back beside its rider. In a trip of 350 miles through the mountains, we met only one wheel vehicle and a few trucks for hauling railroad ties, which were being gotten out of the forests. Our own camp waggons, though carrying only light loads, had to double their teams in climbing the ridges. All that had been done in most cases to make a road over a mountain was to clear an avenue through the dense growth of timber, so that it proved, as a rule, to be just short of impassable. For this reason the public of the mountains prefer to keep to the valleys with their streams, to which they have given many expressive and picturesque names, while the knobs and mountains are rarely honored with a name. We have Cutshin creek, Hell-fer-Sartain, Bullskin creek, Poor Fork, Stinking, Greasy, and Quicksand creek. One trail leads from the waters of Kingdom-Come down Lost creek and Troublesome, across the Upper Devil and Lower Devil to Hell creek. _Facilis decensus Averno,_ only no progress is easy in these mountains. The creek, therefore, points the highway, and is used to designate geographical locations. When we would inquire our way to a certain point, the answer was, "Go ahead to the fork of the creek, and turn up the left branch," not the fork of the road and the path to the left. A woman at whose cabin we lunched one day said, "My man and me has been living here on Quicksand only ten years. I was born up on Troublesome."

All passenger travel is on horseback. The important part which the horse plays, therefore, in the economy of the mountain family recalls pioneer days. Almost every cabin has its blacksmith's forge under an open shed or in a low outhouse. The country stores at the forks or fords of the creek keep bellows in stock. Every mountaineer is his own blacksmith, and though he works with very simple implements, he knows a few fundamental principles of the art, and does the work well. Men and women are quite at home in the saddle. The men are superb horsemen; sit their animals firm and erect, even when mounted on top of the meal-bag, which is the regular accompaniment of

the horseman. We saw one day a family on their way to the country store to exchange their produce. The father, a girl, and a
large bag of Indian corn were mounted on one mule, and the mother, a younger girl, and a black lamb suspended in a sack from
the saddle-bow on the other. It is no unusual thing to see a woman
on horseback, with a child behind her and a baby in her arms,
while she holds an umbrella above them.

But such travel is not easy, and hence we find that these
Kentucky mountaineers are not only cut off from the outside world,
but they are separated from each other. Each is confined to his
own locality, and finds his little world within a radius of a few
miles from his cabin. There are many men in these mountains
who have never seen a town, or even the poor village that constitutes their county-seat. Those who have obtained a glimpse of
civilization have gone down the head-waters of the streams on
lumber rafts, or have been sent to the state penitentiary at Frank-
fort for illicit distilling or feud murder. The women, however,
cannot enjoy either of these privileges; they are almost as rooted
as the trees. We met one woman who, during the twelve years of
her married life, had lived only 10 miles across the mountain
from her old home, but had never in this time been back home to visit
her mother and father. Another back in Perry county told us she
had never been farther from home than Hazard, the county-seat,
which was only six miles distant. Another had never been to the
post-office, 4 miles away, and another had never seen the ford of
the Rockcastle River, only 2 miles from her home, and marked,
moreover, by the country store of the district.

A result of this confinement to one locality is the absence
of anything like social life, and the close intermarriage of families
inhabiting one district. These two phenomena appear side by side
here as in the upland valleys of Switzerland and other mountain
countries where communication is difficult. One can travel for
40 miles along one of the head streams of the Kentucky River
and find the same names recurring in all the cabins along both
its shores. One woman in Perry County told us she was related
to everybody up and down the North Fork of the Kentucky and
along its tributary creeks. In Breathitt County, an old judge,
whose family had been among the early settlers on Troublesome,
stated that in the district school near by there were ninety-six
children, of whom all but five were related to himself or his wife.
This extensive intermarriage stimulates the clan instinct and
contributes to the strength of the feuds which rage here from
time to time.

It is a law of biology that an isolating environment operates
for the preservation of a type by excluding all intermixture which
would obliterate distinguishing characteristics. In these isolated
communities, therefore, we find the purest Anglo-Saxon stock in
all the United States. They are the direct descendants of the
early Virginia and North Carolina immigrants, and bear about them
in their speech and ideas the marks of their ancestry as plainly
as if they had disembarked from their eighteenth-century vessel

but yesterday. The stock is chiefly English and Scotch-Irish, with scarcely a trace of foreign admixture. Occasionally one comes across a French name, which points to a strain of Huguenot blood from over the mountains in North Carolina; or names of the Germans who came down the pioneer thoroughfare of the Great Appalachian Valley from the Pennsylvania Dutch settlements generations ago. But the stock has been kept free from the tide of foreign immigrants which has been pouring in recent years into the States. In the border counties of the district where the railroads run, and where English capital has bought up the mines in the vicinity, the last census shows a few foreign-born, but these are chiefly Italian labourers working on the road-bed, or British capitalists and employees. Four of the interior counties have not a single foreign-born, and eight others have only two or three.

Though these mountain people are the exponents of a retarded civilization, and show the degenerate symptoms of an arrested development, their stock is as good as any in the country. They formed a part of the same tide of pioneers which crossed the mountains to people the young States to the South-west, but they chanced to turn aside from the main stream, and ever since have stagnated in these mountain hollows. For example, over a hundred years ago eleven Combs brothers, related to General Combs, of the Revolutionary army, came over the mountains from North Carolina. Nine of them settled along the North Fork of the Kentucky river in the mountains of Perry county, one went further down the stream into the rough hill country of Breathitt County, and the eleventh continued on his way till he came into the smiling regions of the Bluegrass, and there became the progenitor of a family which represents the blue blood of the state, with all the aristocratic instincts of the old South; while their cousins in the mountain go barefoot, herd in one-room cabins, and are ignorant of many of the fundamental decencies of life.

If the mountains have kept out foreign elements, still more effectually have they excluded the negroes. This region is as free from them as northern Vermont. There is no place for the negro in the mountain economy, and never has been. In the days of slavery this fact had momentous results. The mountains did not offer conditions for plantation cultivation, the only system of agriculture in which slaves could be profitably employed. The absence of these conditions and of the capital wherewith to purchase negroes made the whole Appalachian region a non-slave-holding section. Hence, when the rupture came between the North and South, this mountain region declared for the Union, and thus raised a barrier of disaffection through the center of the Southern States. It had no sympathy with the industrial system of the South; it shared the democratic spirit characteristic of all mountain people, and likewise their conservatism, which holds to the established order. Having, therefore, no intimate knowledge of the negro, our Kentucky mountaineers do not show the deep-seated prejudice to the social equality of blacks and whites which characterizes all other Kentuckians. We find today, on the western margin of the Cumberland Plateau, a flourishing college for the co-education of the Bluegrass blacks and mountain whites; and this is probably the only geographical location south of the Mason and Dixon line where such an institution could exist.

Though the mountaineer comes of such vigorous stock as the Anglo-Saxons, he has retained little of the ruddy, vigorous appearance of his forebears. The men are tall and lank, though sinewy, with thin bony faces, sallow skins, and dull hair. They hold themselves in a loose-jointed way; their shoulders droop in walking and sitting. Their faces are immobile, often inscrutable, but never stupid; for one is sure that under this calm exterior the mountaineer is doing a deal of thinking, which he does not see fit to share with the "furriner", as he calls every one coming from the outside world. The faces of the women are always delicately moulded and refined, with an expression of dumb patience telling of the heavy burden which life has laid upon them. They are absolutely simple, natural, and their child-like unconsciousness of self points to their long residence away from the gaze of the world. Their manners are gentle, gracious, and unembarrassed, so that in talking with them one forgets their bare feet, ragged clothes, and crass ignorance, and in his heart bows anew to the inextinguishable excellence of the Anglo-Saxon race.

The lot of a mountain woman is a hard one. Only the lowest peasantry of Europe can show anything to parallel it. She marries between twelve and fifteen years a husband who is between seventeen and twenty. The motive in marriage is very elemental, betrays little of the romantic spirit. Husband and wife speak of each other as "my man" and "my woman". A girl when she is twenty is put on the "cull list," that is, she is no longer marriageable. A man is included in this undesirable category at twenty-eight; after that he can get no one to take him "except some poor wider-woman," as one mountain matron expressed it, adding, "gals on the cull-list spend their time jes' bummin' around among their folks." During a ride of 350 miles, with visits at a great many cabins, we met only one old maid; her lot was a sorry one, living now with a relative, now with a friend, earning her board by helping to nurse the sick or making herself useful in what way she could. The mountain system of economy does not take into account the unmarried woman, so she plunges into matrimony with the instinct of self-preservation. Then come children; and the mountain familes conform to the standard of the patriarchs. A family of from ten to fifteen offspring is no rarity, and this characterizes not only the mountains of Kentucky, but the whole area of the Appalachian system. In addition to much child-bearing, all the work of the pioneer home, the spinning and weaving, knitting of stockings, sometimes even the making of shoes and moccasins, falls on the woman. More than this, she feeds and milks the cow, searches for it when it has wandered away "in the range," or forest, hoes weeds in the corn, helps in the ploughing, carries water from the spring, saws wood and lays "stake and ridered" fences. A mountain woman who had a

husband and two sons, and who had been employed all day in mak-
a fence, lifting the heavy rails above the height of her own head,
replied in a listless way to the question as to what the men did,
with, "the men folks they mostly sets on a fence and chaw tabac-
co and talk politics."

The mountain woman, therefore, at twenty-five looks forty,
and at forty looks twenty years older than her husband. But none
of the race are stalwart and healthy. The lack of vigour in the
men is due chiefly to the inordinate use of moonshine whiskey,
which contains 20 per cent more alcohol than the standard liquor.
They begin drinking as mere boys. We saw several youths of
seventeen intoxicated, and some women told us boys of fourteen
or fifteen drank. Men, women, and children looked underfed, ill
nourished. This is due in part to their scanty, unvaried diet, but
more perhaps to the vile cooking. The bread is either half-baked
soda biscuits eaten hot, or corn-pone with lumps of saleratus
through it. The meat is always swimming in grease, and the eggs
are always fried. The effect of this shows, in the adults, in their
sallow complexions and spare forms; in the children, in pimples,
boils, and sores on their hands and faces. This western side of
the mountains, moreover, has not an abundant water-supply, the
horizontal strata of the rocks reducing the number of springs.
Hence all the mountain region of Kentucky, West Virginia, and
Tennessee shows a high percentage of diarrhoeal diseases, ty-
phoid, and malarial fever.

The home of the mountaineer is primitive in the extreme,
a survival of pioneer architecture, and the only type distinctly
American. It is the blind or windowless one-room log cabin,
with the rough stone chimney on the outside. The logs are sometimes squared with the hatchet, sometimes left in their original
form with the bark on; the interstices are chinked in with clay.
The roofs are covered with boards nearly an inch thick and 3
feet long, split from the wood by a wedge, and laid on, one lapping
over the other like shingles. The chimneys, which are built on
the outside of the houses, and project a few feet above the roof,
lend a picturesque effect to the whole. They are made of native
rock, roughly hewn and cemented with clay; but the very poorest
cabins have the low "stick chimney," made of laths daubed with
clay. In the broader valleys, where the conditions of life are
somewhat better, the double cabin prevails--two cabins side by
side, with a roofed space between, which serves as a dining-
room during the warmer months of the year. Sometimes, though
rarely, there is a porch in front, covered by an extension of the
sloping roof. In some of the marginal counties of the mountain
region and in the sawmill districts, one sees a few two-story
frame dwellings. These are decorated with ornamental trim-
ming of scroll-saw work in wood, oftentimes colored a light
blue, along the edges of the gables, and defining the line between
the two stories. The regulation balcony over the front door and
extending to the roof has a balustrade of the same woodwork in
excellent, chaste design, sometimes painted and sometimes in

the natural color. These houses, both in their architecture and style of ornamentation, recall the village dwellings in Norway, though not so beautiful or so richly decorated. But the usual home of the mountaineer is the one-room cabin. Near by is the barn, a small square log structure, with the roof projecting from 8 to 10 feet, to afford shelter for the young cattle or serve as a milking-shed. These vividly recall the mountain architecture of some of the Alpine dwellings of Switzerland and Bavaria, especially when, as in a few instances, the roofs are held down by weight-rocks to economize hardware. Very few of them have hay-lofts above, for the reason that only a few favored districts in these mountains produce hay. ...

Conditions point to agriculture as the only means for the Kentucky mountaineer to gain a livelihood. Mineral wealth exists in abundance in this section, but the lack of transportation facilities prevents its exploitation; so the rough hillsides must be converted into field and pasture. The mountaineer holds his land in fee simple, or by squatter claim. This is based, not upon title, but merely on the right of possession, which is regarded, moreover, as a thoroughly valid basis in a country which still preserves its frontier character. Large tracts of Kentucky mountain lands are owned by persons outside the state, by purchase or inheritance of original pioneer patents, and these are waiting for the railroads to come into the country, when they hope to realize on the timber and mines. In the meantime the mountaineers have been squatting on the territory for years, clearing the forests, selling the timber, and this with conscious impunity, for interference with them is dangerous in the extreme. Every lawyer from the outside world who comes up here to a county courthouse to examine titles to the land about, keeps his mission as secret as possible, and having accomplished it, leaves the town immediately. If further investigation is necessary, he does not find it safe to return himself, but sends a substitute who will not be recognized.

The pioneer character of the region is still evident in the size of the land-holdings. In the most mountainous parts near the eastern border-line the farms average from 160 to 320 acres; in the western part of the plateau, from 100 to 160 acres. Of the whole state, the mountain counties show by far the largest proportion of farms of 1000 acres and over. Pike County has sixty-six such. Mountaineers in two different sections told us that the land on the small side creeks was better, and there farms averaged about 200 acres; but that on main streams, like the North Fork of the Kentucky river and Poor Fork of the Cumberland, the farms were usually 600 acres, because the soil was poorer. The cause for this was not apparent, unless it was due to exhaustion of soil from long tilling, as the valleys of the main streams, being more accessible, were probably the earliest settled.

Only from thirteen to thirty per cent of the acreage of the farms is improved; the rest is in forest or pasture. Land is cleared for cultivation in the Indian method by "girdling" or

"deadening" the trees, and the first crop is planted amidst the
still standing skeletons of ancient giants of the forests. Indian
corn is the chief crop raised, and furnishes the main food-supply
for man and beast. Great fields of it cover the steep mountain
sides to the very top, except where a farmer, less energetic or
more intelligent than his fellows, has left a crown of timber on
the summit to diminish the evil of washing. The soil on the
slopes is thin, and in the narrow V-shaped valleys there is almost
no opportunity for the accumulation of alluvial soil. Hence the
yield of corn is only from ten to twelve bushels to an acre, only
one-third that in the rich Bluegrass lands of Central Kentucky.
But the population is so sparse that the harvest generally averages
forty bushels per capita. In the "upright" farms all ploughing is
done horizontally around the face of the mountain, but even then
the damage from washing is very great, especially as the staple
crop forms no network of roots to hold the soil and requires repeated ploughing. In consequence, after two successive crops of
corn the hillside is often quite denuded, the soil having been
washed away from the underlying rocks. The field then reverts
to a state of nature, growing up in weeds and briars, and furnishing a scanty pasturage for cattle. Level land is very scarce, and
is to be found only in the long serpentines of the main streams;
but even here, from long cultivation and lack of fertilizers, a
field is exhausted by two crops, and has to "rest" every third
year. Clover is almost never seen. The mountaineers maintain it will not grow here, although on our circuit we did see
two fields. ...
    In spite of the hard conditions of life, the Kentucky moun-
taineer is attached to this rough country of his. Comparatively
few emigrate, and many of them come back, either from love of
the mountains or because the seclusion of their previous environment has unfitted them to cope with the rush and enterprise
of life in the lowlands. One mountaineer told us that, though it
was a poor country, "the men mostly stays here." Another who
had travelled much through the district in his occupation of selecting white oak timber for a lumber company, estimated that
about one man in five emigrated; such generally go to Missouri,
Arkansas, and Texas. We met several who had been out West,
but the mountains had drawn them back home again. The large
majority of the population, therefore, stay in their own valley,
or "cove," as they call it, divide up the farm, and live on smaller estates, while the cornfields creep steadily up the mountains.
The population of these twenty-eight counties with their 10,000
square miles area was about 220,000 in 1880, or over twenty
to the square mile; that in 1890 was 270,000, showing an increase
of 25 per cent. As the ratio in the past decade has risen, there
is now a population of 340,000, or thirty-four to the square mile,
while for the state at large the ratio is fifty-four. This growth
of population is to be attributed almost entirely to natural increase; and as the accessions from the outside are practically
limited to the foreign element, only two or three thousand all told,

employed in the coal-mines and on the railroads, so large a percentage of increase precludes the possibility of much emigration. Cities there are none, and the villages are few, small, and wretched. This is true also of the county-seats, which in the interior counties average only from 300 to 400 souls; while those of the marginal counties and located on railroads encircling the mountain districts sometimes rise to 1500, but this is rare.

In consequence of his remoteness from a market, the industries of the mountaineer are limited. Nature holds him in a vise here. As we have seen, a few of his sheep may find their way to the railroad, but his hogs are debarred by the mountains from becoming articles of commerce. The same is true of his corn, which is his only superabundant crop; and this, therefore, by a natural economic law, the mountaineer is led to convert into a form having less bulk and greater value. He makes moonshine whisky, and not all the revenue officers of the country have succeeded in suppressing this industry. At our first camping-place, only 15 miles from the railroad, we were told there were twenty illicit stills within a radius of 5 miles. Two women, moreover, were pointed out to us who carried on the forbidden industry; their husbands had been killed in feuds, so they continued to operate the stills to support their families. Living so far from the arm of the law, the mountaineer assumes with characteristic independence that he has a right to utilize his raw material as he finds expedient. He thinks it laudable to evade the law--an opinion which is shared by his fellows, who are ready to aid and abet him. He therefore sets up his still in some remote gorge, overhung by trees and thickly grown with under-brush, or in some cave whose entrance is effectually screened by boulders or the dense growth of the forest, and makes his moonshine whisky, while he leaves a brother or partner on guard outside to give warning if revenue officers attempt a raid. It is a brave man who will serve as deputy marshal in one of these mountain counties, for raiding a still means a battle, and the mountaineers, like all backwoodsmen, are fine marksmen. In Breathitt County, called "Bloody Breathitt," four deputy marshalls have been killed in the past six months. The moonshiner fully understands the penalty for illicit distilling, and if he is caught, he takes his punishment like a philosopher--all the more as there is no opprobrium attached in his community to a term in the penitentiary for this crime. The disgrace falls upon the one who gave testimony against the illicit distiller; and often a mountaineer, if summoned as a witness in such a case, leaves his county till the trial is over, rather than appear for the prosecution. Most of the moonshine is sold within the mountains. The natives, physically depressed by lack of nourishment and by the prevalent diseases of the district, crave stimulants; so the demand for spirits is steady. Not content with the already excessive strength of moonshine whisky, they often add pepper or wood-ashes to make it more fiery. The result is maddened brains when under its influence, and eventually ruined constitutions. ...

As the isolation of his environment has left its stamp upon every phase of the outer life of the mountaineer, so it has laid its impress deep upon his inner nature. The remoteness of their scattered dwellings from each other and from the big world beyond the natural barriers, and the necessary self-reliance of their pioneer-like existence, has bred in them an intense spirit of independence which shows itself in many ways. It shows itself in their calm ignoring of the revenue laws, and in their adherence to the principle of the blood-feuds which inculcates the duty of personal vengeance for a wrong. In consequence of this spirit of independence, and of its antecedent cause in their slight dealings with men, our Kentucky mountaineers have only a semi-developed commercial conscience. They do not appreciate the full moral force of a contract; on this point they have the same vague ideas that most women have, and from the same cause. At all times very restive under orders, when they have taken employment under a superior, their service must be politely requested, not demanded. If offended, they throw up their job in a moment, and go off regardless of their contract and of the inconvenience they may occasion their employer. Every man is accustomed to be his own master, to do his own work in his own way and his own time. And this brings us to another curious characteristic of the mountaineer, also an effect of his isolation. He has little sense of the value of time. If he promises to do a certain thing on a certain date, his conscience is quite satisfied if he does it within three or four days after the appointed time. For instance, some mountaineers had promised to furnish horses for our camping party, which was to start from a certain village on July 15; when that day came half a dozen horses had failed to appear, but their places were supplied and the party moved off. During the succeeding week, delinquent mountaineers dribbled into town with their horses, and were surprised to find they were too late, explaining that they did not think a few days would make any difference.

Living so far from the rush of the world, these highlanders have in their manner the repose of the eternal hills. In the presence of strangers they are quite free from self-consciousness, and never lose their simplicity or directness. There is no veneer about these men; they say exactly what they think, and they think vigorously and shrewdly. Endowed with the keen powers of observation of the woodsman, and cut off from books, they are led to search themselves for the explanation of phenomena or the solution of problems. Though hampered by ignorance, their intellects are natively strong and acute. Conscious of their natural ability, conscious too that they are behind the times, these people are painfully sensitive to criticism. Cut off so long and so completely, they have never been able to compare themselves with others, and now they find comparison odious. They resent the coming of "furriners" among them, on the ground that outsiders come to spy upon them and criticize, and "tell-tale," as they put it, unless they are convinced that it is some commercial mission or a political campaign that brings the stranger. His suspicions allayed, the mountaineer is the most generous host in the world. "Strangers, won't you light and set? Hitch your beasties. This is a rough country, and I'm a poor man, but you can have all I've got." This is the usual greeting. If it is a question of spending the night, the host and his wife sleep on the floor and give the guests the bed. In a one-room cabin, the entertainment of strangers involves inconvenience, but this discomfort is never considered by the Kentucky highlander. When he says, "You can have everything I've got," this is no lip-service. At one cabin where we spent the night, when we were making our toilettes in the morning, the daughter of the house, with infinite grace and simplicity, offered us the family comb and her own toothbrush. Hospitality can go no further. This quality the Kentucky mountaineer has in common with the inhabitants of all remote, untrodden regions where inns are rare. But if he refuses to be reimbursed for his outlay and trouble, he is repaid in part by the news which the stranger brings, and the guest is expected to be very communicative. He must tell everything he has seen or heard on his journey through the mountains, and must meet a whole volley of questions of a strictly personal nature. Inquiries come as to his age, married or unmarried condition and the wherefore, his health, ailments, symptoms, and remedies. ...

Men who, from the isolation of their environment, receive few impressions, are likely to retain these impressions in indelible outline; time neither modifies nor obliterates them. Thus it is with the Kentucky mountaineer. He never forgets either a slight or a kindness. He is a good lover and a good hater; his emotions are strong, his passions few but irresistible; because his feelings lack a variety of objects on which to expend themselves, they pour their full tide into one or two channels and cut these channels deep. Like all mountain-dwellers, they love their home. They love the established order of things. Their remoteness from the world's great current of new ideas has bred in them an intense conservatism, often amounting to bitter intolerance. For instance, they were so outraged by the divided skirts and cross-saddle riding of some of the women of our party, that in one county they were on the point of blocking our way; in another, they were only dissuaded from a raid on the camp by a plea from a leading man of the town for the two Kentucky women of the party who used side-saddles, and everywhere they gave scowling evidence of disapproval. There were no jeers; the matter was to them too serious for banter or ridicule. Nor was their feeling, as we shall see later, an outgrowth of a particularly high and delicate standard of womanhood; it was more a deep-seated dislike of the unusual. Painfully lax in many questions of morals, they hold tenaciously to matters of form. The women who came into our camp at different times to visit us, in spite of a temperature of 90° Fahr., wore red woolen mitts, their tribute to the conventions.

The upland regions of all countries are the strong-hold of

religious faiths, because the conservatism there bred holds to the
orthodox, while the impressive beauty and grandeur of the natural
surroundings appeals to the spiritual in man. Such a religion, however, is likely to be elemental in character--intense as to feeling,
tenacious of dogma, but exercising little or no influence on the
morals of everyday life. This is the religion of the Kentucky
mountaineer. By nature he is reverential. Caves are "God's
houses," sun time is "God's time," indicated by the noon-mark
traced with charcoal on the cabin door. A God-fearing man has
the unlimited respect of every one in the mountains. A preacher
is a privileged person. Wherever he goes he finds free board and
lodging for himself and his horse, and his horse is always shod
free. In that lawless country, a man who shoots a preacher is
ever after an object of aversion, and there is a general assumption
that the murderer will not live long--either a superstition or a
generalization from the experience that often some individual constitutes himself an arm of the Almighty to punish the offender.
One who is a preacher must be "called" to the work, and must
serve without pay. The "call" does not presuppose any previous
preparation for the profession, and naturally involves some modern substitute for Paul's tent-making to earn a livelihood. The
result in the Kentucky mountains is sometimes amazing. Preach-
ers there have been known to be whisky distillers. Some have
been seen to take one or two drinks of liquor while delivering a
sermon. We attended an outdoor "meetin' " conducted by one
whose widowed sister ran a moonshine still. The best are farmers
or country storekeepers. All are more or less ignorant, some
densely so. We heard one man preach who could neither read nor
write. At a meeting of some sectarian association in the fall of
1898, a mountain preacher advanced the opinion that the old blue-
back spelling-book gave all the education that a preacher needed.
The style of preaching that appeals to the mountaineer is purely hortatory. It begins in a natural tone of voice, but, like all
highly emotional speech, soon rises to rhythmical cadences, and
then settles to a sustained chant for an hour or more. Any explanatory remarks are inserted parenthetically in a natural voice.
This, and only this, stirs the religious fervour of the mountaineer.
A clergyman from one of our cities who was doing missionary work
among these people was met with the criticism after his service,
"Stranger, I 'lowed to hear ye preach, and ye jest talked." ...
        The prominence given to funeral sermons in the season of
good roads lends a sombre cast to the religion of the mountaineer,
and strengthens in him a fatalistic tendency which is already one
of his prominent characteristics, born doubtless of the hopeless-
ness of his struggle with natural conditions. This feeling is so
strong that it goes to astonishing lengths. It frankly condems
missions and Sunday schools as gratuitous meddling with the
affairs of Providence. An Episcopal bishop recently, on arriving
in a mountain village, heard that one of the families there was in
great distress, and went immediately to make a visit of condolence.
When he inquired as to the cause of their grief, he learned that a

ten-year-old son had disappeared the evening before, and they had reason to suppose he had been lost in a large limestone cave which ran back two miles under the mountain not far away. In answer to his question if their search had been fruitless, he learned they had made no attempt at search, but "if he's to die, he's to die" came the wail, with pious ejaculations as to the will of God. In a few moments the man of God was striding along the trail to the cave, a posse of men and boys armed with candles and lanterns pressing close upon his heels, and in two hours the lost child was restored to the bosom of its family.

The morals of the mountain people lend strong evidence for the development theory of ethics. Their moral principles are a direct product of their environment, and are quite divorced from their religion, which is an imported product. The same conditions that have kept the ethnic type pure have kept the social phenomena primitive, with their natural concomitants of primitive ethics and primitive methods of social control. Such conditions have fostered the survival of the bloodfeud among the Kentucky mountaineers. As an institution, it can be traced back to the idea of clan responsibility which held among their Anglo-Saxon forefathers: and it is this Old World spirit which animates them when the eldest man of a family considers it a point of honor to avenge a wrong done to one of his kindred, or when a woman lays upon her sons the sacred obligation of killing the murderer of their father. In a community that grows from within by natural increase, hereditary instincts are strong, and clan traditions hold sway. But if the bloodfeud was decadent among the colonial ancestors of our Kentucky mountaineers, the isolation of this wild upland region was all-sufficient to effect its renascence, and today in some counties it is a more powerful factor of social control than the courts of law. The mountains, by reason of their inaccessibility and the sparsity of their populations, saw a great prolongation of pioneer days and pioneer organization of society, where every man depended on his own strong arm or rifle to guard his interests and right his wrongs. When the law invaded this remote region, it found the feud established and the individual loath to subordinate himself to the body politic. This individual was justified to himself by the almost universal miscarriage of justice. For the administration of the law is almost impossible in a feud case. It is next to impossible to convict a murderer in his own county, because the jury, and often the witnesses, are intimidated by the party of the defendant, and will fail to render a verdict of guilty; or, if the murder was committed to avenge some real wrong, the mountain jury, trained by tradition in their peculiar ideas of family honor, feels itself in sympathy with the criminal and acquits him. This they do without compunction, for they have as yet only a rudimentary conception of the sacredness of the law. ...

In all mountain regions of the world crimes against persons are far more frequent than crimes against property. So in the Kentucky uplands the former are frequent, the latter rare. There is no real disgrace attached to killing an enemy or a government officer who attempts to raid a moonshine still. There is little regard for the law as such, little regard for human life; but property is sacred. If a mountaineer is asked what, in the eyes of the mountain people, is the worst crime a man can commit, the answer comes, "Horse – stealing. If a man up here steals a horse, his best friend would not trust him again with fifty cents." Here speaks the utilitarian basis of his ethics in the almost impassable roads and trails of a pioneer country. To further inquiry, he replies, "And the next worst thing is to steal logs out of a stream--indeed, to steal anything." The mountaineer is honest, scrupulously so. If a log from a lumber-camp is stranded on his field from a subsiding flood in the river, he rolls it into the water at the next rise; or if this is impossible on account of its weight, he lets it lie and rot as a matter of course, for it never occurs to him to cut it up for his own use. He never locks his door. If a robbery occurs, the punishment is swift and sure, for the hue-and-cry is raised up and down the valley or cove, and the escape of the culprit is almost impossible. Primitive in their shortcomings, these mountain people are primitive also in their virtues. The survival of the clan instinct has bred in them a high degree of loyalty; and their free, wild life, together with the remoteness of the law, has made them personally brave. They carry themselves with a certain conscious dignity which peremptorily forbids all condescension. Every man recognizes man's equality; there are no different classes. The consequence is the prevalence of that democratic spirit which characterizes the mountains of Switzerland and Norway. ...

When a mountain lad comes down to the State University at Lexington, it is a foregone conclusion that he is going to carry off the honors. We find at work in him the same forces that give success to the youth from the Swiss Alps and the glens of the Scotch Highlands, when these too come down into the plains to enter the fierce struggle for existence there. For the Kentucky lad, the change has meant a stride over an intervening hundred and fifty years. ...

Though these people came into the mountains with eighteenth-century civilization, their isolation and poverty not only prevented them from progressing, but also forced them to revert to earlier usages which at the time of their coming were obsolescent. This is the explanation of the feud, as has been shown above, of the use of the hand-mill and shortbow, and especially of the old English ballad poetry which constitutes the literature of these mountain folk today. This has survived, or, more properly, flourished in its mediaeval vigor because it has not felt the competition of books. The scant baggage of the pioneer immigrants from colonial Virginia and Carolina could not allow much space for books, and the few that did make the trip across the Appalachian mountains were used up, from much reading and handling, by one generation. Poverty and inaccessibility prevented an invasion of new books from without, and from within there was no competition from newspapers. There are to-day twenty contiguous mountain counties, covering altogether an area of 6,000 square miles, not one of which can boast a print-ing-press. Under these circumstances, the Kentucky mountaineer reverted to this ancestral type of literature and revived ballad poetry. This has now been handed down from lip to lip through generations, the slightly variant form and phrase only testifying to its genuineness. The ballad of "Barbara Allen," popular in Great Britain three hundred years ago, and known now in America only to the musical antiquarian, is a stand-by in several of the mountain counties. The tragic ballad of "Little Sir Hugh," or "The Jewish Lady," as it is variously called, traces back to the Prior's Tale of Chaucer. The lengthy ballad of "Lord Bateman," or "The Turkish Lady," shows unmistakable identity with the poem of the same name in Kurlock's "Ancient Scottish Ballads," though the Scotch version is longer.

Animated by the spirit of minstrelsy, the mountaineers have composed ballads on the analogy of the ancient. These are ro-mantic or heroic and of narrative length. We heard a woman sing a native ballad of fifty-two stanzas, entitled "Beauregard and Zollicoffer," which recounted the deeds of these two generals of the Civil War. The music for all these ballads is in a weird minor key, and is sung in a nasal tone. So far as we were able to judge, the women are the chief exponents of mountain minstrelsy, and the accuracy of their memories for these long poems is sug-gestive of Homeric days. Spain and Sicily are perhaps the only other parts of the civilized world, at least in Europe and America, where modern folk-songs are still composed in the form of ballad poetry.

The whole civilization of the Kentucky mountains is eloquent to the anthropogeographer of the influence of physical environment, for nowhere else in modern times has that progressive Anglo-Saxon race been so long and so completely subjected to retarding conditions; and at no other time could the ensuing result present so startling a contrast to the achievement of the same race else-where as in this progressive twentieth century.

CHAPTER 5

Analytical Economic Geography

By 1920 the first generation of geographers trained professionally in America had appeared on the scene and had undertaken seriously the task of developing a subject of popular interest into an academic discipline. In this effort a significant contribution was made by C. C. Colby, and his study "An Analysis of the Apple Industry of the Annapolis-Cornwallis Valley", 1925, is taken to represent a fifth type in this series of field studies.

The analysis is of an economic activity carried on in a specific area. The field method is that of general observation, systematic inquiry about the industry among leading people engaged in it, and the gathering of statistics and other data locally available. The article is written for an audience of geographers, particularly economic geographers.

Part of the inspiration for this study came from Mark Jefferson, under whom Colby had begun his training in geography. A clear statement of Jefferson's viewpoint appears in his Presidential Address to the Association of American Geographers in 1916: "Geography is not to be regarded in its human aspects as the story of Earth and Man but as the study of Man using and living on the Earth"[1]. This viewpoint is exemplified in "The Apple Industry of the Annapolis-Cornwallis Valley".

Another part of the inspiration for this work came from J. Russell Smith's economic geography[2], which represents a similar approach though more generalized and less systematically localized than Colby's field study.

AN ANALYSIS OF THE APPLE INDUSTRY OF
THE ANNAPOLIS-CORNWALLIS VALLEY [3]
by C. C. Colby

The apple industry of the Annapolis-Cornwallis Valley is the most highly specialized and prosperous agricultural industry in Nova Scotia. In fact, in 1922, when this survey was begun, the industry and the small district in which it is developed, stood out in striking contrast to the general dullness of the agricultural fabric of Maritime Canada. The apple industry is particulary significant in the district because it represents the principal cash crop on many farms and an important cash crop on many others.

STATUS OF THE INDUSTRY AND
ITS GEOGRAPHIC CHALLENGE

The annual production of commercial apples in Nova Scotia during the last decade has been approximately 1,400,000 barrels, and in 1919 and again in 1921 it exceeded 2,000,000 barrels. The value of the crop in 1920 as represented by the prices paid to growers approximated $4,000,000, while the total value of the pack in that year as represented by the wholesale market prices of graded fruit, including all charges such as packing, insurance, transportation, and marketing, was more than $10,900,000. In a

1. M. Jefferson: "Some Considerations on the Geographical Provinces of the United States," in Annals AAG., vol. 7 (1917), pp. 3-15.
2. J. R. Smith: Industrial & Commercial Geography (N.Y.: Henry Holt & Co., 1913).
3. Econ. Geog., vol. 1 (1925), pp. 173-197, 337-355.

normal year 60 per cent of the crop or more is exported to Great Britain, and this overseas market is of the utmost significance to the continued prosperity of the industry and the district. In the fiscal year ending March 31, 1923, 1,060,819 barrels of apples valued at $4,500,000 to the growers, were exported from Nova Scotia to Great Britain. This represented 80 per cent of the exports of apples from Canada to that market. Although small shipments of apples from other provinces may have been made through Nova Scotian ports, and although some apples from other sections of the province are included in the total, at least 90 per cent of the apples exported from Nova Scotia to Great Britain originate in the Annapolis-Cornwallis District. The volume of this trade approximately equals the exports of apples from the United States to Great Britain and is the largest regular movement of apples from a single producing district to an overseas market. It is of sufficient importance to affect the operation of many ships plying the North Atlantic in the autumn and early winter when the fruit is moving.

While an apple orchard, or at least a kitchen plot containing a few apple trees, is a feature on most farms in the Maritime Provinces, commercial production practically is limited to the Annapolis-Cornwallis Valley, which is a long, narrow, relatively level, sedimentary floored lowland, open at its ends to the sea. At the north it is separated from the Bay of Fundy, to which it is roughly parallel, by North Mountain, which, from the floor of the valley or from the bay, appears as a fairly steepsided, even-crested, forested ridge. The summit of this ridge varies from one to six miles in width and in some places is level enough to be farmed. At the south the valley is flanked by South Mountain,--the steep, north-facing escarpment of the irregularly surfaced, rocky, crystalline upland occupying Central and Southern Nova Scotia. Much of the fine forest originally covering this upland has been cut or burned, so that today, except for tiny farmed patches or mining camps along the river valleys, most of the upland is unoccupied. Between these two relatively unproductive uplands lies the Annapolis-Cornwallis Valley, which, with the contiguous lowlands bordering Avon River, makes up the most productive agricultural district in Nova Scotia. This district is not more than one hundred miles long and varies from three to ten miles in width. It extends in a general west-east direction from Digby on the Annapolis Basin to Windsor on the Avon River. In it apples are associated with hay and potatoes as the more important money crops. While, on most farms, diversified farming is practiced, in a majority of cases the apple crop constitutes the center of interest. Locally the apple district and the Annapolis-Cornwallis Valley are thought of as synonymous and that practice will be followed in the present analysis.

The localization of the Nova Scotian apple industry in the Annapolis-Cornwallis District is striking. Seventy-seven per cent of all of the apple trees in the province are in Annapolis, Kings and Hants counties, the three counties in which the Annapolis-Cornwallis Valley lies; 68 per cent are in Annapolis and Kings

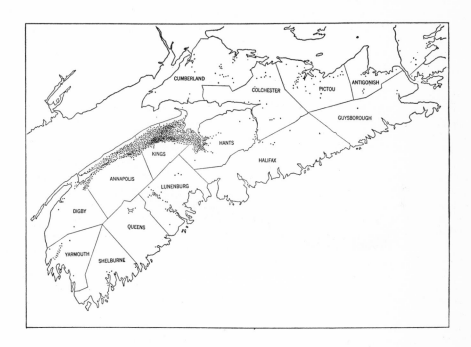

Fig. 5. *"The distribution of Apple Trees in Nova Scotia in 1921". An example of a dot map, the style most popular just before adoption of the mosaic map based on qualitative or quantitative uniformity and diversity. "The dots are placed more accurately in the western part of the province than in the eastern. The outline of the principal producing district is practically correct, for apple culture is so definitely adjusted to the Annapolis-Cornwallis Valley that the boundaries of the area are well known....In the eastern counties, where production is not on a commercial basis, the actual distribution of apple trees is probably more widespread than the dots suggest.....In western Nova Scotia the percentage of distributive error probably is not over 20 per cent; in the eastern part of the province it may be in some places as high as 50 per cent". Each dot represents 2,000 trees. Scale: 1 inch to 58.9 miles.*

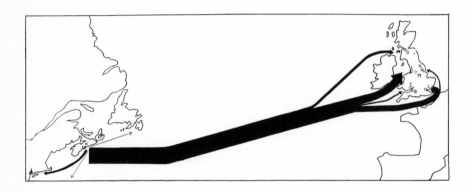

Fig. 6. "*The Distribution of the exports of apples from Nova Scotia in 1921-22. Sixty-six per cent were shipped to Great Britain, of which 33 per cent went to Liverpool and Manchester, 17 per cent to London, 10 per cent to Glasgow, 3 per cent to Cardiff and Bristol, and 3 per cent to Hull. In addition 6 per cent were exported to the United States, 1 per cent to Newfoundland, and less than 1 per cent to the West Indies. Twenty-seven per cent were consumed in Nova Scotia, either in local markets or in factories. Practically all the exports moved through the port of Halifax*". *The map is an expression of the approach through economic human activity and not through landscape.*

counties, and 47 per cent are in Kings County alone (Fig. 5). Kings County includes the eastern end of the Annapolis-Cornwallis Valley, and it is claimed that within twenty-five miles of Kentville, the shiretown of the county, are grown 75 per cent of the apples produced in the province. In fact, Kentville may be said to be the center of the industry, for here are located both the United Fruit Company, through which most of the apples are marketed, and the headquarters of the Dominion and Atlantic Railway, over which the fruit moves to Halifax. ...

PRODUCTION AS RELATED TO CLIMATE

Apple culture in the Annapolis-Cornwallis Valley is closely related to climate both as to general success and as to fluctuations in volume of production. In general, apple culture flourishes in the climate of this valley. Winter killing is rare, the normal blossoming time is late enough to minimize damage from frost, the growing season is adequate in length and has the conditions requisite for maturing the fruit, and under the autumn conditions the fruit usually can be picked and packed efficiently. Extremes of heat, cold, wind or rain seldom occur. The climatic factor is positive rather than negative. During the sixteen years from 1911 to 1924 inclusive the ratio of favorable to unfavorable years is 10 to 6. Moreoever, two of the years classed as unfavorable probably would have been called favorable in many fruit districts. ... A close relation exists between the nature of the season and the volume and quality of the crop. Thus the large production from 1919 to 1924 inclusive was associated with a series of favorable seasons, while the small volume of the crop from 1915 to 1918 inclusive was due to the occurrence of unfavorable weather at some critical stage in the development of the fruit or at harvest time. The sharply contrasted yields of 1910 and 1911 are explained by equally sharp contrasts in the character of the seasons. The abnormally low yield of 1910 occurred in one of the most unfavorable seasons on record, while the conspicuously large crop of 1911 marks a season of nearly ideal apple weather. ...

LOCALIZATION OF CLIMATIC ASSETS FOR APPLE CULTURE

Locally the general belief is that the Annapolis-Cornwallis Valley possesses a modification of the regional climate which makes it more suited to apple culture than other parts of Maritime Canada. It is argued that the valley has fewer severe frosts at critical periods, has less likelihood of cold, wet, cloudy weather during the blossoming period, has more sunshine throughout the summer and is more protected from high winds than other areas in the region. Generally these advantages are attributed to the maritime position of the peninsula of Nova Scotia, to the trough-like structure of the valley, and to the "protection" offered by North Mountain. Unfortunately crop and weather records do not exist in sufficient detail from enough places in the region to test the truth of this claim satisfactorily. Therefore, in some instances it is difficult to lift the contention above the level of personal opinion.

The claim that the Annapolis-Cornwallis Valley has climatic assets for apple culture not enjoyed by other areas in the region is supported by the absence of commercial orchards in Prince Edward Island. Experience has demonstrated that in this fertile province, which is almost a replica of the Annapolis-Cornwallis Valley in underlying rock, topography, soil, and drainage, apple culture on a commercial basis is impractical. On account of the prevalence of floating ice in the Gulf of St. Lawrence in late spring, the growing season in most years opens too late and is too cool and foggy for apples. In evaluating this evidence it should be borne in mind that until 1917 produce from Prince Edward Island could not be shipped to the mainland by rail, for only when the exigencies of war made it imperative, was car-ferry service inaugurated across Northumberland Strait. Even as recently as 1922 rail-roads in the island were not completely changed to the standard gauge.

The question of the success or failure of apple culture on a commercial basis in other sections of Maritime Canada, and the generally accepted belief that the climate of this district really is more favorable for horticultural activities than neighboring districts, are receiving the convincing test of practical experience in a number of places in the region. An outstanding case is in the Fredericton section of the St. John Valley in New Brunswick, where a number of young, thriving orchards and an increasing apple production will demonstrate in time whether apples of good quality and in considerable quantity can be produced with sufficient frequency to warrant specialization in this fruit. If these orchards are damaged or the crop decreased in quantity or quality by weather more frequently than those in the Annapolis District they will be under a considerable handicap. In New Brunswick it is claimed that well managed orchards on proper sites in the St. John Valley are no more handicapped by climatic conditions than similar orchards in the Annapolis District. ...

PRODUCTION AS RELATED TO ORCHARD SITES

The Annapolis-Cornwallis Valley is not and never has been a district of continuous orchards. Such statements as "one may ride for fifty miles under apple blossoms," which by certain writers have been applied to the valley, are literally untrue and figuratively unhappy. In riding along the country roads, a casual observer gains an exaggerated impression of the amount of land devoted to orchards, for the time-honored practice of placing the orchards near or about the farm homes has been followed rather consistently. Likewise looking into the Cornwallis Valley from a position on South Mountain or on North Mountain, the impression is gained of closely spaced orchards, for the orchards are most numerous along the valley slopes. In fact, however, orchards probably occupy less than 15 to 20 per cent of the slopes and floor of the valley. Moreover, the total orchard acreage in Nova Scotia, as stated in the census of 1921, is not more than 20 per cent of the total area of this apple district. The explanation of the relatively small amount of land devoted to orchards is that not all of the land in the valley is suited to orchards, that as yet orchards do not occupy all of the sites in the valley suited to their culture, and that not all of the farmers owning suitable land are convinced of the wisdom of specializing in apple culture as a long run proposition.

Because orchards of some size and of some degree of productiveness are growing in a considerable diversity of drainage situations, in varieties of soil from heavy clay to sands, on various slopes, and at many elevations, generalizations concerning the distribution of orchards must possess a considerable degree of inaccuracy. However, the sites best adapted to orchards have become recognized by the slow process of practical experience. They have been revealed by the paying orchards, those which represent a commercial asset to their owner. A statement which approximates the truth is that with proper management, orchards in this area thrive best on sites which possess three qualifications: (1) adequate drainage, (2) a soil and subsoil which, while gravelly enough to permit of good drainage, contain sufficient fine materials to retain a requisite amount of water, and (3) sufficient slope to afford air drainage on frosty nights during critical periods. Such sites occur in many places on the floor of the valley, along the slopes of North Mountain, and particularly along the lower slopes of South Mountain. They are entirely absent on the intervales of the streams and on the dyked marshes near the bays. As it has taken years to develop the present knowledge of orchard location and as it requires from fifteen to twenty years to bring an orchard to bearing in a commercial way, it is probable that some orchards were located years ago on sites which would not be selected at present. Conversely, farmers owning land so unsuited to cereals and forage crops that formerly they scarcely were able to make a living from mixed farming, through the establishment of orchards, have risen to prosperity on the high tide of success which in recent decades has characterized the apple industry. ...

CROP ASSOCIATIONS IN THEIR RELATION TO THE NATURE OF THE LAND

Although apple culture is without question the center of interest in the economic activities of the Annapolis-Cornwallis District, the importance of the apple crop to the individual farmer varies from farm to farm. Some farmers give little or no attention to apple culture, others divide their attention between apples and other crops, while a few devote practically their entire effort to their orchards. Although this diversity of crop association is due in part to the special interest of the individual farmer, it also reflects the nature of the land being farmed. In many situations the nature of the land practically dictates the crop association if the farms are operated at a profit, while in others the range of choice is greater. In general, the farmers whose operations do not include apple culture are those whose farms include principally dyked marshes or intervale meadows. As has been stated, the heavy silt and clay loams of these natural meadows are not suited to orchards and, when properly managed, yield remarkable quantities of hay. On the other hand, the farmers specializing in apples occupy sites which combine the advantages for apples and the disadvantages for diversified farming such as are characteristic of the slopes of South Mountain and the sandy areas near the divide between the Annapolis and the Cornwallis rivers. For the most part, farmers in this group plant only such field crops as are necessary to keep their orchards in shape. In the foregoing two types of situations the necessary relation between crop association and site is so close that it represents what may be termed a geographic relationship of the first order. In the case of farms which include intervale or dyked meadows as well as well-drained hill sites, it is practicable for the farmer to engage successfully in either mixed or fruit farming or, as commonly is the case, in a combination of both. As the last named combination is representative of much of the district, the number of farmers in this class is large. Farmers operating land of this type can and do exercise an option as to the crops which they emphasize. Consequently sharp differences of opinion exist as to the percentage of land and time which it is wise to devote to apple culture. Some maintain that a system of mixed farming combined with apple culture constitutes the best economy, others argue that any effort spent on other crops, except in so far as the raising of such crops is an essential part of efficient orchard practice, represents economic waste. ...

ORCHARD PRACTICES WHICH AID PRODUCTION

Apple culture developed as it is in the Annapolis Valley becomes a highly specialized business. A grower must be familiar with the generally accepted orchard practices and must know how to adapt them to his orchard and site. The aim of the grower obviously is to produce regularly as large a crop of high quality apples as possible. To this end he prunes, plows, cultivates, fertilizes, sprays, dusts, keeps bees, plants a cover crop, harvests, and packs in the way and to the extent which he considers best. Each of these operations requires special knowledge and equipment and adds to the cost of orchard operation. Some of them are varied from site to site, their efficacy fluctuating from year to year and with the time of the season when and the skill with which they are done. It must be recognized that the job of the orchardist continues practically throughout the year and that it goes forward under the hazard of the weather over which the grower has no control, on a site which he can modify but slightly, and under the attack of insect and other pests. However, by the skillful handling of orchard and land the trees are kept healthy and, therefore, better adapted to withstand the ravages of pests and the vagaries of the weather. ...

THE HARVEST

Although the summer apples ripen as early as the middle of August, the harvest of the commercial varieties begins about the first week of September and continues for approximately two months. The early varieties, such as the Red Astrachan and the Duchess of Oldenbury, are only of local importance because they do not keep long enough to enter the export trade. The Gravenstein, the most important as well as the earliest of the commercial varieties, is harvested in September and makes up the bulk of the exports during the autumn. Other autumn varieties are the Blenheim, the Rebston, and the King, the last named being a handsome table apple of high quality which reaches the London market for the Christmas and holiday trade. These are followed by the Baldwin, Northern Spy, Golden Russet, Ben Davis, and other standard winter apples. As all of the foregoing are grown throughout the Annapolis-Cornwallis District, and as the harvest season at best is a busy time, it is considered good practice to include a number of varieties in an orchard in order that the harvest may be extended over as long a period as possible.

No matter how large and fine a crop of apples may hang on the trees at the beginning of harvest, the size and quality of the commercial crop depends upon the way in which the fruit is picked, upon the labor available for this work, and upon the weather during the harvest period. For the most part the crop is picked by hand, as bruised fruit will not stand overseas transportation. Apparently the degree of care exercised is about intermediate between that of the carefully picked fancy box apples produced in the Pacific Northwest and the indifferent, careless pack of some of the districts in eastern United States. Considerable criticism of the method of picking employed is voiced by packers and others, so that improvement in picking practices may be expected in the future. It should be understood, however, that the crux of the success of the apple industry lies in selling apples in large bulk and of medium quality at a low price in the British markets. Therefore any change of method involving considerable cost must prove its worth before being adopted generally.

The apple picking and packing season creates a much greater demand for labor than exists at other times of the year. Fortunately the apple harvest comes later than most of the other crops. Wheat, if grown, is winter wheat and is harvested in July, oats come into harvest in August, while most of the hay is off the meadows by the first of September. Therefore, the apple crop conflicts mainly with the potato and the other root crops. The individual farmer during this busy period augments his farm crew by one to a dozen or more men, depending upon the size of his orchard and the acreage of his other crops. ...

MARKETING PERFORMANCES IN THEIR RELATION TO THE NATURAL ENVIRONMENT

Apples in the Annapolis-Cornwallis Valley are raised pri-

marily for export. In fact, the industry so definitely depends upon
its overseas trade that a permanent decline in exports would lead
to a corresponding decline in the industry.

In a normal year approximately 60 per cent of the crop is
shipped out of the province. In 1920-21, 71 per cent was exported
and during the five-year period from 1920 to 1925 the exports
averaged 65 per cent of the production. The close resemblance of
the trend of production and export shows that in general the exports
rise and fall with production, and suggests a steady demand for Nova
Scotian apples. Naturally, profits to the growers vary with prevailing prices as well as with the quantity produced, but the important fact is that year by year a market exists for this fruit. In
some fruit districts this does not appear to be the case. The sight
of fruit hanging on the trees because no market exists for it, is all
too familiar in many fruit-growing areas. While in general agriculture in Maritime Canada is handicapped by a similar inability
to market the crops produced, ordinarily this is not true of the
apple industry. It is this characteristic more than any other on
which the success of the industry depends, and an explanation of it
reveals the outstanding geographical asset of the apple industry in
Nova Scotia. Curiously enough, this same condition almost as
definitely constitutes a geographical liability to much of the agriculture of the Maritime Provinces.

MARKETS FOR NOVA SCOTIAN APPLES

The trade in Nova Scotian apples is illustrated by Figure 6,
which shows the distribution of the exports. Great Britain is the
principal market, and in the year in question 66 per cent of the
crop moved to British ports. Without this trade the industry would
not have developed to its present size and importance. The exports
to Newfoundland are customary business, for the fishing fleets and
villages, the logging camps, the paper and lumber mill communities, and the city of St. Johns import much food and other supplies
from Prince Edward Island and Nova Scotia--the nearest agricultural areas. The small export of apples to the West Indies represents an outgrowth of the much larger trade in fish and potatoes
which long has been carried on between Maritime Canada and the
West Indian and Caribbean islands. The item not representative
of the trade in every year is the export to the United States. At
rare intervals Nova Scotian apples are sold in considerable quantities in Eastern United States, the amount varying according to
the size of the crop in Western New York, Maryland-Virginia,
and other districts which normally supply the American markets.
Shipments to other Canadian provinces, ordinarily small, are
principally to New Brunswick. At times, however, when the crop
in Ontario is short, shipments to interior Canada reach considerable quantities. In some years small quantities of Nova Scotian
apples are shipped to Norway, Sweden, Germany, and other markets.

PLACE OF NOVA SCOTIA
IN BRITISH IMPORT TRADE IN APPLES

The trade between Nova Scotia and Great Britain is an outgrowth of the large consumption of apples in the industrial and
commercial centers in England and Scotland. Although a considerable quantity of apples is produced in the agricultural districts of southeastern and southwestern England, the local crop is
not sufficient to meet the demands of the British market and consequently approximately 3,000,000 hundred weight are imported
annually. The English fruit has a local reputation for quality,
and the preference of the British consumer for certain varieties
long grown in England finds expression in the varieties grown in
Nova Scotia and other districts catering to the British trade.
Historically apple culture in Nova Scotia and in the other apple
districts of Canada and the United States is an offshoot of the
early development of this fruit in the Mother Country, for many of
the commercial varieties and much of the knowledge of apple culture developed in England. ...

Of the imports into Great Britain in recent years 70 per cent
or more came from North America, 10 to 18 per cent from distant
Australia, and approximately 10 per cent originated in near-by
countries of western Europe. The apple districts in these European countries are, with the exception of those in Germany, near the
coast and therefore only a short sea haul is required to place fruit
in London and other cities on the east coast of England. The increasing imports from Australia (principally of Tasmanian
apples) arrive in the early summer and therefore for the most
part do not compete directly with those from the Northern Hemisphere districts. As a result of this Australian trade, apples are
on sale in England practically throughout the year. The trade
from North America, the largest long-distance overseas movement of apples (and probably of any fresh fruit) in the world, is
divided about equally between United States and Canada, the total
from the former normally being slightly in excess of that from
the latter. While exports from the United States to all countries
make up considerably less than 10 per cent of its total production
of commercial apples, and while no United States district depends
primarily upon export business, nevertheless exports of raw and
dried apples add materially to the success of the industry in the
seaboard and far western districts. Of the exports of raw apples
from the United States, approximately 70 per cent go to Great
Britain, and therefore the British market is the crux of its export business. Of Canadian exports to Great Britain, Nova Scotian
apples normally make up 80 per cent. Thus Canadian participation
in this trade rests primarily on the ability of the Annapolis-Cornwallis District to compete with other producing districts, especially those in eastern United States. To Nova Scotia, the
British business is the life blood of the industry, for no other
important market is open to its fruit. ...

NOVA SCOTIAN ASSETS IN TRANSATLANTIC APPLE TRADE

In marketing apples, the continued success of the apple industry in the Annapolis-Cornwallis District is due to the relatively
low cost and the effectiveness with which its product is placed in
the British markets. These advantages are an expression of an
outstanding geographic asset, namely the position of the producing
district in relation to Great Britain via the North Atlantic Trade
Route. In this respect it has advantages as compared with other
North American fruit districts.

IMPORTANCE OF HALIFAX IN
OVERSEAS TRADE IN APPLES

The North Atlantic trade in apples consists primarily of
shipments from New York and Halifax to Liverpool, Manchester,
London, and Glasgow. The total volume of the trade and the proportions from and to the individual ports varies somewhat from
year to year. In the season of 1923-24, 82 per cent of all apples
exported from North America and 90 per cent of those in barrels
were from the two ports of New York and Halifax. Into Great
Britain, 73 per cent of the imports entered via the four great ports
of Liverpool, London, Manchester and Glasgow, and 52 per cent of
the total entered through Liverpool and London. From New York
go apples in barrels from a number of producing districts near
that port, and also large quantities of fancy box apples, most of
which originate in the Pacific Northwest. From Halifax practically
the entire export is of apples in barrels from the Annapolis-
Cornwallis District. Canadian box apples originate principally
along the Canadian Pacific Railway in British Columbia and are
shipped via that line for export at Montreal or its winter port, St.
John. Exports of boxed apples from Vancouver, Seattle, and Portland mark a growing trade via the Panama Canal. At Liverpool
and Manchester by far the larger proportion of the imports in the
year under survey were a barrel pack destined for the industrial
cities tributary to those ports. At London and Glasgow, box apples
make up a greater fraction of the imports. This fact possibly indicates a proportionally larger demand for fancy apples in those
cosmopolitan centers.

LOW RAIL RATES TO POINT OF EXPORT

The seaboard position of the Annapolis-Cornwallis Valley
gives it a short and cheap rail haul to the point of export. Digby
at its western end and Kentville in its center are by rail only 151
and 72 miles respectively from Halifax. Most places in the district
enjoy a minimum freight rate and can place apples on the docks in
Halifax in from twelve to fourteen hours after they leave the
warehouses. With respect to proximity to either of the two major
exporting points, viz., New York and Halifax, the Annapolis-
Cornwallis District has an advantage as compared with other

United States and Canadian districts, with the possible exception of
the Hudson Valley District in New York. This advantage translates
into a lower rail rate. In the current season shippers in the
Annapolis-Cornwallis Valley have enjoyed an advantage in the rail
rate to the point of export, of eight cents as compared with Western
New York, and of twenty-one cents in the case of Ontario. As this
advantage has prevailed in other years, it may be taken as a long-
run or permanent asset. The higher insurance rate from Montreal
as compared with the rate from Halifax and New York represents
the customary differentiation among these ports in this respect.
Moreover, navigation on the St. Lawrence closes before the apple-
shipping season gets well under way, thus eliminating Montreal as
an exporting point and greatly increasing the length of the rail
haul required for the export of Ontario fruit. This condition seriously handicaps Ontario in competing in the overseas markets.

The Dominion Atlantic Railway handles practically all of the
apples shipped from the Annapolis-Cornwallis District to Halifax.
In fact, in Kings and Hants Counties it is the only railroad. As
apples for export represent an important part of the freight
hauled by this road, it endeavors to handle them to the satisfaction
of the fruit companies and other shippers. In the winter most of
the fruit moves in refrigerator cars, for otherwise the apples
might be injured by frost. During the spells of extremely cold
weather occurring in some winters, the transfer of apples from
the cars to the ships at Halifax is suspended. The Halifax representative of the United Fruit Companies in 1922-23 pointed out
that "there were days when it was impossible to move cars in the
yards and when it was not fit to open the hatches of the ship on
account of the severe cold." He called attention to the need of a
large heated car shed at Halifax to protect apples waiting to be
transferred to the ship. Although the need for this improvement
is endorsed by the Halifax Board of Trade and the provincial government, its accomplishment is difficult because the railway
yards and the railway facilities at the deep water terminal in
Halifax are controlled by the Intercolonial Railway. As this organization receives practically none of the revenue from carrying
apples, naturally, it does not consider practicable large expenditures to facilitate the fruit shipments. The matter is complicated
by the fact that the Dominion and Atlantic is a subsidiary of the
Canadian Pacific System and that the Intercolonial is one of the
Canadian National lines. To a slight extent, therefore, this question of railway ownership handicaps the establishment of a more
scientific adjustment of the facilities at the port to the business
of one of its principal tributary areas. However, because of the
generally satisfactory terminal layout at Halifax, apples apparently are handled there as expeditiously as at any North American
port.

POSITION OF HALIFAX ON NORTH ATLANTIC TRADE ROUTE

The development of the apple industry in the Annapolis-

Cornwallis Valley has been favored by the position of the port of
Halifax on the North Atlantic Trade Route. Most of the apples
shipped from Halifax to United Kingdom ports are carried as part
cargo in first-class cargo liners. The usual passage from Halifax
to Liverpool consumes from eight to nine days, although the faster
ships make the voyage in seven-and-a-half days. The voyage to
London takes a day or two longer. The shipments carried by a
single vessel average between 10,000 and 20,000 barrels. The fruit
is placed in ordinary stowage, damage from foul air and gases
being prevented by artificial ventilation. Small quantities of
fruit are carried by passenger liners and at times a steamer is
chartered for the trade. The departures from the usual custom
of shipping on the cargo liners in the past have been made as experiments or as protests against the rates charged by the liners.
Thus in 1920, when the rate on apples from all seaboard ports in
America to Great Britain was $2.50, the United Fruit Companies
of Nova Scotia chartered twenty-two Norwegian fruit steamers
and, certain other exporters doing likewise, the rate on the regular liners was reduced to $1.25 per barrel.

Although apples, as compared to many fruits, ship well,
nevertheless they must be handled carefully and moved quickly if
they are to reach the markets in first class condition. On account
of the care with which some of the cargo liners handle the fruit,
some of the shippers consider space on a cargo liner worth at
least 25 cents more than that on a chartered vessel. Thus in the
season of 1922-23 the officials of the United Fruit Company chose
to ship via the regular services furnished by Furness, Withy and
Company, although the rate charged was 25 cents per barrel more
than some shippers paid on chartered ships. It was argued that
the better condition of the fruit upon arrival, together with a lower
insurance rate, more than offset the higher freight rate. While
apples are carried at times by the International Mercantile Marine,
the Cunard, Canadian Pacific and other lines, and by vessels of
the Canadian Government Merchant Marine and the United States
Shipping Board, the line most interested in this trade is Furness,
Withy and Co., Limited. During the shipping season this company
operates regular sailings at about weekly intervals from Halifax
to London, Liverpool, Manchester, Glasgow, and also occasional
sailings to Hull, Belfast and other ports. In fact this company takes
great pains to handle the fruit satisfactorily. Expressions of appreciation of the service rendered appear in a number of instances
in the publications of the Fruit Growers Association and of the
United Fruit Companies.

A regular flow of apples from Nova Scotia to Great Britain is
furthered greatly by the large number of sailings from Halifax to
Great Britain during the exporting season. These frequent sailings
are due in part to the shipping conditions prevailing on the North
Atlantic at the time when the fruit is moving, and in part to the
attractiveness of apples as cargo. Probably, with the exception of
New York, no other port in North America is as well situated as
Halifax to take advantage of these conditions. During the summer

few regular overseas sailings are made from Halifax, for at that season trans-Atlantic shipments from the Maritime Provinces are small, and the St. Lawrence being open, Montreal becomes the principal Canadian port and regular services by many lines are maintained to it. In September, when exports of apples begin, an occasional vessel is diverted from the Montreal run in order to call at Halifax for early shipments of apples. Late in November, after the close of navigation of the St. Lawrence, the lines operating to Montreal in the summer shift their ships to St. John and Portland, with Halifax in many instances a port of call. A few ships at this time of the year operate directly from Halifax. However, the greater number of steamers calling at Halifax for apples, especially from September to the end of November, have their terminals at United States ports in the range from Boston to Newport News. At the terminal port, such ships take on part cargo of a general nature, some of which may be apples from one of the fruit districts in Eastern United States, and en route call at Halifax to complete their cargo by loading apples. If it were not for the apple traffic and the convenient position of Halifax on their route these ships would not call at that port. During the autmn and early winter the sea off the southeast coast of Newfoundland is free from icebergs, and therefore from September to the end of January during the period when most of the apples are exported, ships from New York and other Atlantic ports of the United States calling at Halifax can follow a direct course across the Grand Banks. A call at Halifax, therefore, involves little additional time except that spent in port. Thus precisely at the time when apples are moving, abundant tonnage and frequent sailings are available. In the season of 1922-23, the trans-Atlantic shipments of 362,598 barrels and 5,301 boxes made by the United Fruit Companies were carried in a total of one hundred and two sailings. This is an average of more than three sailings per week during the shipping season from September to March inclusive.

An important feature of the export of apples to Great Britain is the necessity of regulating the amount of apples shipped to any one port at any one time. The problem arises from the relatively perishable nature of the commodity and from the fact that cold storage facilities available in the British ports are not utilized for apples. It is complicated by the length of the trans-Atlantic voyage, by variations in the time required by ships in making the voyage, by the movement of apples to the British markets from other producing districts, and by the relatively large number of Nova Scotia shippers. Exporters agree that it is wise not to allow any one ship to carry to any one port a cargo of more than 15,000 barrels at a time, for otherwise the markets tributary to the port would be glutted. In order to regulate the trade, shipments from Nova Scotia for the most part are governed by a local organization known as the Shippers Association. In order to avoid serious conflict with other American shipments, the United Fruit Company, and probably the other Nova Scotian shippers, watch the movement of apples with great care. Once each week this company learns the exact quantities of apples shipped from all ports to all ports for the week previous, and the probable clearances for the ensuing week. Its officials know a week ahead, of all ships sailing from New York, Portland and Boston, and the space booked for apples on these ships. Interest in regulating apple shipments to the British markets probably is not matched elsewhere, for no other apple district, in America at least, depends to the same extent upon that market. In regulating shipments, frequent sailings to the several British ports are of the utmost importance. The fact that they are available attests the commercial significance of the geographic position of the port of Halifax and the Annapolis-Cornwallis District.

IMPORTANCE OF ADAPTING THE MARKETING SYSTEM TO REGIONAL ASSETS

Present Market System

For some years the system by which Nova Scotia apples are marketed has been in the process of change, and it bids fair to change still further in the future. At present (1925), although approximately 60 per cent of the fruit is handled by local coöperative companies, apples also are packed and consigned by individual growers and by buyers or speculators. Most of the coöperative companies belong to the United Fruit Companies of Nova Scotia, Limited. This organization consigns to one or more of the several British firms through which the apples reach the retailers. Some of the buyers are representatives of British importing companies and others operate independently. On account of fluctuations in price which characterize the market in many years, the job of the buyer is highly speculative. It is said that more men have failed than have succeeded at it. Certainly in order to succeed a man must be highly conversant with every aspect of the industry. Formerly buyers handled most of the crop, but since 1908 the trend has been toward coöperative marketing. This decided change has been due to dissatisfaction with the old system on the part of the farmers, and to the initiative of a small group of farmers whose success with the original coöperative company stimulated interest in coöperation. It represents an attempt to perfect a system by which a relatively perishable product may be sold successfully in an overseas market approximately 2,500 miles from the place of production. It grew out of the somewhat disorganized situation which developed as apple culture slowly evolved from an unimportant side line to a major farm interest. ...

PROBABILITY OF FURTHER EXTENSION OF COÖPERATIVE MARKETING

... The relatively small size and continuity of the producing district, the homogeneity of the social group, the success of the present organizations and the sentiment which they promote, and any increase in the competition in the British markets on the part of other fruit districts, will operate toward further coöperation. On the other hand, the continued success of some growers in handling their own fruit, the satisfactory business relations which certain buyers have maintained for many years with their clientele, and the natural distrust which many farmers have of leadership among their group, are conditions which will operate against it. Some of the men who have given considerable attention to this matter argue that the continued success of the industry on the present basis hinders, to a certain extent, any movement toward further coöperating. They point out that the management of an orchard is a full-sized job and as long as the grower gets a fair return from his effort he is content to go forward on the existing basis. They argue that a few unsuccessful years might speed up the coöperative movement considerably. By some it is believed that further coöperation would increase the returns to the growers and promote the general welfare of the industry. Others are convinced as definitely that the opposite would be true. While the question carries economic aspects quite beyond the scope of the present study, its solution involves careful and constant recognition of the geographic relationships of which the industry as developed today is an expression.

The first of these geographic relationships may be termed the <u>productive performance</u> of the industry. The present production has been attained only by long years of experience and experimentation, and represents the degree to which, through orchard management, the natural productive capacity of the district is being utilized. In this respect the industry is well advanced and is advancing. The second is the <u>marketing performance.</u> In order to realize fully upon the productive capacity of the orchards, the market system should be adapted as effectively as possible to the job of placing a relatively perishable product, in good condition and at low cost, in an overseas market. Here the natural endowments consist of a definitely delimited district directly facing the North Atlantic Trade Route. The industry is developed in a peninsula province, the outlook of which is to the sea rather than to the continent. The position of this peninsula at the Atlantic apex of North America gives it an insular rather than a continental character. Its commercial structure is vitalized by its water routes to Britain and other oversea points rather than by its rail connections to the United States or interior Canada. Continentally its position as far as the apple industry is concerned is a liability, oceanically it constitutes an asset. The marketing aspect of the industry should be adapted to these fundamental geographic conditions. Whether this will be accomplished by a further development of coöperative marketing or by some system not yet over the horizon, remains to be seen.

C H A P T E R   6

Geography of
Areal Uniformity and Diversity

Under the same impulse, to develop a sound academic discipline, other stages came on in rapid succession. "Detailed Field Mapping in the Study of the Economic Geography of an Agricultural Area" by W. D. Jones and V. C. Finch, 1925, is taken to represent a sixth type in this series.

Although so close in time to the previous type-study and also labelled as economic geography, the viewpoint is entirely different, on another tangent of the circle of geography. This is not a "study of Man using and living on the Earth",[1] but a study of the Earth itself divided into bits of landscape.

The intention in this stage is clear and justifiable: to avoid even more emphatically the unsubstantiated theory, unsound explanation and loose rationalization of environmentalism; to discover geographic relationships empirically from coincidental occurrence of phenomena, depending as in other sciences on the direct evidence of the senses; to acquire a distinctive object of study in geography, and to develop a systematic method of studying it.

1. *pp. 78, 79 above.*

The object chosen for study is a unit of area uniform throughout in its natural and man-made characteristics and different from adjacent areas. Any land to be surveyed is subdivided into such units and viewed as a mosaic of spaces. The field method involves the mapping of units recognized as uniform in the landscape, the classification of similar units into types, and the description of whatever types are found.

The idea of recognizing general uniformity over an area from one or more criteria was not new. It was exemplified in Herbertson's natural regions of the world[1] already well known in America. An innovation in this study is the application of the idea to areas so small as to have substantial uniformity in all characteristics of nature and culture which the field observer cares to include.

Clearly this approach does not follow Mark Jefferson's suggestion in 1916 to study "Man using and living on the Earth", but does follow the different advice of N. M. Fennemann in his Presidential Address to the Association of American Geographers in 1918, to study "the areal unit as such", "areas in their compositeness or complexity", "areas generally of course in relation to man", "the comprehensive, rational, systematic study of regions", which "belongs solely to geography".[2]

1. A. J. Herbertson: "The Major Natural Regions: An Essay in Systematic Geography," in Geog. Jour., vol. 25 (1905), pp. 300-310.
2. "The Circumference of Geography," in Annals AAG, vol. 9 (1919), pp. 3-11.

The study by Jones and Finch is addressed to an audience of geographers interested in field methods. It represents the work of a larger group, as indicated in the article, a group which met for a few days every year to confer on problems of geographic methodology in the field.[1] Soon after the article by Jones and Finch was written, more complex symbols were adopted by the group, in the form of a fraction in which the denominator is descriptive of the land itself (natural environment) and the numerator of what is on it (land use). This system is represented here by part of the field map and excerpts from the accompanying text of "Geographic Surveying" and "Montfort: A Study in Landscape Types in Southwestern Wisconsin" by V. C. Finch, published in 1933 but worked out before 1930, and considered to be the classic case of "the fractional complex code", the name attached to the method exemplified by the following selections.

---

1. *In the first year of meeting, 1923, at Holland, Michigan, the group consisted of W. D. Jones, C. C. Colby, D. S. Whittlesey, and R. S. Platt from the University of Chicago; V. C. Finch and A. K. Lobeck from the University of Wisconsin; C. O. Sauer and K. C. McMurry from the University of Michigan; D. H. Davis from the University of Minnesota; W. O. Haas from Northwestern University; and A. E. Parkins from Peabody College.*

DETAILED FIELD MAPPING IN THE STUDY OF THE ECONOMIC GEOGRAPHY OF AN AGRICULTURAL AREA[1]

by W. D. Jones & V. C. Finch

Sound conclusions in geography, as in any other subject, must be based on facts. A large proportion of the facts needed by the geographer can be obtained only in the field, and since observations of workers in other sciences and of untrained travelers have proved quite inadequate for the geographer it is clear the latter must make and record his own fundamental observations as a basis for description and interpretation. Field maps constitute a vital part of the record of these observations, and a problem of primary importance therefore is the determination of what observed facts shall be mapped and how the mapping shall be done.

Recently a group of geographers met in the field to consider this problem of mapping, in so far as it is involved in the study of a region dominantly agricultural. It was agreed that the objective of an economic geographic study of a region is the determination of relations between its economic life and its natural environment.

It was further agreed that sound generalizations about a region should be based on intensive studies of typical small areas. The considerations set forth in this paper deal with the field mapping which is essential in such intensive studies.

Three propositions were considered as to the type of maps to make; (1) five or more separate maps showing (a) land utilization, and (b) such facts of the natural environment as slope, soil, drainage, and natural vegetation; (2) two maps, one of land utilization and one of natural environment (the combination of such facts as slope, soil, drainage, and natural vegetation); (3) one map combining land utilization and natural environment, this map being in effect a synthesis of the several maps noted in the first proposition.

The five separate maps of land utilization, slope, soil, drainage, and natural vegetation, if properly made, are of exceedingly great value in a study of the economic geography of an agricultural area. The chief problem in making these maps is in each case the recognition of types worthy of differentiation.

The following major types of land utilization were recognized in the areas studied by the group whose conclusions are reported in this paper:

    (a) Tilled land, differentiated into types on the basis of crop combinations;

1. *Annals AAG*, vol. 15 (1925), pp. 148-157.

(b) Grass lands, used for pasture or wild hay;
(c) Wooded land, differentiated into types on the basis of utility;
(d) Idle land;
(e) Settlements, both towns and villages and separate farm-steads;
(f) Permanent streams and lakes, not navigable waterways;
(g) Navigable waterways;
(h) Land transportation routes, railroads and roads, with a differentiation between roads good all year and good at certain seasons only.

For slope it seemed desirable to distinguish at least three types, each enough different from the others in possibilities of use to warrant differentiation:
(a) Slope so slight as to lead to no undesirable soil wash and not to interfere with the use of machinery in cultivation;
(b) Slope great enough to be likely to lead to undesirable soil wash except in the case of very permeable soils and to interfere with the effective use of machinery in cultivation;
(c) Slope so great as to preclude continuous cultivation except by terracing.

As to soils, the group making this study did not come to anything like a final classification which would clearly differentiate soils into types differing in utilization possibilities. It seems as though not only surface soils must be taken into account, but the entire soil profile to a depth of several feet. Study on a classification of soil profiles suitable for the use of geographers is urgently needed.

On the basis of drainage, land may be classed as inadequate, satisfactory, and excessive. Drainage is a resultant of slope, soil profile, climate and vegetation, but this resultant is observable and for most areas its recognition seems worth while.

Natural vegetation in any given area can without great difficulty be classified, on the basis of characteristics which bear on use and landscape aspect, into well defined types.

The scheme of making two maps, one of land utilization and one of natural environment, in the place of five just described, has certain distinct advantages. In the first place, it greatly simplifies field procedure, it being easier to carry on work on two rather than on five sheets. In the second place, it combines in a useful manner the outstanding facts of the natural environment as they are combined in nature. The procedure is to mark off on the one map areas which are essentially uniform throughout in utilization, and on the other map areas possessing essential uniformity in their combination of slope, soil, drainage, and natural vegetation (where the latter exists), and to set down in the notebook a detailed description of each type of area. It seems likely that comparison of the land utilization map with a map of natural environment will prove more productive of significant conclusions than comparison of the land utilization map with separate maps of slope, soil, drainage, and natural vegetation.

The idea of making a single field map that combines observed facts of land utilization and of natural environment grew out of the making of the two maps described in preceding paragraphs. Such a map was made in the Hennepin (Illinois) area and is here presented for consideration. As far as the routine of mapping is concerned, it is simpler to make one map than to make two or more. In directing attention to what is significant, the making of this single synthetic map offers peculiarly promising possibilities. The procedure in the field is as follows. A given spot is observed, as to utilization and as to the complex of natural conditions there existing. A note is made of these facts and of the known or probable relations between them. The area within which these facts of use and environment are essentially uniform is then outlined on the map. Adjacent but different areas are similarly distinguished, described in the notes and outlined on the map. Presently certain types of land are found to recur within a district, and to be typical of the region of which the district is a part. If an area marked off on the map is uniform throughout in land utilization and in natural environment it would seem to follow that it is uniform throughout in the relation between these two sets of facts, and experience in the Hennepin district bears out this conclusion. The single field map just described thus becomes in effect one showing types of areas according to fundamental geographic relationships.

On the field map of a small area some four or five miles northeast of Hennepin, Illinois, (Fig. 7 is a reproduction of this in line drawing) colors were used to show major types of land utilization. At a glance one can determine from the map the distribution of tilled land (yellow), grassland used for pasture or wild hay (orange), wooded land (green), idle land (gray), farmsteads (pink), roads and railroads (black), and water areas (blue). Closer scrutiny of the map shows that the tilled areas, the grass areas, and the wooded areas are subdivided and numbered. Each of these numbers distinguishes a type of area that is different from the others in the complex of observed facts of land utilization and natural environment. Brief descriptions of each type are to be found in the legend accompanying the map, these descriptions set forth the oustanding characteristics of each type of area, and serve as a condensed but clear and effective characterization of the variety of conditions which exist in the district mapped. ...

The chief justification for detailed mapping of small areas is that it helps greatly in accumulating the facts which serve as the basis of sound, broad generalizations with reference to regions, which generalizations constitute the ultimate goal in geographic study. The making of one map showing types of land according to the combined facts of use and natural conditions compels the observer to group together in the field phenomena which occur together and thus is much superior to synthesis in the office of related facts. ...

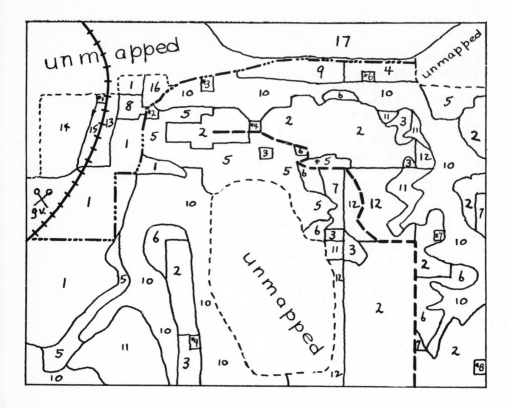

Fig. 7. *"Types of Land near Hennepin, Illinois, differentiated according to observed facts of land utilization and natural environment." Scale: 1 inch to .3 mile. An example of a mosaic map based on areal uniformity and diversity.*

The types numbered and described below and shown in Figure 7 were established in a two days' field trial of the proposed method of mapping, ...

    A. Tilled Land (yellow)

        1. Slope and topographic location--flat; valley bottom.
            Soil--silt loam surface soil, low in humus; sub-soil not examined.

            Drainage--good, except in very rainy weather; water table fairly close to surface, so that in dry weather this type of land does not get so dry as to injure crops seriously.

            Vegetation--originally forested; maple, elm, oak; valley floor type.

            Use--tilled, chiefly for corn; excellent crops, suffering occasionally from wetness.

        2. Slope and topographic location--flat; upland.
            Soil--silt loam surface soil, low in humus; sub-soil, at a depth of a few feet, clay.

Drainage--good; in rainy weather this land may get too
wet; in dry weather it is likely to get too dry because of rapid run-off into bordering ravines and
because of low water table.

Vegetation--originally oak forest; upland type.

Use--tilled; corn, oats, hay in rotation; excellent
crops, not so good as No. 1 in dry seasons.

3. Similar to No. 2 except in the following respects:

Slope and topographic location--slope great enough to
lead to some soil wash and to impede somewhat
the effective use of machinery; upland slopes to
bordering ravines.

Soil--clay loam.

Drainage--so rapid that the fields almost never are
too wet, and they dry out at times even more than
those on No. 2 type.

Use--similar to that of No. 2, but yields are somewhat less and fields deteriorate somewhat from
wash.

4. Surface and topographic location--slope steep enough
to lead to some soil wash and to impede somewhat the use of machinery; lower bluff slopes.

Soil--clay loam, stony in places; sub-soil clay.

Drainage--good, with water table close enough to
surface to prevent serious drying out in droughty
weather.

Vegetation--originally oak forest; slope type.

Use -- tilled; corn, oats, hay; in quality between No.
2 and No. 3.

B. Grass Land, for Pasture or Marsh Hay (orange)

5. Slope and topographic location--slope so steep as to
be unsuited to ordinary tillage; bluff slopes, valley sides, ravine heads.

Soil--clay loam, gravelly in places; sub-soil clay.

Drainage--good to excessive.

Vegetation--rather a dry type of grass sod; in places
scattered trees, mostly oak.

Use--fair pasture, with some slight use as woodlot.

6. Slope and topographic location⎫
Soil   ⎬ Similar to No. 3
Drainage   ⎭

Vegetation--good grass sod, with scattered trees,
mostly oak.

Use--good pasture, with some slight use as woodlot;
potential tilled land similar to No. 3.

7. Slope and topographic location⎫
Soil   ⎬ Similar to No. 2
Drainage   ⎭

Vegetation--good grass sod, with scattered trees,
mostly oak.

Use--good pasture, with some slight use as woodlot;

does not dry out as much as No. 5 or No. 6; potential
tilled land similar to No. 2.

8. Slope and topographic location ⎫
   Soil   ⎬ Similar to No. 1
   Drainage   ⎭
   Vegetation--good grass sod.
   Use--good pasture; does not dry out as much as No. 5
       or No. 6, or even No. 7; potential tilled land simi-
       lar to No. 1.

9. Slope and topographic location ⎫
   Soil   ⎬ Similar to No. 4
   Drainage   ⎭
   Vegetation--good grass sod and scattered trees, most-
       ly oak.
   Use--good pasture.

C. Wooded Land (green)

10. Slope and topographic location ⎫
    Soil   ⎬ Similar to No. 5
    Drainage   ⎭
    Vegetation--oak forest, mostly second growth; slope
        type.
    Use--woodlot and summer pasture.

11. Slope and topographic location ⎫
    Soil   ⎬ Similar to No. 3 and
    Drainage   ⎭ No. 6
    Vegetation--oak forest, mostly second growth; upland
        type.
    Use--woodlot and summer pasture; potential tilled
        land similar to No. 3.

12. Slope and topographic location ⎫
    Soil   ⎬ Similar to No. 2
    Drainage   ⎭
    Vegetation--oak forest, mostly second growth; upland
        type.
    Use--woodlot and summer pasture; potential tilled
        land similar to No. 2.

13. Slope and topographic location ⎫
    Soil   ⎬ Similar to No. 1
    Drainage   ⎭
    Vegetation--forest of valley floor type; maple, elm,
        oak.
    Use--woodlot and summer pasture; potential tilled
        land similar to No. 1

14. Slope and topographic location--flat; high valley ter-
        race of Illinois Valley.
    Soil--dark silt loam; sub-soil at a depth of 3 feet,
        glacial outwash sand and gravel.
    Drainage--good.
    Vegetation--forest.
    Use--timber and woodlot; potential tilled land of
        fairly good quality.

15. Slope and topographic location--steep slope from ter-
    race to valley bottom.
    Soil--Sandy, gravelly loam.
    Drainage--good.
    Vegetation--forest.
    Use--woodlot
D. Idle land (gray)
 16. Slope and topographic location--flat; valley floor.
    Soil--peaty.
    Drainage--poor; under water all year.
    Vegetation--cattail marsh.
    Use--waste; perhaps potential tilled land if drained.
E. Water (light blue)
 17. Shallow bayou of the Illinois River; perhaps potential
    tilled land if drained.
F. Farmsteads (pink)
    Each farmstead is given an identifying number, and is
    described in detail in the notebook, as to character of
    buildings, numbers of animals, orchards and gardens,
    and a variety of other significant facts.
G. Roads and Railroads
    Two types of roads are shown, those good except in
    wet weather (dashes), and those poor at all times
    (dashes and dots). A third type, good in all weather,
    does not occur in this area. The conventional symbol
    is used for railroads.

GEOGRAPHIC SURVEYING, AND MONTFORT, A STUDY IN LANDSCAPE TYPES IN SOUTHWESTERN WISCONSIN[1]

by V. C. Finch

The immediate objective of the map record in field geography is to put upon one map, so far as it may be done in two
dimensions, all of the significant features of both the natural and

1. Bull. #9, Geog. Soc. of Chicago (Univ. of Chicago Press, 1933), pp. 6-40.

the cultural landscapes and to put these varying combinations in
their areal relationships to one another. For the improvement
of the degree of map accuracy plane tables, open-sight alidades,
pace scales and methods of rough triangulation are employed in
the field. In the Montfort study, the notations were made upon a
base-map drawn, in advance of the field work, from United States
topographic sheets and the available township surveys, upon a
scale of approximately 1:15,840. The map record for any given
combination of slope, soil, drainage, major land use, specific
crop and quality thereof was made in the form of a fractional
notation. This unit areal complex was bounded by lines drawn
as nearly as possible along the positions which marked a change
in any one or more of these elements. The nature of the record
and an explanation of the symbols used is exemplified by the
map (Fig. 8). ...

  The utility of the map record. The system of map records,
when properly carried out, provides a vast quantity of information. In the map of the Montfort area the geographical complexes
recognized and numbered vary from about 40 to considerably more
than 150 per square mile. Since each numbered compartment
represents a complex of six elements involving six records of
fact, it follows that there are available in this map from 250 to
nearly 1000 specific facts of geographic significance per square
mile of area, and for the whole area surveyed (approximately 47
square miles) more than 20,000 such facts. This obviously is not
the ultimate limit of detail to which such a map might be carried.
It was believed to be the practical limit, since all changes in
complex that involved a minimum of about one acre of area were
recorded. ... Within the limits of error imposed by the surveying
instruments used, and by the variability of human judgment the
record is accruate.

  The utilization of such a vast number of facts about so
small an area might be a difficult problem were it not for the
fortunate fact that the map record lends itself to accurate measurement and statistical analysis. By means of the polar planimeter the area of each of the numbered compartments or geographical complexes of the map may be determined with reasonable
accuracy. The values thus obtained may, by simple, though somewhat tedious manipulation, be spread and sorted according to almost any desired order. By such means total areas and percentages of total area may be obtained for any one of the elements
represented by a digit in the fraction, or for coincidences of any
two or more of them. Some such percentages have been determined from the map of the Montfort area and are used in its
geographical description and interpretation. It is obvious that
this type of correlation may be applied also to the three-point
relationships of use, slope and soil; to the four-point relationships of use, slope, soil and drainage; or to any other association of elements in the cultural and natural landscapes that the
probability of usefulness may indicate. ... A more ambitious
project might recommend the use of the Hollworth machines or

NUMERATOR

Left-hand Digit MAJOR USE TYPE	Second Digit SPECIFIC CROP OR USE TYPE		Third Digit CONDITION OF CROP
1. TILLED LAND	1. CORN (MAIZE) 2. OATS 3. HAY, (IN ROTATION) 4. PASTURE (" ") 5. BARLEY 6. WHEAT	7. PEAS (Mainly for canning). 8. SOY BEANS 9. POTATOES T. TOBACCO X. SUDAN GRASS ⅖. OATS AND BARLEY MIXED	1. GOOD 2. MEDIUM 3. POOR
2. PERMANENT GRASS LAND	1. OPEN GRASS PASTURE 2. PASTURE WITH SCATTERED TREES OR BRUSH 3. WOODED PASTURE 4. PERMANENT GRASS CUT FOR HAY		1. GOOD 2. MEDIUM 3. POOR
3. TIMBER LAND	1. PASTURED 2. NOT PASTURED		1. GOOD 2. MEDIUM 3. POOR
4. IDLE LAND	1. IS CAPABLE OF USE		

DENOMINATOR

Left-hand Digit SLOPE OF LAND	Second Digit SOIL TYPE (Wis. Soil Survey terminology).		Letter X (If indicated). CONDITION OF DRAINAGE
1. LEVEL, 0° TO 3° 2. ROLLING, 3° - 9° 3. ROUGH, 9° - 15° 4. STEEP, Over 15°	1. MARSHALL SILT LOAM 2. KNOX " " " 3. " " " (STEEP PHASE). 4. LINTONIA " " 5. WABASH " " 6. ROUGH, STONY LAND		X POOR XX VERY POOR

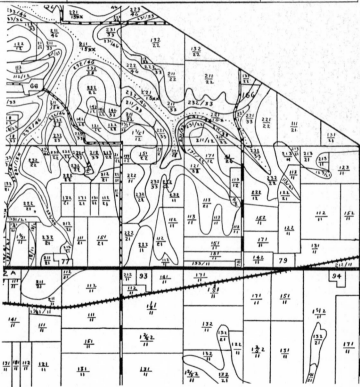

Fig. 8. Part of the fractional complex code map of the Montfort area, another example of a mosaic of uniformity and diversity qualitatively distinguished. The Prairie Upland district in the southeastern half, the Cuesta-Escarpment district in the northwestern half. Scale: 1 inch to .4 mile.

other mechanical devices in a more facile accomplishment of this tedious statistical analysis.

It is of course true that the facts recorded in the Montfort map and the interpretation based thereon are true in detail for only the year of observation, 1928. It is not probable however that this fact much affects the value of the record or the soundness of the interpretation. Changes from year to year in the specific use of land in normal crop rotation greatly affect neither the relative proportions of the major uses of the land nor, is it probable, the relative importance of the specific crops with respect to each other. Such changes come about slowly with the evolution of agricultural practice or from changes in the whole agricultural outlook of the region. For such a future time this map of present-day use will serve as a valuable historical record, and a basis for accurate measurement of the changes that time may have accomplished.

The map produced by this method of geographical surveying has also other advantages. By a process of coloring, according to any one digit or combination of digits in either the numerator or denominator of the recorded fractions, there may be shown areally the same sorts of phenomena or coincidences thereof that may be brought out by the statistical method. Thus there may be produced a slope map, a soil map, a timber map or a crop map. Also there may be shown the subdivision of cultivated lands according to their slopes, or for example the distribution of corn fields according to their slope or soil conditions. It is possible that a method employing the measurement of a beam of light passed through photographic plates of maps colored to show any desired fact or coincidence of facts might provide a means, even less laborious than the Hollworth machines, for obtaining the relative areas of sets of landscape phenomena.

It is indeed these supplementary and analytical labors which, at present, more than the field surveying, impose a severe limit upon the extent of area that may be so treated. Most important of these were the construction of a finished map (Fig. 8) from the fragmentary field maps; the planimeter measurement of each of its compartments; the making of a statistical record or distribution of each of these areas according to the digits of its fractional index; the totaling of these assorted groups and the computation of their relation to one another in terms of percentage; the checking of the statistical columns for coincidences of use and slope and their expression in terms of percentage; the preparation of color maps showing features of natural or cultural landscape according to digits of the fractional indices and of coincidences of these; and the re-drawing of these maps to a form suitable for publication. Altogether these matters required the expenditure of nearly twice the 120 days of man time required to complete the field survey. This would not prove a difficult task for an organization provided with a staff of clerical assistants and draftsmen. It is a large investment of time for the unaided geographical research worker.

The written description and interpretation. The attempt at
a verbal portrayal and interpretation of the Montfort area has
been purposely limited to depicting and interrelating the landscape forms, and to such facts about the historical sequence of
physiographic or human events as leave visible imprint upon the
area or its present institutions. The treatment is therefore brief.
The essentials of the landscape forms, both physical and cultural,
are presented succinctly in maps, photographs and tables. For
that reason no verbal summary is required. In the present state
of the writer's knowledge of the area, and his belief regarding the
function of geographical writing, any attempt to project the historical sequence of events into the future and to predict economic-
geographic trends has been avoided.

The general landscape. Montfort, Wisconsin, is one of a
series of villages,...that stand upon the crest of the Galena-Trenton cuesta in the southwestern part of the State. The outlook
northward from these villages is over an irregularly eroded
escarpment where peninsular projections of the upland alternate
with the deeply eroded valleys of tributaries to the Wisconsin
River. Southward their views include the gently-undulating back
slope of the cuesta, a region of broad ridges and open valleys. ...

The landscape bordering the approach to Montfort from the
east is an interesting one but not particularly impressive. (Fig. 8)
Upon the south lie level farm lands, rectangular fields of corn,
oats and hay interspersed with spacious farmsteads that include
comfortable homes with large, painted barns. All of these features are reminiscent of the adjacent Illinois corn belt of which
this locality is indeed a northward projection. To the north also
appears a seemingly level or gently rolling surface. Fields of
less regularity, the less frequent spacing of farmsteads upon the
horizon and a more persistent fringing of timber give faint notice
of a different landscape from that which lies on the other side of
the highway. How different it is the observer does not realize
until his course carries him past the end of one of the valleys
tributary to the Blue River, valleys which rapidly-flowing, spring-
fed brooks have cut through the Galena-Trenton limestone, the
St. Peter sandstone, the Lower Magnesian limestone and, in their
lower courses, into the Cambrian sandstone below. These valleys
are almost completely hidden to an oblique view across the escarpment of the cuesta but have in their relief of from 200 to 300
feet a detail of rugged beauty to which no photograph does justice. ...

Geographical subdivision of the Montfort area. Although
the rural landscape about Montfort bears many features that are
common throughout, some significant differences appear upon close
analysis. These include differences in population character and
distribution, in type and location of farmsteads, in land use, in
crop systems and animal industries. Most of these differences
appear to be adaptations, conscious or unconscious, to differences
in the natural environment, differences in part of soil and drainage but primarily and fundamentally to differences of topography. ...

Extended detail in picturing these differences would be

tedious. Therefore attention is directed to the more striking contrasts in the land and in the characteristics of its occupancy and use to be seen in passing from the Prairie Upland district of the Pecatonica drainage area, on the back slope of the cuesta southeast of Montfort, to the district on the escarpment slope in the Blue River drainage area north of the village. (S.E.versus N.W. in Fig. 8) ...

The prairie upland district.--In the district southeast of the village of Montfort the general view is across the gently undulating surface of one of the islands of prairie which characterized the native vegetation of certain localities in southern Wisconsin. Slight indeed is the dissection, 80 per cent of the surface has a slope of less than 3 degrees, only 0.2 per cent exceeds a slope of 9 degrees and there are no steep slopes of more than 15 degrees. Almost exactly coincident in distribution with the gentlest slopes are the tilled lands, 74 per cent of the total area. Rectangular fields of corn look exceedingly prosperous, and, wherever a cultivator is at work, expose a well-drained dark-brown or black upland soil which closer investigation shows to be the Marshall silt loam of the Wisconsin soils classification. This soil is usually deep and stoneless being largely of loessial origin. Its upper horizons are characterized by a relatively high proportion of organic matter, the inheritance from the native prairie grass vegetation and the cause of the dark color. The subsoil is less deep and sometimes contains cherts derived from the underlying Galena limestone. The surface soil is generally friable and loose and excellently adapted to general farming.

So significant is corn in the rural economy of this district that it occupies a greater surface area than any other crop, 22 per cent of the total area and 30 per cent of the tilled-land area. Alternating with the corn fields are those of thrifty small grains, chiefly oats and barley, which obviously are in rotation with it. Their combined areal extent is nearly the same as that of corn, 31 per cent of the tilled-land area. Not only are oats and barley the important small grains but frequently they are sown together. This reflects the fact that they are not grown for sale but for farm use, mainly as a ground feed in conjunction with corn. The other major crop in the rotation is hay; timothy, clover and an occasional field of alfalfa, soy beans or sudan grass. The hay crop is also of generally good quality save where drifing snows on this wind-swept prairie upland have bared parts of fields to damage by ice storms and winter desiccation. The combined area in hay and pasture in rotation (22 and 9 per cent respectively of the tilled land) is about equal to that of corn or the small grains.

Only about 9 per cent of the tilled land is devoted to crops other than corn, small grains, hay and rotation pasture. The major part of this is occupied by two principal cash crops, peas and sweet corn for canning, 5 and 1 per cent of the total tilled area respectively. ...

In this prairie district, where less than 20 per cent of the land exceeds 3 degrees in slope and where 74 per cent actually is tilled, it is probable that as much as 95 per cent is capable of tillage. That so much as 24 per cent of the land is in permanent grass pasture is related (I) to the fact that the farms average large (190 acres) in proportion to the farm population (4.4 persons) and (2) to the large numbers of farm animals which require more summer pasture than can be supplied by pasture in the common rotation. Almost invariably these permanent pastures occupy the shallow depressions of the upper valley ends which have slightly inferior drainage. Often the site chosen for the farmstead is on or near the edge of one of these shallow depressions. Particularly is this true of the sites chosen on account of spring water. From farmsteads so situated the pasture lot is directly accessible and stock does not require driving. Elsewhere extension of the pasture across the flat land or the use of broad farm lanes serves the same purpose.

A few of the prairie farmsteads appear upon the horizon half obscured in shallow valleys, where the advantage of spring water influenced the original choice of site. In most cases the springs are near the base of the Galena limestone, a formation which is separated from the underlying Trenton limestone by the thin band of the Decorah shales. In the upland these inconspicuous shales are exposed only in the bottoms of the broad ravines, generally below the 1100 foot contour. However, the majority of the farmsteads are located at irregular intervals upon the rectangular pattern of the highways. Many of them were laid out in the day of cheap land and, being physically unrestricted, are large; the average size is 3.9 acres. Nearly all of them, being unrestricted by conditions of surface slope, are rectangular in shape and are squared with the points of the compass. ...

The cuesta-escarpment district.--Certain contrasts may now be drawn which will serve to give emphasis to some of the landscape forms and patterns in the more dissected cuesta-escarpment district which lies in the Blue River drainage basin north of the village of Montfort. It is possible to show also some of the associations involved and to suggest their interpretation.

First it may be noted that the agricultural use of area in this district is different from that which characterizes the prairie. Permanent grass for pasture predominates. It occupies 54 per cent of the total area, which contrasts sharply with the 24 per cent so used in the prairie. This is a sensible adaptation of farm practice to slope and soil conditions, since only 22 per cent of the total area is flat, while 31 per cent exceeds a slope of 9 degrees and may be called rough or steep land. The relation of the grassland to the physical landscape will be seen from its distribution, for it is confined principally to the bluffs and narrow bottom lands of the streams. In the prairie only 1 per cent of the grassland exceeds a slope of 9 degrees, while in this district 50 per cent of it is so situated. It is significant also that 65 per cent of the permanent pasture in this district is wholly or partly uncleared; 40 per cent being wooded and 25 per cent having scattered trees or brush. Of the wooded pasture 74 per cent occupies rough or steep land; i.e., slopes of more than 9 degrees. Among the pastures characterized by scattered trees or brush are some that were originally timbered and in which a few trees have been left standing. Some have been so recently cleared that young oak and hickory brush and saplings are thickly interspersed among the stumps. In other pastures thickets of hazel brush are found, some of these being the native vegetation on the thin soils of the steeper slopes, others the result of continuous pasturage and neglect after clearing. In addition to pasture the hillside woodlands supplement the farm income by furnishing oak firewood, while small quantities of second growth hickory or an occasional black walnut tree on the bottom lands are cut for sale.

That so much as 18 per cent of the permanent grassland occupies flat land may be attributed to the fact that the stream bottoms are seldom tilled. Though characterized by dark-colored silt-loam soils (Wabash) they are subject to overflow, are locally very deficient in drainage and are usually narrow and cut up by the creeks, affording but small fields. Also they are generally reached by gullied lanes, down bluffs too steep for the easy ascent of loaded farm wagons.

In the cropping system of the escarpment district hay, instead of corn, takes the foremost place, occupying 36 per cent of the cropped land area as compared with 22 per cent in the prairie. This implies a somewhat longer rotation, with less frequent plantings of corn involving tillage and its attendant soil erosion on steeper slopes. Most of the land used for rotation crops lies on the uplands, frequently narrow, which project northward between the stream valleys. Only 30 per cent of the land so used is flat, as compared with 90 per cent in the Prairie, while 64 per cent is rolling and nearly 8 per cent has a slope of more than 9 degrees. On such land soil erosion is a constant menace. Few means of prevention, other than the cropping system, are employed, although some farmers have narrow strips of sod along the bottoms of the draws in their tilled fields. On these peninsular projections of the cuesta upland the field and road patterns are not so rectangular as in the prairie and several of the narrower projections end in round-nosed fields. Some of the cultivated land lies on terraces developed in the St. Peter sandstone adjacent to the Blue River.

The rank of the tilled crops reflects not only the dissection of the escarpment district but to a degree also the presence of less satisfactory corn soils. A broad ridge or peninsular projection of the upland, situated just east of the Montfort area at Cobb, was also originally a northward extension of the Prairie and likewise is characterized by the Marshall silt loam soil. Within the surveyed area however the ridges are narrow. ... These ridges were originally forested and are now characterized by the Knox silt loam soil on a generally rolling surface and by the "steep phase" of that same soil, where the slopes pitch toward the valley walls. The Knox is a light-brown or grayish friable silt loam. The light color of the soil indicates its relatively small content of organic matter. (About 2,700 pounds of nitrogen per acre as compared with 5,000 pounds in the surface 8 inches of the Marshall). The subsoil is a compact silt loam in which the clay content increases with depth. The surface soil is of variable thickness. On the steep phase and sometimes also on the ridge tops it is thin or even wanting, exposing the heavy yellowish subsoil. The compactness of this soil and its topographic situation make it subject to severe erosion. Although there is an important loessial component in this soil, as in the Marshall, its lower organic content and the greater prevalence of erosion make it a less satisfactory corn soil, yields averaging about two thirds those obtained in the Prairie district. ...

One consequence of the smaller areas of corn land and less productive corn soils in the escarpment district is that a smaller proportion of the total corn crop is raised for grain and a larger proportion is raised for silage. The dairy industry is predominant in this district also and silos are as common as in the prairie. Although exact figures are wanting, it is estimated that in the prairie as much as 50 to 60 per cent of the total acreage of corn is raised for grain while in the escarpment district this figure falls to 25 or 20 per cent. The average escarpment farm has therefore only about 15 acres of corn of which 10 or 12 are destined for the silo. The average prairie farm has about 45 acres of corn of which nearly 20 are for silage, leaving a considerable amount for grain production.

Along with the corn of the escarpment farms are the small grains, as in the prairie district. Indeed on these poorer soils they are relatively more important than in the prairie, since their combined acreage exceeds that of corn by a greater percentage of the total cultivated area than is true of the small grains in the prairie.

Of cash crops the escarpment district has three; peas, potatoes and tobacco. The first named crop, where raised as a cash crop for canning, is found almost entirely on the upland adjacent to the prairie and near a pea viner and the canning factory at Cobb. This distribution is explainable upon the basis of the physical association of this part of the district with the prairie and the community of economic interest. The potato industry is not an important one. Few farmers raise more than an acre or two of the crop. ...

The farms of the escarpment district average smaller than those of the prairie, 165 as against 190 acres. The acreage of tilled land per farm is even smaller, about 70 as compared with 150 acres, yet the average farm population of 4.8 persons is slightly larger than in the prairie. The farmsteads also are smaller, averaging 2.5 as against 3.9 acres. In general they are not arranged upon the main highways. Some are found upon spring sites in valley heads. Others are situated upon terraces, accessible to both tilled land above and pasture land below, or surrounded by the cultivated crops of the terrace itself. Still other farmsteads occupy the upland edge or even the slope of a ravine (e.g. No. 66, Fig. 8) where they are reached only by a short but difficult road up the bluff or by a long, poor, private road through the fields along the ridge. Not many are rectangular in shape and, due to the conditions of their sites, many do not square with the compass. Only a few are in the valley bottoms (e.g. No. 52); chiefly they are those of the upper portion of the Blue River valley itself where a weaker phase of the St. Peter sandstone has permitted the development of a broad valley with broad low terraces. These terraces are characterized by Lintonia silt loam soils of alluvial and colluvial origin. They are sufficiently above the Wabash soils of the first bottoms to be free from flood and are excellent agricultural land. ...

From this comparison of crops and their geographic relationships in the two districts, as well as of other features of the local landscape patterns and associations it may be concluded that the prairie farmer has a greater range of choice than the escarpment farmer in the nature of his farm operations.

CHAPTER 7

Geography of Areal Organization

Mark Jefferson's advice to study "Man using and living on the Earth" was not entirely lost in the general acceptance of Fennemann's "areas in their compositeness and complexity". A dilemma appears in the Fennemann program between the objective on the one hand of studying areas in relation to man, natural environment in relation to human life, and on the other hand of approaching the subject through the visible landscape in which man is hardly visible and is only occasionally and indirectly introduced: looking for man in the landscape and seeing only areas of complexity produced by diverse processes, agglomerations of discrete elements graded separately in the fractional complex code.

The steady advance of human geography has seemed to call for less concern with visible landscape or with the generalization of this in a simplified categorical uniformity within subdivisions of area, and more concern with occupance of areas by people. An escape from the dilemma is found in recognizing man as the organizer of areas in a process of using and living on the Earth, and in studying land use from the viewpoint of the land users, who give it coherence. Thus the phenomena suggested by Mark Jefferson and analyzed by Colby appear together in an areal pattern of organization, unified but not uniform.

"A Detail of Regional Geography: Ellison Bay Community as an Industrial Organism" by R. S. Platt, 1928, is taken to represent a seventh type in this series. In this the idea of detailed field mapping developed in connection with areal uniformity is retained, but the phenomena mapped are points of focus, areas of organization, and lines and limits of movement, rather than static areas of uniformity in a generalized mosaic. The phenomena belong together in a functional pattern of occupance as organized by a group of settlers or inhabitants in the process of living and making a living in an area.

The field method is one of detailed field mapping in which observation of visible features is less important than in the previous stage and in which inquiry among inhabitants of the area is more important - inquiry as to the function-with-reference-to-area of establishments which they operate and their own areal pattern of activity, checking for reliability by observation and further inquiry. Thus in this approach to human geography emphasis is shifted from pure observation and inference, inherited from geology, to gathering data from the people who make and operate the pattern of occupance under investigation.

As in the preceding case the study is addressed to an audience of geographers interested in field methods. The title of the article is outmoded, the comparison of human organizations with living organisms having been overdone and

properly criticized in other cases. Also outmoded is an implication of determinism or at
least of possibilism in the reference to relationships "latent in the arrangement of natural
features."[1]

A DETAIL OF REGIONAL GEOGRAPHY:
ELLISON BAY COMMUNITY AS AN INDUSTRIAL ORGANISM[2]

by R. S. Platt

I. INTRODUCTION

The Project.--In this article is presented a bit of regional
geography dealing with a minute area. In such an area intensive
study has been possible, and in the presentation the many facts
need not be reduced to sweeping generalizations. The investigation represents a type of geographic experiment, and might
later, with other detailed studies, form a basis for significant
generalizations. The study of Ellison Bay is a primary case,
an elementary unit in the science of geography.

Even for this small community only certain phases of the
geography are here presented. Maps of "The Natural Environment" and "The Cultural Landscape" of most of the area have
been published in a previous issue of the Annals of the Association
of American Geographers. Attention is here confined to the point
of view suggested in the title, omitting various topics which might
be included in a "complete geography" of Ellison Bay. Whether
such a discussion from an all-inclusive view point would be
worthwhile is very doubtful.

The area dealt with is not defined arbitrarily, but by the
trade bounds of a village community. It is a geographic unit, and
regional geography in its lowest terms is the objective of the
study. The aim has been to limit the discussion in accordance
with the subject discussed. When the investigation began it dealt
with an area whose limits were unknown and did not correspond
with any measured division; attention was fixed not on certain
square miles of land but on the occupancy of land by a certain
group of people. In the course of investigation the distribution

1. *p. 128 below.*
2. *Annals AAG, vol. 18 (1928), pp. 81-126.*

and range of their activities assumed definite form, a pattern woven to fit the patchwork background of their environment. In the presentation of the study the organized life of this areal unit of human activity provides the theme and limits the discussion.

The Setting.--The village of Ellison Bay, Wisconsin, has about a hundred inhabitants. In it are centered the interests of a community lying round about and found by investigation to occupy an irregular territory two or three miles in radius.

The community occupies land and water--a bit of land near the tip of the Door Peninsula, a bit of the adjacent water of Green Bay. It sees passing ships of the Great Lakes as a farmer sees express trains pass his fields; it contributes its mite to the streams of traffic through little boats on Green Bay and motor trucks on the peninsula. It has a share in the fishing grounds of the Great Lakes, a share in the fruit lands of the Great Lakes shores, and a share in the northern woods of the Great Lakes region. It is within the extensive hay and pasture province of short summers and diversified glaciated lands; and within that part of the province accessible but not close to great markets where dairying has been developed, particularly for cheese making. It bestrides the Niagara cuesta, and so holds attractions of rugged land and water, which gives it a place among summer playgrounds.

The peninsula as a whole is a salient feature of the cuesta. The jagged edge of the Niagara limestone escarpment overlooks Green Bay; the long back-slope dips gently eastward beneath Lake Michigan. The crest is not an even line but is broken by a series of grooves cutting diagonally across the peninsula and forming indentations on both shores. Between these transverse depressions are the undulating uplands sloping from rocky headlands above Green Bay to low points on Lake Michigan. Deep water lies close to shore on the Green Bay side, and the indentations between the bluffs form sheltered harbors. On each of the harbors is a village. On the last of the westward facing harbors, sixty miles northeast of the base of the peninsula, is the village of Ellison Bay.

The Village.--The white village nestles among trees at the head of its bay and spreads scatteringly up the lower slopes of the bordering uplands.

The buildings cluster about three points close together; the landing place, the crossroads where the highway is met by a transverse road terminating at the landing place, and the nearby road fork where the highway turns northward (Fig. 9). From this triple center the village spreads along the roads and along the shore, an irregular six-pointed star. Twenty-seven households are contained in it, twenty-five places of business or village activity, and fifteen summer cottages.

At the landing place there are two storehouses on the dock and two elevators. Along the shore are scattered fish docks and summer cottages reached by lanes from the village center. At the crossroads is one of the stores, and at the road fork is the

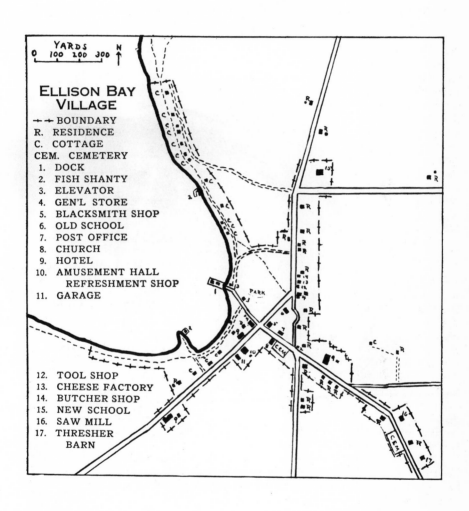

Fig. 9. *Ellison Bay Village: Functional establishments.*

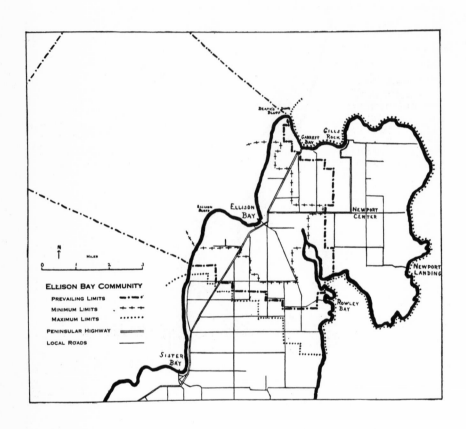

Fig. 10. Ellison Bay Community: Lines and limits of movement.

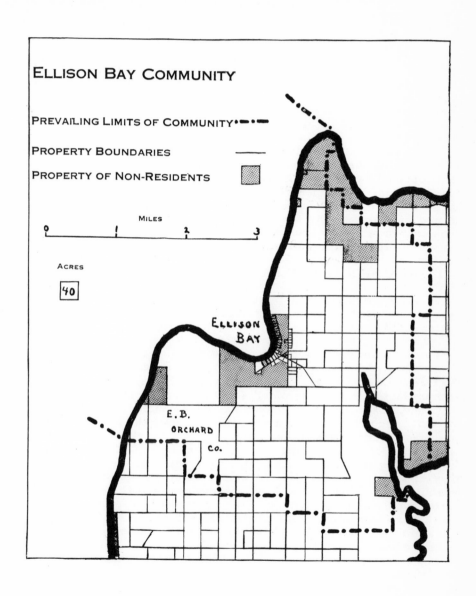

Fig. 11. Ellison Bay Community: Basic units of areal organization.

other, while within a stone's throw are the post office, the church, the old school buildings, the commercial hotel, the amusement hall, the blacksmith shop, the garage, the tool shop, the butcher shop, and the cheese factory. Beyond this central group are most of the dwelling houses and a few other buildings; the new school, the sawmill, the thresher, and two summer hotels.

In the dwelling houses live the people who operate the village institutions, and in addition some people who are institutions in themselves: the nurse, the notary public, the barber, the cobbler, the carpenters, the laborers. The other householders, although not active, can all give a good account of themselves: two retired farmers, a retired hotel keeper, a retired ship captain and three widows.

The life of the village is in the activity of the village institutions. These reach out beyond the village into the surrounding territory and depend for their activity upon the enterprises there which draw directly upon resources of land and water. In the surrounding territory there is a sense of common interest and unified life centering in the village. The community is an economic organism, occupying its own domain reaching to the bounds of other communities.

II. TRANSPORTATION FACILITIES OF THE COMMUNITY

Transportation is of the essence of the community. The heart of the community is a spot reached by transportation routes from the outside world and by local routes focusing upon it. The body of the community is the territory reached by the local routes and looking to the village as the center of its life.

Green Bay Waterway.--Of the routes from the outside world the Green Bay waterway bears the heavier loads. The season of activity lasts about seven months and for five months the harbor is closed. Generally this season has been considered long enough for most requirements; in winter it is not only the harbor that has been inactive: the whole community has barely existed, hibernating until the spring renewal of activity.

During the season, from May to November, the principal regular service is that of a steamboat which makes three trips weekly between Green Bay City, Menominee, and Door County ports, supplying to the northern Door Peninsula a freight and passenger connection with railroad centers on the south and west sides of Green Bay. Ellison Bay is the northernmost stop on the mainland. . . .

Peninsular Highway.--Much more numerous than the arrivals and departures by water are those by land at the village crossroads. The main highway cuts northeasterly along the peninsula, functioning as an extension into the peninsula not only of highways from the south and southwest but also of the railway from the south terminating near the base of the peninsula at Sturgeon Bay. It runs near the Green Bay side of the peninsula, passing through each of the little ports which lie at the heads of the little bays

(Fig. 10). In Ellison Bay, the northernmost of the port villages on the Green Bay shore, the highway forks and thence two branches extend to points on the northern end of the peninsula. The width of the peninsula at Ellison Bay is so constricted by indentations on both shores and a swamp on the Lake Michigan side that there are no roads paralleling the highway; all roads join in one and bring through the village all the traffic to and from the northern end.

Regular service on the highway is supplied by a stage company which carries mail, express, and passengers between the railroad terminus at Sturgeon Bay and the peninsular villages, including Ellison Bay and beyond to the northern shore. The mail stage makes one trip daily throughout the year, rarely interrupted by storms. Occasionally a sleigh is substituted in winter. The passenger stage makes one trip daily from July to September. . . .

A railway extension to the northern end of the peninsula has often been proposed and twice surveyed, but probably will not be constructed. The meager traffic of an area so narrow, so slightly productive, and so well supplied with waterway and highway service, is not likely to afford an attractive return on railway capital investment. The project is not favored in Sturgeon Bay, which now holds a key to the peninsula. . . .

Local Transportation.--Local traffic within the community, in smaller units of greater frequency, focusses on the village and there connects with the outside world through the mediation of the village enterprises.

The fact that the peninsula is constricted at Ellison Bay is perhaps a slight advantage to the village, as previously stated, in bringing through traffic into it, but it is more of a disadvantage in reducing the tributary area. The swampy and sandy transverse lowland is relatively unproductive. On both sides of the lowland local roads reach out into the bordering uplands to meet there the rival limits of other communities (Fig. 10).

The mail carrier makes a daily round of the community, winter and summer, by automobile, except on winter days when a one-horse sleigh is substituted and a few spring days when a two-horse buggy is used.

Most other service within the community is a private matter. Almost every household outside of the village is provided with an automobile, and some of them more than one. The most regular service is the daily visit of each patron to the cheese factory. But each of the village institutions receives visits of similar significance. Even on the water there is local transportation focusing on the village. Four fishing boats make daily trips during the season to take out set lines and to bring back fish, and six other boats make triweekly trips to bring in the catch from the pound nets.

It is these local connections which give the village enterprises their status as institutions of the community. Without these connections there would be no unified community.

III. EXTENT OF THE COMMUNITY

The radius of the community is measured by the reach of the village institutions. In general, the area of the community is the territory nearer to Ellison Bay than to any other center. Each of the village enterprises tends to reach half way to the nearest similar enterprise in a neighboring community. If the neighboring villages and their road connections were exactly similar to Ellison Bay, then the boundaries of the community would tend to be definite and to lie half way to the rival centers. Since the neighboring villages are somewhat dissimilar in the number and character of their enterprises, there is disconformity in the territory served by the Ellison Bay enterprises. Some activities reach farther than others, and the exact boundaries of the community are difficult to define. . . .

At the Ellison Bay village site are the fundamental features of sheltered landing place, highway passing close by, and local road focus. A similar and slightly stronger combination of landing place, highway and local roads occurs at Sister Bay, five miles to the southwest (Fig. 10). There is a less concentrated occurrence of similar elements northeast at Gills Rock and Newport, and there is a suggestion of them southeast at Rowley Bay.

Each of the Ellison Bay enterprises, with one exception, is matched if not surpassed by a similar enterprise at Sister Bay; several of them are matched in the Newport-Gills Rock area; and one or two of them are matched at Rowley Bay.

Regardless for the moment of superiority in certain respects, Sister Bay has the same boat service as Ellison Bay and similar dock service. Since traffic tends to seek the nearest port to obtain this service, the boundary between the areas tributary to the two ports is almost exactly half way between, for automobile traffic on the local roads. The boundary crosses the peninsula from shore to shore, there being no boat service on the Lake Michigan side. The lake shore is far from the boat routes to railway ports on Green Bay and far from the better road routes of the Green Bay shore.

Northeast of Ellison Bay the only significant landing place is at Gills Rock. Being almost at the end of the peninsula in a northward facing bay, Gills Rock is less of a road focus and village center than Ellison Bay--even less of a focus than Newport Center, two miles inland. Like Ellison Bay, Gills Rock has a dock storehouse and "hooker" service, but it does not have the steamboat service nor agricultural warehouse and elevator service. Consequently the Ellison Bay dock serves the territory more than half way to Gills Rock and in some ways, particularly in connection with farm shipments, it serves the entire northern end of the peninsula.

The stores, shops, and garage of Ellison Bay similarly are matched at Sister Bay by active competitors, strengthened by the business of a more productive farming area and a more numerous summer colony. The boundary between the territories of the two

shopping centers is not definite nor fixed. The services are so
diverse, the personal considerations so weighty, and the mobility
of the customers so great that the factor of distance alone does not
decide the matter. There is a zone containing customers of both
centers. In general, however, the people shop in the village where
they are served in other ways, and the boundary may be considered
approximately the same as that for dock service. In fact, the
storehouses on the dock should be considered among the stores, as
they are used for a merchandising business in certain commodities,
catering particularly to dock patrons. . . .

The elevators are even more closely related to the dock
service than are the stores. They are both located beside the dock
and one of them is operated by the dock management. Peas and
grains are brought to the elevators from the farms for cleaning
and potatoes for grading. From here they are shipped by water or
land. There is similar service at Sister Bay, but not at Gills Rock.
The Ellison Bay elevators receive produce from the territory about
half way to Sister Bay and all the way to the end of the peninsula.

The cheese factory has a more definite territory; distance
is a more compelling factor than in the case of the stores or even
of the elevators. It requires an early morning trip six days a
week throughout the year, seven days a week in summer. Road
distance by automobile, wagon, or sleigh is of daily consequence.
The service rendered is simple, and, although the business is
competitive, it is the same from place to place even in details of
operation, standardized under state supervision. Personal considerations have little weight and only in exceptional cases does
the cheese factory reach more than half way to the nearest
competitor. . . .

An institution performing a service comparable to that of
the cheese factory is the threshing machine. The commodity with
which it deals does not require daily attention in small quantities
like milk, but annual attention in one large quantity. For that one
occasion each customer is visited by the machine. This system
leaves to the farmer the marketing of the product, either through
another village institution or otherwise, whereas in the case of
cheese the factory handles the marketing. The fact that grain is
more easily marketed than cheese is a secondary factor in favor
of the moving machine.

This system does not lead to activity in every direction
around the village. The thresher moves out in one direction,
leaving the village, perhaps invading the territory of one competitor while conceding territory on the other side of the village
to another competitor. There are differences from year to year
in the route followed and the territory covered. Therefore it is
only in an average of years that the changeable limits of activity
may be said to reach half way to the headquarters of competitors
at Sister Bay and Gills Rock. . . .

The fishing establishments are like most of the other commercial institutions in depending on the village as a focus of local
routes connecting with outside transportation service. They are

different in having no relation to the landward extent of the community. Their local water routes mark the extent of the Ellison Bay domain along the shores and out into Green Bay (Fig. 10). The limits of pound net fishing along shore are definite: southwest around Ellison Bluff half way to Sister Bay and north to Death's Door Bluff half way to the fishing settlement of Gills Rock. Out in the bay the limits are less definite: there are no exclusive private holdings as in pound net sites and farm lands; motor boat mobility is so great that a few miles' distance is not a strong factor against opportunities to make a catch. The one definite limitation is the middle of Green Bay, not due to competition from the fishermen on the opposite shore, but due to state jurisdiction. The cost of a Michigan license keeps most of the Ellison Bay fishermen on the Wisconsin side of the bay. On their side Ellison Bay fishermen mingle on the fishing grounds with men from other ports, sometimes fishing near Ellison Bay and sometimes near Sister Bay or Gills Rock. There are no fishing grounds used exclusively by Ellison Bay fishermen, and the extreme limits of their operations are many miles southwest, beyond Sister Bay, many miles north, beyond Washington Island, and even east beyond Gills Rock in Lake Michigan. These limits are hardly to be considered community boundaries, and perhaps the arbitrary limits of greatest proximity to Ellison Bay are the best indication of Ellison Bay waters.

The hotels at Ellison Bay, only in a minor phase of activity, have the same relationship to the community as the typical village enterprises. This phase is the small amount of commercial business which has to do with the focus of local routes and the external connections. One hotel is open all year and is patronized by traveling salesmen who make Ellison Bay their headquarters for covering the end of the peninsula beyond Sister Bay. There are similar accommodations at Sister Bay but not in the Newport-Gills Rock area.

As summer resorts, the hotels and cottages have important connections with the outside world through the village, but no community lines focusing upon them. In this respect they are like the individual farmsteads rather than like the village establishments which handle farm goods. There are hotels at Gills Rock and Garrett Bay and some cottages scattered along the shore north and east of Ellison Bay, as well as numerous hotels and cottages in the opposite direction at Sister Bay and a few cottages at Rowley Bay. The territory within which summer visitors trade and travel through Ellison Bay is about the same as its territory for other trade and travel. Most of the summer places are along the shores and the Ellison Bay boundaries are about the same as for pound net fishing, southwest beyond Ellison Bluff and north to Death's Door Bluff, even though the cottages are reached by land and not by water.

The school is an institution with a definite district fixed by agreement. The radius of the district is based on daily walking distance for the pupils, and the boundaries of the district are equidistant from other similar schools. . . .

The church is a community institution, although its territory is made indefinite by denominational affiliations and other personal considerations. Ellison Bay has a Lutheran Church, while at Sister Bay and Newport Center there are Baptist churches. In general the Ellison Bay community is Lutheran and the others are Baptist, although there is some interchange of people. . . .

The post-office is a village institution whose territory is exactly defined. The nearest post-office on the south is at Sister Bay. Since there is similar service and no competition but unified supervision and organized cooperation between the post-offices to cover both communities, the boundary line between the two is set for convenient mail delivery equidistant from both. The boundary crosses the peninsula from shore to shore. . . .

The amusement hall holds a unique place in that it reaches not only into the Newport-Gills Rock but also into the Sister Bay area, not meeting equal competition in either place. The weekly moving picture show draws an automobile audience from a larger territory than any of the other village enterprises, since there is no such entertainment in the Baptist community of Sister Bay. There are dances at Sister Bay which compete to some extent with the moving picture shows and accompanying dances at Ellison Bay. But even this competition is not direct, since the entertainments are often held on different nights and draw part of the same patronage at both places.

The people who play the role of community institutions have their limits, more or less definite, as do the other institutions. The notary public serves people who do business in the village. The nurse, the carpenters, and the laborers move in the community more widely and irregularly than the thresher. They all meet competition in the direction of Sister Bay rather than of Newport and Gills Rock. . . .

From the examination of individual enterprises it is evident that the boundaries of the Ellison Bay community are not sharply defined. It is also evident that there are extreme limits beyond which Ellison Bay has no power of attraction in any community activity and narrow limits within which Ellison Bay has complete power of attraction in all such activities. Between these limits is the zone of divided attraction where some interests center in Ellison Bay and others elsewhere. This zone is narrow in the south, where Sister Bay matches almost every activity, and broad on the northeast, including all of the Newport-Gills Rock area. It is not surprising that in a broad sense this latter area is considered part of the Ellison Bay community, in view of its relative weakness in some activities and its lack of others, and in view of the absence of a concentrated village focus. In Newport Center is seen the rise of a new community, in an area which formerly was an outlying but integral part of the Ellison Bay territory, but which now in the course of more intensive development is acquiring its own community institutions--cheese factory, store, and church all new within a few years. In this study it is not included in the territory "served principally by Ellison Bay," for already it may be considered a separate community subordinate in some respects to Ellison Bay, just as Ellison Bay is overshadowed in some respects by Sister Bay, and Sister Bay in turn by Sturgeon Bay.

The idea of these communities as equals side by side is incomplete, for equality in some respects is accompanied by inequality and subordination in others. Rural activities look to the smallest village focus for immediate services needed close enough for daily visiting or heavy hauling, and to greater centers for more centralized and larger scale services visited less frequently or reached indirectly. The farmer at the northeastern end of the peninsula takes his milk daily to the Newport cheese factory and goes less frequently to Ellison Bay to ship his potatoes and for some other purposes. Farmers of both Ellison Bay and Newport go occasionally to Sister Bay for a variety of merchandise in larger stores, for the disposal of cherries and the grinding of wheat, for the Chicago steamboat, for town meeting and for the undertaker. They telephone or take a trip to Sturgeon Bay for telegraph office, bank, hospital, courthouse and other establishments centralized for the whole county in the county seat and railroad terminus. With the people of the whole county and other counties they look to Green Bay for wholesale houses, purchasers of their products, and headquarters of their boat service. With the people of the whole state and of other states they look to Chicago for mail order houses and larger wholesalers, for their ultimate market, for the source or destination of many things.

These relationships, patent in the present development of community life, are latent in the arrangement of natural features: the head of Lake Michigan as the focus for a national inland metropolis; the head of Green Bay for a regional center; the head of Sturgeon Bay for a county seat; and the head of Ellison Bay for a village focus, slightly inferior to Sister Bay and superior to Newport and Gills Rock, the heart of a community lying within a three-mile radius.

IV. ACTIVITIES OF THE COMMUNITY

Through the commercial establishments of the village there are seasonal flows of goods in reciprocal streams. . . .

In addition to the outward and inward flows of goods, community life is evident in other activities, involving movement within the community, focusing on the village. . . .

The community is organized around certain industries which have been developed to take advantage of certain resources of the area. The community center is a focus coordinating the farms and other basic units of the industries, the living cells of the community organism. These activities are considered in succeeding pages.

FARMING

Ellison Bay is primarily a farm village, the center of a farming community. This is indicated by the products shipped and the supplies received. Three of the principal village institutions handle farm products exclusively: the cheese factory, the elevators, the thresher. Most of the others also handle farm products or farm supplies or serve farmers in other ways.

The basic units of farm activity are the individual farms. Of these there are sixty-five in the community. The land is divided among them in accordance with a square section survey. A regular pattern of rectangular farms is superimposed on the irregular pattern of hills and swamps, sands and silts, as economic units apparently set down upon and not cut to fit their natural setting (Fig. 11).

Most of the farms are of forty acres or a multiple thereof. But the property areas and boundary lines are not significant. The "forties" are merely convenient measuring squares for dealing out to each farmer enough cultivable land for him to work as a unit with whatever family aid he has available. In the best areas one of these units is enough for a farm; in mediocre areas two. In poor areas many forties are appended to better farm lands and some do not belong to farms. Seventeen per cent of the land of the community is not in farms. Forty-six per cent of the community is cut-over, marsh, and timber land, belonging to farms, some of it used as rough pasture, some of it supplying a little wood, but a large part of it lying idle and almost none of it taxed as productive land. The rest of the land, thirty-seven per cent of the community, is agricultural land.

Naturally the unproductive areas are not evenly distributed among farms, the large appendages of a few farms raising the average farm size to 102 acres, although more than eighty per cent of the farms have no more than 80 acres.

The agricultural land is distributed more evenly, the average amount of 43 acres per farm being about the normal quantity. This is designedly the case in this community of economic equality and similarity of organization. Forty-acre farms have a little less than the average of agricultural land and eighty-acre farms generally a little more, although the best forty-acre farms have more than the poorest eighty-acre farms. At one extreme are a few properties which are hardly to be classed as complete farms, having less than 10 agricultural acres giving part time work to men otherwise engaged. At the other extreme are only four farms with 80 or more agricultural acres. Of these four, two represent the burdensome heritage of over-extension, one represents the energy of the families of two brothers, and one, the largest of all, represents a distinct development not to be classed with the other farms, a specialized corporate enterprise. Evidently significance lies not in total farm areas, but in productive farm areas.

Even the agricultural land shows the influence of the rectangular survey. Fields commonly are rectangular, although they are made large or small for placement on good land and are modified in form where circumstance demands. In some places good land is separated from poor land by a sharp line of demarcation--a steep slope, a rocky ledge, or a marsh border. But in many places there is no such sharp distinction; deep silty soil merges into shallow, stony, or sandy soil through a marginal zone, into which some fields penetrate farther than others to complete the rectangular pattern or for other reasons.

The clearing of the marginal land has depended generally on its relations to other land, on its distance from roads, or on the energy or needs of its owners. The clearing even of relatively good land has been laborious on account of the large number of stones to be gathered and piled as well as the stumps to be pulled. The marginal quality of some land is due to excessive stoniness to be overcome by extra costly clearing. Very little clearing has been done in recent years of farm depression.

In general most of the good cultivable lands have been cleared. They fit into the landscape, concentrated in the uplands, where silty soils overlie the limestone; dispersed along shore and in the transverse lowland, where steep, stony, sandy or swampy areas prevail; they spread on into other communities uninterrupted except by farm boundaries for convenience of administration and by community boundaries for convenience of transportation.

Thus is emphasized the complexity of geographic delimitation and the necessity of boundary settlement by a sharply defined viewpoint. In this study the community as a trade organism supplies the viewpoint and limits the discussion. . . .

General Farming.--The Ellison Bay community was once an area of wheat farming indistinguishable in aspect from the rest of the Door Peninsula. But that day has long since passed, with the decline in yields and the increase in western competition. Stony fields of small extent offer scant opportunity for competition in grain markets against regions of large scale, extensive farming.

The one crop system has been succeeded by general farming with livestock and rotation of crops; and by some specialization in fruit growing, a subject for separate consideration.

Dairying is the central feature of the farm system. There is much land available for pasturage, too stony for cultivation, included in the great area of cut over and wooded lands of the community. The relatively cool short summers are unfavorable for the ripening of corn but favorable for silage corn, oats, hay and other fodder crops as well as for pasture grasses. Cool temperatures are favorable also for the handling of milk.

There is no accessible market to consume much of the fresh milk and the product must go to the consumer in a less perishable form. There are only about three hundred cows in the Ellison Bay area, too few to support a milk condensery in the community and too isolated for a condensery in an area including the Ellison Bay community. Formerly there was a creamery at Sister Bay taking cream from such an extended area including Ellison Bay. It flourished where a condensery was impracticable, because it needed only cream in mediocre condition instead of whole milk in perfect condition and therefore could accept infrequent and delayed deliveries from distant farms.

Now butter making has been superceded by cheese making, which generally pays a little more for the farmer's output. The cheese factory requires the whole milk in fresh condition and cannot endure the delayed deliveries of a creamery. However, it needs the milk of only about three hundred cows to be successfully operated, instead of the cream of a thousand cows needed by the creamery. Therefore the cheese factory can exist in a part of the territory of the creamery and take the milk from a small compact group of farms. The Ellison Bay cheese factory offers a more convenient and profitable market for the milk of a part of the territory formerly supplying material to the creamery. Other similar factories occupy other parts.

The factory is a small frame building containing one cheese vat operated entirely by one man. Probably there is no more conspicuous example of a manufacturing industry impelled to small scale operation by the peculiar advantage of close proximity to the source of raw material.

Early every morning each farmer brings his milk to the factory and by afternoon the cheese maker has converted the day's receipts into the day's output of American cheese, biproduct cream, and whey. Most of the whey is wasted because its use for pig feed is not well known in the community and not many pigs are raised. The biproduct cream is taken by an ice cream delivery truck on its return journey to a Sturgeon Bay creamery. The cheeses are collected weekly by the truck of a buyer on a round of the peninsula, to be taken to Sturgeon Bay for storage and distribution. . . .

Ellison Bay farms are not specialized dairy enterprises, although dairy cows are the center of farm life and milk is the most regular and dependable source of income. There are no more than five cows per farm on the average, and there are no very large herds, there being similarity among the farms in this respect as in others. . . .

Among the miscellaneous farm products are certain crops which do not contribute to dairying or other livestock interests. Almost every farm has four or more fields, and in them generally a three or four-year rotation of crops is practiced. The first place in rotation is occupied in many cases by silage corn, a dairy crop. About half of the farms have silos. But equally common are crops of potatoes or peas, well adapted to the short growing season, light soil, and small scale methods of the community, and suitable for marketing.

The potato crop is so important and the problems of marketing it so serious that the Ellison Bay Potato Association has come to be the chief organization of farmers in the community. By cooperation it is hoped to consummate sales at prices more favorable than those obtained by individual farmers. The association has been active and helpful in connection not only with potatoes but also with other farm interests. Through its elevator and management of the dock the association performs for commercial crops such service as the cheese factory performs for milk, and through its supply service it supplements the village stores. . . .

Small grains occupy a larger but less distinctive place among the crops, second in rotation, or first when intertilled crops are omitted, providing fodder, food, and seed, and in a few cases a surplus hauled to the elevators to be cleaned and shipped away. . . .

Hay and pasture occupy the last but largest place in rotation. In fact they occupy the only place on some farms where years of unprofitable farming have discouraged all efforts at producing any but the simplest of field crops. . . .

In dairying and in the raising of potatoes, peas, and other field crops the Ellison Bay community is not peculiar, but merely shares the advantages of a larger area. Cheese making is a Wisconsin industry. Potatoes find favorable conditions in many parts of the Upper Lakes region. . . .

The community is distinct only in its organization with reference to the village transportation focus, and beyond it are similar farms similarly related to other centers.

Fruit Specialization.--One farm has been mentioned as different from the rest, the large special enterprise of the Ellison Bay Orchard Company. Although this is but one special farm among more than sixty general farms, it is no less characteristic of the area. Ellison Bay, in its climate modified by the bodies of water east and west and in its silty limestone lands, has excellent possibilities for fruit growing, especially for pie cherries. The cold backward spring retards fruit blossoms in the period of frosts and prevents rapid tender growth; the long mild autumn perfects the growth of twigs and buds; the winter is not dangerously cold for cherry trees nor the summer injuriously hot for the ripening of the fruit. Thorough drainage and lightness of fertile soil are more advantageous, and stoniness and shallowness of soil less objectionable for fruit than for field crops.

The production of cherries is an attractive modern venture, but requires special knowledge and labor, special equipment and materials, without any returns for three years or more. Therefore a majority of the family general farms have not engaged in the enterprise and most of the production is from the one special fruit farm organized and financed by outside interests, in the choicest site of the silty upland, holding 5 per cent of the farm area of the community, 9 per cent of the "agricultural" land, and 14 per cent of the farm capital investment.

The community is not a separate unit in cherry growing; it is merely an outlying part of the Door Peninsula fruit district centering at Sturgeon Bay. Ellison Bay shares the advantages of climate and soil which make the peninsula fit to be the greatest pie cherry district in the world. . . .

The Ellison Bay Orchard Company is in the southern part of the Ellison Bay territory (Fig. 11) and it is therefore natural that the plant should be on the next harbor to the south, around which there are other orchards. In spite of its name the big orchard is less attached to Ellison Bay as a community phenomenon than any other farm enterprise in the area. While the Ellison Bay Potato Association and the cheese factory handle other farm products, it is the Door County Fruit Growers' Association, through its Sister Bay plant, which handles cherries. The fruit is collected by truck immediately after picking and taken to the plant to be chilled, pitted, sugared and barreled; and thence it is sent by truck to Sturgeon Bay for storage and distribution.

The Ellison Bay Orchard Company is the main factor but does not monopolize the cherry industry in the Ellison Bay area. The excellent conditions for cherries and the success of the industry as now organized in the peninsula have encouraged progressive Ellison Bay farmers to put a few of their eggs into the new basket of cherry raising. Thus cherries have become an item in the general farms of the area, handled through the Sister Bay plant as in the case of the orchard company. Some of the land used formerly for field crops in rotation is occupied now by orchards. . . .

Apple raising is a less spectacular part of the fruit industry and probably a less profitable part. Apples are less exacting than cherries in their climatic requirements and have a wider range, the Door Peninsula being merely one minor competitive district among many in the Great Lakes region. At the same time apple trees require a longer period to mature and are more exacting in labor required of the producer; seven sprayings are needed annually for various apple pests as compared with four sprayings needed for cherries; and apple packing needs to be done at the orchard to avoid bruising instead of at a central plant, thus increasing the responsibility of the producer and making district standardization difficult.

One fact at least has favored the planting of apples: they do not require such intensive work as cherries during the harvest season, since they are less perishable and since there are more varieties available to ripen successively. The cherry harvest is confined to a period of about three weeks, within which both of the two available varieties must be picked. Indeed the major part of the work falls within the ten days of harvesting the late variety, which is preferred by producers, because in Ellison Bay orchards the trees are more prolific than those of the early variety, the blossoms are less liable to frost injury, and the fruit is larger, easier to pick and more in demand. Of apples on the other hand there are nine varieties found available and produced in quantity. The harvesting season is spread over six weeks. Picking is accomplished with less labor on a smaller scale than in the case of cherries and the fruit can be shipped at leisure without preservative treatment. Whereas the cherry picking season requires the energetic mobilization of all available labor in the district, two or three hundred people for the orchard company alone and two 12-hour shifts at the packing plant, the apple harvest requires hardly more than the regular orchard workers and farm shipping facilities. Many apples grown in the Ellison Bay district are shipped like other crops from the village dock. . . .

Forest Exploitation.--Ellison Bay was founded as a wood-choppers' settlement. The narrow, forested peninsula with its many indentations on both sides offered a supply of timber so accessible that it was exploited early in the history of Wisconsin Lumbering. For years timber and cordwood were shipped from Captain Ellison's land around the bay, until no valuable virgin timber remained. Similar exploitation was taking place at Gills Rock, Newport, Rowley Bay, and Sister Bay. Probably the forest area reached from Ellison Bay was about the same as the area of the present Ellison Bay community.

Today about 55 per cent of the area of the community is still uncleared and most of this is woodland. But the forest industry as an independent activity has vanished; the woodland has been stripped of its timber value and that which remains is of secondary importance in other connections. Hardly 2 per cent of the area of the community is assessed as timber land, and most of this is not virgin timber. The rest of the woodland is assessed as cutover and waste land.

All of the assessed timber lands and most of the cutover and waste lands are in farms. The productivity of these lands is low. Most of them are unsuitable for agriculture, and are in farms for want of other holders. They play a part in the farm economy by supplying rough pasturage, firewood, and some timber. Most of the farms have more than enough firewood, and on many farms incidental lumber requirements are met by hauling a few logs to the Ellison Bay mill and having them sawed into boards.

Some areas contain growing stands of second growth pines, cedars, or hardwoods, which some day may have value as timber. But the great days of the Ellison Bay woods as a primary timber resource are passed. On fertile land they have been superseded permanently by agriculture. Elsewhere they are destined to remain of small obvious value in supplying minor needs of people who are in the area on account of other resources, and to become of greater intangible value standing as an essential element of attraction for summer visitors. The present status of forest exploitation emphasizes the fact that in this generation the community is organized primarily on the basis of farming. . . .

FISHING.--Ellison Bay is secondarily a fishing village. Apparently an Indian fishing village once occupied the same site, and white fishermen used the harbor before permanent settlement. Now on the water front docks and shanties stand conspicuously. While these face in the opposite direction from the farm interests and operate in a different realm, yet their relations to the community are not different: boats from the fishing grounds bring in their catch to the village where the product is prepared and whence it is shipped along with products of the farms. Most of the regular

fishermen do some farming and many of the farmers are part
time fishermen.

The basic units of the fishing industry, paralleling the family
farms of agriculture, are partnerships of two or three men, having
boats, tackle, dock shanties, pound net sites and license to use the
common ground of the bay. There are six partnerships, five of
them occupying dock shanties on the village waterfront and the
sixth having a dock on the shore north of the village. Fourteen
partners are the principles in these establishments and at the
height of the season thirty-five or forty other men are engaged,
as well as numerous children to untangle lines.

Almost the whole bay and lake are satisfactory for fishing
of some sort, according to depth and other conditions; at one time
or another there is fishing practically everywhere. But fish are
more plentiful in some places than in others, with periodic variations, and certain areas are known as good fishing grounds.

The close adaptation of the kind and use of equipment not
only to the presence of various kinds of fish but to their moods and
movements in their habitat is illustrated by various details. When
feeding in summer, lake trout can be hooked but not netted, and
when coming on the spawning grounds in autumn they can be netted
but not hooked. The nets must be thoroughly cleaned by boiling in
soapy water when taken up in order to catch fish when used again.
The lines on the other hand need not be cleaned and in some cases
are not dried for years, being merely salted to prevent rotting
when taken up. White fish are not taken by hooks but by nets of one
type out in the bay and by nets of another type when moving close
to shore. White fish are found spawning on sandy bottom in
September and trout on rocky bottom in October. In stormy
weather fish are found in deeper water than in fair weather. In
winter Green Bay freezes over but Lake Michigan remains open,
and, although fish are still present in both bodies of water, fishing
is necessarily different.

About 60 per cent of the fish are caught by means of set
lines. These are used in Green Bay away from shore and are
chiefly to catch lake trout. It is laborious work to handle the
"gangs" of lines, four miles in length, fitted with two thousand
hooks, to be baited, set, and on a subsequent day hauled in, unloaded and taken ashore to be disentangled. This work occupies
every day, morning and afternoon, for the regular fishermen. Yet
it is more efficient than small scale hook-and-line fishing,
particularly in view of the fact that the fish are near the bottom
and that the lines must be sunk accordingly, to depths of from
eight to twenty fathoms.

Motor boats are used for the work. Usually they operate
near enough to the village to return every night to the dock,
cleaning the catch on the way. Summer is the season of greatest
activity, from May to September, when the trout are feeding in
the bay.

In May and September, just before and just after the
principal set line season, gill nets are used. The net of fine cord

hangs as an invisible fence in the water, to entangle the gills of fish swimming near the bottom. Like set lines, gill nets are distributed out in the bay at depths of from eight to twenty fathoms, and are set and taken in similarly. The method is effective, but the season is short and the equipment is expensive, fragile and difficult to handle, a single set of nets being several miles in length. Therefore only the largest establishment has them. Gill nets account for about 10 per cent of the annual catch.

At certain times a few gill nets of small mesh are set at the surface instead of the bottom to catch herring. Other gill nets of small mesh can be used throughout the year at the bottom at depths of from thirty to one hundred fathoms to catch chubs for smoking. Such depths occur in Lake Michigan but not in Green Bay, so that Ellison Bay fishermen seldom engage in chub fishing.

Through the spring and autumn there are runs of fish along the shores of Green Bay. To take advantage of this fact pound nets are used. As in gill netting, a barrier net obstructs the movement along shore. In this case it is a visible barrier, turning the fish aside in search of a way around, and trapping them in labyrinthine pound at the outer end of the obstacle.

Each of the fishing establishments has one or two of these set at intervals north and south of the village. They account for about 30 per cent of the annual catch, and they are of even greater significance than is indicated by this fraction of the annual marketable product, because they furnish the bait for set lines. Herring are the fish caught in largest quantities. Of these the smaller ones are used for bait and the larger ones are marketed for food. Trout, white fish, perch, and pickerel make up a substantial and valuable portion of the catch.

The nets are lifted generally three times a week, to ship the iced product by the steamboat. Their operation requires little time, in contrast with set line and gill net fishing; visiting and lifting them is a mere incident of the day's work. At the same time they represent a relatively large investment, each net being worth about a thousand dollars.

In summer when the catch becomes smaller and netting rots in the warm water, some of the nets are taken out, the others being left to supply bait. In the autumn before freezing, not only the nets, but also the sixty-foot supporting stakes are drawn out to avoid destruction by ice.

In the winter there is fishing in Green Bay by hand lines through holes in the ice. Boats and expensive tackle are not needed, preserving fish by freezing is easy, and other occupations languish at that season. Therefore other people as well as regular fishermen engage in the industry. Some of the regular fishermen continue their operations by moving their headquarters to the east side of the peninsula, fishing in the unfrozen waters of Lake Michigan, and shipping their product directly by road to Sturgeon Bay, thus creating a minor seasonal focus of activity apart from the village.

Each fishing partnership operates separately. Whereas farmers make use of the centralized services in the village for preparing and shipping their products, the fishermen need no assistance. The nature of their occupation brings them to the village with time and ability to carry forward the urgent processes of cleaning, packing, and shipping the catch. The fresh fish product is packed with ice in boxes and shipped promptly by stage to Sturgeon Bay or by boat to Green Bay or Menominee, consigned to dealers for distribution to interior cities. Most of the larger herring of the pound net catch are cleaned, salted, barreled, and stored for shipment by hooker to Menominee distributors, by whom they are sent to various markets west as far as Montana, south as far as Texas, east as far as Virginia, supplying a particular demand for a kind of cheap food which keeps better than salt water herring.

In recent years the fishing industry has been more prosperous than farming. Moderately good prices and relatively low overhead expenses have resulted in fair financial returns. However, the catch has diminished and depletion through overfishing is in evidence, in spite of restrictive regulations and government fish propagation. Further decline seems likely, unless more effective measures are taken to prevent it.

RECREATION

Along the shores, less conspicuous and unsightly than the fishing establishments, are the evidences of summer resort activity. This newest and most rapidly expanding interest seems likely to become the most valuable one to the community. The northern end of the peninsula has reached the narrow limits of its possibilities as a fishing center and is of mediocre value as a farming area. But it has unique advantages for summer resort purposes. The rocky wooded bluffs and sheltered beaches characteristic of the Niagara Cuesta, exposed to summer breezes both from Green Bay and from Lake Michigan, are unmatched so near to various large interior cities.

Something of an inversion of values has resulted from the development. The more rugged, rocky or sandy shore property, of relatively low value for farming and consequently left wooded, has on these accounts assumed high value for resort purposes. Most of the shore frontage of the community is held for this purpose.

Recreation is still in the development stage. A considerable part of the shore is in large tracts owned by non-residents who saw the possibilities and acquired the land cheaply.

The trend of the times is seen in little changes. Several old fish landings on small pieces of property apart from the village have been purchased recently for cottage sites. The fishermen have been the more ready to sell on account of recent years of lowered lake level hindering the use of their docks. The only active fishing establishment away from the village has a "shanty" built to accommodate a children's camp during the mid-summer off season for net fishing. In the village there is talk of remodeling one of the grain elevators as a summer cottage.

Hotels and cottages are the active units of the resort business. There are three hotels in the village; and there are fifteen cottages along the village waterfront, five or six on the shore outside of the village, and one or two in the interior outside of the village. Most of the cottages have been built by summer visitors for their own use, on lots bought for the purpose from the Ellison Bay Company, a corporation of non-residents which has acquired and is developing resort property. The best company land is on or near the village waterfront, which is both accessible and attractive (Figs. 9 and 11).

It is a striking fact that whereas most of the cottages are on the shore, two of the three hotels are not on the shore, and the third, although possessing a desirable shore frontage, occupies the landward end of its lot, faces a road, and has the shore view obscured by its barn. This is probably to be accounted for by the fact that, unlike the cottages, all of the hotels have been established by local people on their home property. The hotels are used as family dwellings throughout the year, and the hotel keepers are likely to engage in farming or some other occupation. The one hotel which has waterfront property is the all-year-round commercial hotel, and has not catered to summer tourists; it is a business house of the community in the heart of the village.

It is difficult to compute the accomplishments of the resort business in the same terms as those of farming and other industries which produce commodities. The prices of the service can perhaps be compared with the price of commodities. The total receipts of the hotels is about $5000 a season and the total rental value of the cottages is less than $1000 a season. These figures indicate a low scale of values, considerably below the potential advantages, but corresponding to the present lack of resort development. The hotels are not profitable at present and there are only two or three cottages built for profit.

From the summer visitors' point of view the most peculiar advantage of Ellison Bay at present is perhaps not in its scenery and climate, but in its people and its unspoiled community life. This is an advantage which is decreased by increasing numbers of resorters and greater commercial development. If it becomes widely appreciated it will no longer exist, but will be destroyed by those who seek it.

Yet other attractions will remain and are more likely to be increased by building and landscaping than decreased by forest fire or other injury. The change depends on continued prosperity in the cities and on a continued demand for a sedentary rather than nomadic type of summer vacation. If the trend continues the old community may dissolve and a new form of crystallization appear, as farmers and fishermen fail to prosper in the old ways and as new men enter to guide the resort development.

V. CONCLUSION

The community life flows and ebbs through the year. In the warm season there is a crescendo of activity: the farms are producing crops, the fishing grounds are scenes of activity and the fishing establishments are preparing the catch and untangling the lines, the cottages and hotels are occupied by city visitors, the cheese factory is making ten cheeses daily and sending away seventy weekly; the thresher starts on its rounds after the sawmill has filled its orders; the elevators clean the peas and grains for sale and grade the potatoes; the commercial dock ships these crops and apples and fish, and receives merchandise; the stores distribute the merchandise to visitors, householders, farmers and fishermen; the post office sends out eggs and miscellaneous produce and takes in mail-order merchandise; the garage sells supplies and repairs cars and machinery; the refreshment shops receive daily consignments by truck and dispense their wares over the counter: the amusement hall is crowded on Saturday nights and the church on Sundays.

Activity is evident from spring to autumn, but there is a varying medley within this period. Fishing declines in the heart of summer and increases again thereafter, while visitors flock in chiefly at that time. The activities of planting, cultivating, harvesting, threshing, cleaning and shipping proceed in an orderly succession of crops and processes through the period. The blacksmith opens his shop for spring and autumn sessions.

Then comes winter. School is in full swing, but other activities languish. Not only do visitors depart, but a conspicuous fraction of the farming population migrates to the city for work, or to the South for recreation, leaving enough hands to care for the livestock and take the milk to the cheese factory. The docks are deserted except to fill the ice houses. The stores operate on a reduced scale and some patrons have to be carried through the winter on credit. Transportation is laborious and there is little to be transported.

Then spring again and high hopes of great and prolonged activity. The cycle is repeated, varying a little from year to year, and changing gradually through the decades. In the few generations of its existence the logging camp has become a general farming and fishing village, and this, now discouraged, turns hopefully to the cherry and the summer visitor.

CHAPTER 8

Geography of Culture Origin and Dispersal

There had been strong reactions against environmentalism but no alternative approach to explaining ways of life to replace the discredited ideas of simple and direct relations between natural environment and human activity. The three stages in the 1920's just previously exemplified were almost free from environmental explanation, but they were kept so only by careful exclusion of any explanatory statements about ways of life. When care was relaxed, hints of environmental explanation crept in.

Before 1930 an ample and suitable replacement for environmental explanation was found for geography in the anthropological concept of cultural process. "Pueblo Sites in Southeastern Arizona" by C. O. Sauer and D. Brand, published in 1930 but worked out before then, is taken to represent an eighth and last type up to 1930 in this series of field studies.

In this work the concept of culture origin and dispersal is taken to account for areal uniformities in certain diagnostic items. This implies the idea of localized invention, local persistence, and social transmission of culture traits, as a causal process through which man-made objects or ways of life reach their places in a receptive natural environment.

In this particular study the diagnostic items are archeologically selected, but this is merely incidental to the specific subject. In more general form the idea is of universal application in human geography to replace that of direct cause and effect relations between Nature and Man - to intervene, as it were, between human activity and natural environment.

The field method in this study depends on archeological in association with geomorphological techniques. It involves observation and explanatory description of land forms, observation of associated land use, reconnaissance of archeological sites, a search for critical diagnostic items of culture, and a classification and mapping of culture-distributions. The study is addressed to an audience of scholars, particularly in the social sciences.

PUEBLO SITES IN SOUTHEASTERN ARIZONA[1]

by C. O. Sauer & D. Brand

INTRODUCTION

Origin of study -- In the Southwest, land of desert, steppe, and short mountain range, the records that are left by those who occupied it in former days are tangibly and cumulatively expressed in ruins and other material remains that form an essential part of the scene. Archaeology is of common interest: cattle-man and peon know the places and the outlines of the ancient sites, and the ranch house may harbor an important collection.

The geographer also is readily tempted to consider those prehistoric agricultural people who dwelt in pueblos and then disappeared mysteriously from the greater part of their realm before the white man's discovery of the country. Here indeed are some

1. _Univ. of Calif. Publ. in Geog._ vol. 3, 1930, pp. 415-448.

of the earliest and most significant scenes of human occupation in our country, involving an important cultural succession, a careful selection of site, and its skillful and intensive utilization. Inevitably, the question of climatic change in that period presents itself.

During a summer's field work in Sonora in 1928, Pueblo ruins and artifacts were encountered so frequently that we had to reckon with an occupation of that country prior, and perhaps unrelated, to the historic Indian cultures of the area. Bandelier had looked over a number of Sonora ruins in 1884, but his observations are too remote and obscure as to identifications of material culture to be incorporated into the current reconstructions of Southwestern prehistory. In the spring of 1929 we found occasion to visit the archaeologically known adjacent localities in the United States. These, however, are not directly on the border, but lie farther north in the Gila and Santa Cruz valleys; thousands of square miles in southeastern Arizona and southwestern New Mexico having received scarcely more notice than has Sonora. Kidder, for instance, restricts the extreme limit of Southwestern culture well within the confines of the State of Arizona apparently expressing a state of information rather than of conviction.

A neglected corner -- A belt of country a hundred miles wide on the American side of the boundary had to be reconnoitered before a tie-up between Sonoran observations and published data was possible. To this area, bounded on the north by the Gila, on the west by the Santa Cruz, and on the south by the international boundary, we directed our attention. The present paper is the result of the reconnaissance. Funds for the study were provided through the Board of Research of the University of California.

The neglect of this extreme corner of Arizona is partly to be explained by the fact that the peripheries of the Pueblo country have been regarded in general as of little significance in comparison to the great hearths on the San Juan and upper Rio Grande, though what is periphery and what is hearth may perhaps not be certain as yet. In this particular case the supposed peripheral area gains in interest because we do not know yet whether Pueblo culture was distinguished from Mexican culture by intervening areas occupied by wild peoples, analogous to the Gran Chichimeca of historic time, or whether a continuous and coexistent corridor of higher culture extended down the west coast of Mexico, joining Pueblan and Mexican culture realms, or by a more eastern connection, south through Chihuahua and Durango.

Plan of approach -- We attempted to locate and inspect a maximum number of ruins in the time at our disposal and to make a representative collection of artifacts at each place. The sites are, in general, subject to denudation and the surface of the ground is therefore a cross-section of the human accumulations. Under these conditions random sampling should be fairly representative, and apparently was more so than the tests pits that we tried. In a single opening, disturbed position is always possible. With the great number of rodents present, who like especially to make their burrows in old ash layers, stratigraphic determination of material could not be attempted by anything short of thorough-going excavation. Denudation together with rodent excavation however should make the surfaces of the sites satisfactory for reconnaissance. Through denudation a surface concentration of broken pottery, grinding stones, and other artifacts results. Complete objects other than metates and manos, which are numerous and bulky, are of course not likely to be found thus. Potsherds, however, are legible as specific records of Pueblo cultures. We selected, therefore, all painted potsherds that we found and all otherwise decorated ware, with the exception of the ordinary corrugated ware, which was almost as abundant as plain ware at numerous sites.

We do not repose great confidence in our notes concerning the foundation plans of settlements. To attempt to draw ground plans without excavation would appear to claim an exactness of knowledge which excavation would promptly refute. Concerning one of the most interesting things, the plans of these settlements, we can therefore give only the most tentative notes. In general we relied on the denudational exposure of so-called "foundation stones" in lines for the identification of settlement sites. These rock lines, it will be shown later, are ordinarily simply weathered-out portions of cobble and adobe walls, and are not, properly, foundations. . . .

THE VALLEY FLOORS
WITH PERMANENT STREAMS AND FLOOD PLAINS
SITE QUALITIES

An analysis of the relief of southeastern Arizona has been presented elsewhere. The entire area belongs in the Basin and Range Province, and is bordered on the north by great volcanic mesas that throw a forbidding rim about the southern part of the Colorado Plateau. The Gila River is an important boundary line between plateau country to north and the basin country to south, cold winters prevailing northward, mild winters southward. The division is one of the most striking in the Southwest and has been remarked upon many times, perhaps first by the men of Coronado's expedition, who entered about here into the "second wilderness," where the spiny vegetation ceased, and where the Red House, Chichilticalli, stood. The latter may well have been on a flank of the Pinateno Mountains.

The local country is, however, not all of the same pattern. The Gila, San Pedro, and Aravaipa at the northwest are streams that cut and fill and that have sunk a series of terraces in the once deeply aggraded basins. Hence great dry gravel mesas and ancient, now dissected, clay flats look down upon small, more or less deeply enclosed, modern flood plains. At the extreme southeast, the San Bernardino River, component of the Yaqui drainage, is beginning similar entrenchment. In all cases the modern flood plains occupy only a tiny fraction of the basins and are more or less concealed in the bottom of the greater structural valleys. Here running water is available, more, indeed, than is needed as a rule for simple irrigation. Here also sub-surface irrigation takes place naturally, especially in the sandier stretches of alluvial floors. Here are the lowest, warmest, and least rainy lands of the area. They are of the desert margin as to their rainfall values. But they are also the best watered and the most desirable crop lands for a long distance about and present no serious problem to peoples who had learned flood-plain farming. These oases sites [are] inevitably preferred centers for agriculture, presumably centers of the earliest cultural advances, and probably centers from which expansion took place after a time into sites of lesser advantage.

The invariable association of flood plain with gravel-topped mesa, the latter often cut into conspicuous peninsulas, provided equally good places for farming, as well as good sites for building. The mesas first afforded flood protection, and later sites that could be defended against enemies. The terraced basins, in general, were the major areas of positive attraction south of the Colorado Plateau. Their cultures are of such apparent impressiveness that they alone have been investigated. Data exist from the Gila and slightly also from the San Pedro. For our purposes they constituted, therefore, the known cultures into which we were anxious to tie facts of the more southern archaeology.

SITES IN THE MIDDLE GILA VALLEY

Between San Carlos and San José on the Gila River lies the most valuable agricultural country in this part of Arizona. It is essentially the productive area of modern Graham County. Ruins were noted here even in Spanish days. Thus Father Sanchez, on an expedition into the Apache country, reports from here "ruins of ancient edifices with square patios and other vestiges of earthen ware, jars, ollas, and pots, with variety of colors and paintings." And, he says, "I took notice especially how they had conducted water by ditches to the land which served them for their crops, and of the site sufficiently extensive to sustain a good villa or mission."

Emory and Johnston in their journals of the Kearney Expedition of 1846 described and figured ruins and relics at some length. Fewkes collected and excavated intensively in 1897 in what he called the Pueblo-Viejo Valley, which he limited by the settlements of San José above and Pima below. His report is the principal published information upon the Middle Gila. A further bibliography is contained in Kidder's Southwestern Archeology under the heading, Lower Gila. Kidder does not differentiate between the culture area centering about this part of the Gila and the district about and below Phoenix. Such a division has become necessary. Kidder's polychrome red ware is here called "Middle Gila polychrome," and his "red-on-gray" is here named "Red-on-buff." It is our purpose to introduce some comparative notes on

the area, by a series of selected sites, and to suggest some re-
visions and additions to published data, which have been pretty
well limited to the San José-Solomonsville vicinity.

    <u>Curtis Ranch</u> -- About 2 miles northeast of San José, at the
upstream limit of sites visited by us on the Gila. Apparently the
Buena Vista site of Fewkes, and the only site seen by us on which
full archaeologic data are published.

    Very attractive site for the irrigation of extensive and ex-
cellent bottom land. Irrigating ditches from aboriginal days are
generally known here as elsewhere in the Middle Gila. The village
was situated on a gravel mesa over-looking the flood plain and lies
for the most part west of the Curtis ranch house. Site possesses
no defensive advantages.

    Ruins are extensive and walls are partly preserved above
ground, which is rare in the rest of the area visited by us. Construction was of mud and cobbles, the mud being used perhaps to
hold the cobbles in place. On weathering, the walls become cobble
ridges. Numerous posts (cedar?) remain in position. Size of
some of the mounds suggests that edifices of more than one story
may have existed, and south of barn heavy walls suggest a central
structure similar to Casa Grande. The general structure was
probably that of a compound with linked rooms enclosing a central,
more massive building. Surface has been seriously pitted by pot-
hunters but no real excavations have been made.

    The surficial ruins are identified by a great preponderance
of Middle Gila polychrome pottery. An older occupation is indicated by Mimbres and Red-on-buff ware, which probably will be
disclosed in larger amounts by excavation, for the ruins of the
last occupation form a heavy cover of debris over this site. Casi-
mirio Garcia at San José, near-by, exhibited a 3-inch terracotta
head with coffeebean eyes and mouth, hair coiled about head of
tonsure.

    The next four items are introduced from the valley below
Pima, for which there seem to be no published data.

Fort Thomas. . .
Geronimo River Bluff. . .
Dewey Flat. . .
Gila Bank. . .

SITES IN THE ARAVAIPA VALLEY

    The Aravaipa Valley, at the base of Mount Graham and
above the box canyon of the Aravaipa, was a snug and valuable
territory for settlement. The creek has nearly three thousand
acres of bottom land, much of which is non-irrigable but which
nevertheless enjoys a large measure of natural sub-irrigation and
flooding. The enclosing gravel mesas are sharply fretted and provided defensive sites, as do the recesses of the Aravaipa Canyon
below, and, by report, the cliffs in the Galiuro Mountains to the
west. An easy route leads through Eagle Pass north to the Geronimo

country. The finest sites and largest settlements south of the Gila were met with here. Apparently they have never been reported on, and have been viewed only by local amateurs.

Haby Ranch -- About 30 miles northwest of Bonita and 3 miles southeast of Klondyke Post Office. Site is west of C. J. Haby ranch house on a high gravel mesa.

The defensive position of the major settlement is superior to any site visited. The pueblo was flanked by very steep gravel slopes, about 200 feet high. Only a very narrow neck connected the ridge with the main mesa. At the foot of the hill is an excellent spring, good bottom land, and wood. On an intermediate bench below lay a suburb of the main citadel.

The plan of the village agrees with its site. It seems to have been completely surrounded by a heavy wall. The heaviest walls however, belong to the inner structure. Six and even nine rows of large cobbles mark the thickness of an inside structure. Traces of a commodious central citadel are to be seen. Cedar posts protrude from the ground. The lower village seems to have been without defenses and was also composed of houses placed in less orderly fashion.

The Haby citadel yielded a virtually pure Middle Gila polychrome assemblage, lacking even the common, fine (Little Colorado) ware that seems to have been freely traded in elsewhere. The absence of this ware may indicate the cessation of such trade and a late decadent period for the origin of the town. The fortress site is so situated as to defend one of the principal routes of prehistoric communication -- the so-called Hopi trail from the San Pedro Valley via Post-office Canyon and Rattlesnake Creek over the Galiuros, thence to San Carlos on the Gila, and north to Tusayan. The several villages on the Aravaipa of which this is chief may possibly have accommodated a couple of thousand people.

Wootton Ranch. . .
Wootton-Haby Terrace. . .

SITES IN THE SAN PEDRO VALLEY

The San Pedro River, today entrenched from 20 to 50 feet beneath its flood plain, presented no difficulties for the primitive farmer. Then, apparently a series of swampy pools at low water, with shallow sandy stretches between, it provided water easily carried by gravity to fields, but probably more largely an abundant natural sub-irrigation that has been reduced greatly by the erosion of the past forty years. The San Pedro has become one of the most rapidly eroding arroyos in the Southwest and the channel is sinking deeper and deeper beneath the valley floor over which it once spread harmlessly.

Redington Mesa -- On the mesa north of the school at Redington.

Abundant permanent supply of water, and still an extensive bottom, now largely used in growing clover and alfalfa hay. No defensive quality to village site.

The site covers a good many acres. There are low conical heaps, 6 to 10 feet high and 20 to 30 feet across, that suggest by their prominence the existence of houses of more than one story. The presence of long ridges and mound-enclosed depressions also indicates the Casa Grande compound type of structure.

The shards turned up gave an almost exclusive Red-on-buff site. The site may repay excavation as an illustration of early development of the compound pueblo. It certainly did not consist of loosely clustered houses of similar size.

Shirley Ranch. . .
Cascabel Mesa. . .
Miller Ranch. . .

SITES IN THE SAN BERNARDINO VALLEY

The San Bernardino, in the extreme southeast corner of Arizona, is the last of the permanently flowing streams of the area. Below the international boundary line it has developed an increasingly imposing set of terraces, but north of the boundary it is only beginning to sap a recent surface composed of volcanic ash, cinders, and lava which were spread across the basin floor. The Slaughter (San Bernardino) ranch house is situated at springs that issue from beneath lava sheets in the middle of the basin. Here, at the head of dissection, a few hundred acres of flood plain invite the plow. Chinese and Yaqui labor are maintaining on both sides of the border a small oasis along the cottonwood-shaded stream. It is the same pleasant situation that attracted here in prehistoric time a far more numerous group of farmers that now busy themselves in the fields.

Stevens Ranch -- At western limit of George Stevens ranch, 2 miles northeast of San Bernardino ranch house.

Adjacent to the flood-plain lands and with good and abundant water supply. No defensive advantages.

A rather large settlement, about 20 by 80 rods, with foundation lines in fair condition. The site of the ruins is about as extensive as that occupied by most modern pueblos to the south. Arrowheads and turquoise beads have been carried away by casual relic hunters. The variety of the pottery would indicate that the site was long occupied and that the inhabitants had trade connections northward, southward, and eastward. Stratification, as indicated by one test trench, would make the red, triangularly gouged ware the latest material at this site. The tentative correlation of culture would then be: earlier: Red-on-buff and Mimbres; later: Gouged and Casas Grandes (Chihuahua).

Slaughter Bull Pasture. . .
Sacaton Flat. . .

UPLAND SITES IN DISSECTED BASINS

Marginal to the types of villages that have just been noted are others, which lie in the terraced basins and probably were of the same culture and time as the settlements employing irrigation. They are, however, so situated that the inhabitants could not have had use of flood lands nor of the abundant water that is furnished by perennial streams. These are, in the main, sites that lie farther away from the main valley floors, in tributary valleys which have been cut down as minor flats into the older surface of the basin fill and which are supplied only with intermittent stream flow. The dissection gives a certain quality of defense to these sites, and the earlier entrenchment of streams places the floors sufficiently low so that a fair measure of sub-irrigation takes place, as shown by the luxuriance of mesquite growth. It also appears that the people carried water from higher up the mountain flanks by constructing winding ditches to their fields. These ditches carried only flood waters. Their situation was first noted by Bandelier for the margins of the Gila Valley; they are still pointed out about the margins of Mount Graham against the Gila. This type of site indicates therefore a further step toward straight flood-water farming, away from formal irrigation, though it is not certain that floods and rains were not the major dependence of the farmers who lived in the oases on the alluvial valley floors mentioned above.

Geronimo Mesa -- A mile southwest of Geronimo, and therefore fairly close to site 20. A series of gravel terraces rise toward the Santa Teresa Mountains. A characteristic broad wash sweeps down from the mountains and provided one of the surfaces that were farmed, the floor of the wash being of intermediate soil texture with a large admixture of clay carried down from the higher slopes. This surface at right of picture is well suited, by position and material, to rainy-season farming of quick-maturing crops. The village was located on the mesa at the left, obviously without defense qualities. On the mesa behind the village a considerable area was "swept" of gravels, which are piled in neat small cones, as was noted repeatedly on the San Pedro, and suggest occasional use of the mesa surface for farming.

The site is elongated along the mesa edge, and probably contains a hundred house ruins, in scattered clusters. Foundations are of rectangular outline but do not seem to have included massive structures or compound walls. The site appears to be earlier than the "Chichilticalli" site on the river margin at Geronimo. The most curious feature of the local shards is the predominance of Red-on-buff ware, and the presence in some quantity of a Red-on-buff ware with black interior.

Artesia. . .
Adobe Pit. . .
Veach Canyon. . .

MOUNTAIN PEDIMENT SITES

In southern Arizona mountain slope merges into basin floor in a curving surface which has been developed in the main by the wearing down of the mountain range. The wearing back of the mountain front leaves all about the range a low, bedrock surface, which basin-ward is increasingly deeply buried by detritus, but mountain-ward may be a rock slope only thinly screened with rock spalls. Lawson has called the latter the "subaerial platform," the former the "sub-alluvial bench," both being part of the same surface. The whole base of the mountain ranges above the deeply filled parts of the basins was called by Bryan, after McGee, the "mountain pediment." The term is most apt. A smooth base extends about the ranges in a zone usually at least several miles in width, increases steadily in angle of slope mountain-ward, and has upon it a veneer of slowly moving detritus of lessened thickness and increased coarseness toward the mountain. The surface being of similar slope at similar distance from the mountain front, there is formed an inclined and concavely curved apron upon which the summer rains and the summer streams from the mountains spread out in ephemeral sheet floods. These are most effective about the canyon mouths. They may translate enough debris onto the pediment at the canyon debouchures to be destructive to growing vegetation, but farther basin-ward they leave water and mud in beneficent amounts. At some distance from the canyon mouths, therefore, there exist sites on the basin slopes that are more or less dependable for farming, using summer flood water. On these lower pediment surfaces Pueblo remains are to be found with fairly high regularity wherever one may expect sufficient summer flooding. The important thing in localizing the prehistoric settlement on the pediment is not local drinking water supply, which may or may not be present, but one of the clay stretches, often indicated by sacaton and cat's claw, which enjoys superior frequency of wetting. With some experience of the country, the sites of the ancient villages could probably be anticipated from an inspection of the local drainage and vegetation.

At present this land of undissected basins, that we have designated elsewhere as the Chiricahua area, is almost entirely cattle country. Huntington cites this country as an important exhibit in his theory of dessication, postulating for instance that the ruins about Cloverdale must have been occupied when the climate was less arid.

Average rainfall values for this steppe country are around twelve inches, fully half of which amount comes in three summer months. In parts of the mountains the rainfall reaches amounts that place them in humid instead of semi-arid climate. The flow of mountain streams is spread out on the pediment, further raising the water content of the basin-margin slopes in summer. All the mountain streams are intermittent; but during the summer rains many of them can be depended on to saturate the ground about the base of the canyons. In normal years there is no

difficulty in growing crops on these lands, though occasionally
droughts will wipe out almost any local crop.

In the first decade of the present century many homesteaders
settled in the basins. They have virtually all failed, but their
failure does not disprove the success of Indian cultivation. In the
first place, the homesteaders did not seat themselves cleverly as
did the Indians. The land was surveyed into sections, and the
usual distribution of one homesteader to one quarter-section took
place. Many of them therefore did not own slopes whose rainfall
was reinforced by slope wash, as the Indians were careful to
select in each case. Again the best success that the homesteader
had was in growing beans, which were marketed in adjacent mining
camps. The failure of some of these camps and the elaboration of
Bisbee into a city that commanded supplies from distant markets
injured the local small farmer. The country proved submarginal
for unspecialized white farmers under present economic, not
climatic, conditions. All of this indicates precisely nothing so
far as the subsistence of Indian agriculturists is concerned, other
than that fair success in bean-growing by sheet floods was secured by some of the white farmers.

For Indian agriculture the country is no more difficult than
most of the present Pueblo country and it is better than parts of
it. Pueblo agriculture was well supplied with drought-resistant,
quick-maturing varieties of corn, beans, and squash. Good land
is present all along the lower pediment slopes, and flooding could
be regulated to some extent by auxiliary ditches, which the residents still claim to discern in numerous localities, as for instance
along the western margin of the Chiricahuas. It is even now as-
serted by residents that one good sheet flood will make a bean
crop, and the sites that have expectation of several such soakings
a summer are numerous. In days of greater pressure of population and of more simple standards of living, the area was not
repellent to settlement. With one exception, the sites that were
seen by us were of such character that a frugal Indian population,
growing summer crops of the strains common to Pueblo agriculture, might have good expectations of a harvest. In the years
of great drought, they certainly starved if they had to depend on
their own crop land. That in itself is, however, no more reason
for permanent or complete depopulation than are famines due to
drought in India or China today. A lower standard of living, and
hence a lower margin of agriculture for Indian than for white
agriculture, is all that is needed to make the ancient scene locally
intelligible.

Incidentally, the basins produce a goodly amount of wild
food stuffs, especially of mesquite beans and sacaton seed. Both
grow specifically on sheet-flood lands. We may think of them as
providing a valuable area of wild seeds lying all about the lands
used for agriculture. One competent in the economic botany of
the area could undoubtedly compose an interesting list of plants
from mountain and basin, that were used to help out the diet. Here
belongs for instance the question as to whether the wild potato of

the Chiricahuas is originally wild or whether it has reverted from the potato of early white settlements.

Disaster by arms or epidemic appears to be the only valid reason for depopulation of such villages on the pediment slopes.

The limits of aggregation of people at any one site were, one is inclined to think, determined not so much by the amount of land that could prudently be farmed in expectation of summer floods, but rather by the amount of domestic water available through the year, and perhaps also by the amount of supplementary game and wild seeds that could be foraged from a given spot. The individual settlement was usually of more modest proportions than in the flood plains. The location of the settlement invariably seems to have been determined by the existence, immediately at hand, of farming land subject to sheet floods. In some cases the selection also seems to have been determined by the existence of a spring, but in many cases no source of water is known within several miles. Springs may have been lost sight of, but the fact remains that in the basin margins springs are very few and far between, and that in most of the mountains all-weather streams are not numerous. The judgement of the resident ranchers is that, unless the ancient natives knew how to dig wells, or make covered tanks, they had to carry water in many cases for long distances in the dry seasons. The likelihood of the construction of tanks sufficiently large to hold water during the dry months is a subject on which we have not the least observational information, but it seems difficult to believe, considering the high evaporation, that tanks of sufficient depth could have been constructed. In the dry months the people may well have been more short of drinking water than they were of food.

There remains the possibility of a seasonal migration. The driest months are those of spring. An easy solution would be to have the aborigines go to mountain encampments at this season, taking with them remnants of their stores and returning to pediment sites with the beginning of the rains. The mountains would at that season have the advantage of more vegetation and more game, just as they are now used for early stock pasturage.

There is a village site at the base of Squaw Mountain at the head of the San Bernardino drainage. These sites are normally on topographically nondescript parts of the range margins, there being nothing remarkable about them except the attempts to place them onto slightly drier ground adjacent to surfaces dependably subject to sheet flooding. It will be noted later that these settlements of the undissected pediments were the outlying ones of their particular culture. They formed for their people the pioneer fringe. It is not likely that the greater or wealthier communities of the lost nations lived in this land of dry farming. In contrast to the tree-shaded oases of the perennial rivers, these were mostly rather meager back settlements. Yet they may prove archaeologically important because the sites have been disused since Pueblo days, and if they contained less originally, they have also been less disturbed than the valley homes.

<u>Holmes Maddox Ranch (Animas Valley)</u> —— Hidalgo
County, southwestern New Mexico; in T 29 S R 19 W in Animas
Valley. On low bench west of Animas. Good agricultural land with
high-water table. Cottonwoods flourish here. Site is non-defensive.
A large spring was dried up by the earthquake of 1887.

The site covers 60 to 70 acres and consists of low mounds of
gravel and adobe arranged about depressions in such a manner as
to indicate the collapse of adobe walls arranged in a compound.
The mounds line up into regular, long walls. An occasional post
protrudes at side of old wall. No excavation has been tried at this
important site, which yielded, chiefly from rat holes, an important
and varied lot of shards, Middle Gila polychrome from the north,
Casas Grandes (early and late) from the southeast, and Mimbres
and its associated smoothed corrugated ware from the northeast.
An interesting absence in an otherwise well developed Casas
Grandes site is that of the red gouged ware. At the ranch house a
carved stone tray with four handles like a stretcher suggested
Mexican stone cutting. A legged metate was reported to have been
found in the ruins at an earlier date.

Weber Ranch (San Simon Valley). . .
Squaw Mountain. . .
Cave Creek (San Simon Valley). . .
Whitlock Cienega. . .
Mud Springs. . .
Stark Ranch. . .
Nuttall Ranch. . .
Johnson Ruin. . .
Westfall Ranch. . .
Cochise Stronghold. . .
Fort Grant. . .
Hooker Ranch. . .
Sunset School. . .
Ramsey Canyon. . .

INTRAMONTANE SITES

The larger ranges contain extraordinarily broad valleys
which are most attractive sites for settlement. They enjoy mild
winters, summer protection from the dust storms of the basins,
cool summer nights, a greater rainfall, and greater certainty of
spring water at short distances than is the case in the pediment
situations, and a varied vegetation. One might expect them to be
preferred to the mountain pediment sites.

Relatively little was seen by us or known locally of settlements within the broad valleys that penetrate far into the mountains. One site is two miles above Cloverdale in the Animas
Valley of New Mexico, contains a nice body of valley farm land,
which is not flood plain, but partakes in origin of the nature of the
pediment surfaces. An excellent spring is close at hand, and oaks
on the hillsides provide an additional source of food. It is, more-

over, an open site from which movement in various directions is possible. Since the ancient people lived on the pediment without any regard to defense location, they may as well have lived in mountain valleys without fear of being boxed in by enemies. In that case the mountain valleys should yield numerous sites, whereof we in our hasty acquaintance with the area were unable to get track. Because of the characteristic great breadth of floor, the greater assurance of springs, the greater moisture in the soil, one might expect these valleys to rate high unless the ancients feared getting penned in, and of fear the sites in the area as a whole show no evidence, aside from the north.

Cloverdale Park -- About two miles west of Cloverdale Post Office, most southwestern in the State of New Mexico. Adjacent to dance pavilion in oak park. Good water, good land. Appears to have been a small, poor Casas Grandes colony, judging from the predominance of the red gouged utility ware.

Stewart Ranch. . .
Kimble Ranch. . .
Chiricahua Flat. . .
Pinery Canyon. . .
Hunsaker Ranch. . .
Leslie Ruin. . .
Hicks Ruins, Rucker Canyon. . .

CULTURE AREAS AND SUCCESSIONS AS INTERPRETED FROM ARCHAEOLOGIC DATA

The sites which we visited were fairly well distributed through the area and establish the penetration of the entire section by Pueblo cultures. The most important gaps remaining are probably in the more interior parts of the ranges, where, as in the case of the Galiuro Mountains, cliff dwellings are to be expected, and where further valley settlements also are to be looked for. We saw most of the ruins of which we heard, and perhaps all of the larger ruins barring the cienega of the San Simon, which we were unable to visit, and which is known to have ruins. Excavation, or collecting after the rains of another season have exposed new surfaces, may give different groupings of shards. It would be interesting to go over the area again at some later date and see how two such samplings compare. We are rather of the impression that our random sampling has given sufficiently consistent results to demonstrate its utility and to justify an attempt to reconstruct the culture types that were present in the area. Of their succession less can be said with confidence, though a reconstruction is herewith hazarded.

It is apparent that with probably one or two exceptions southeastern Arizona held no hearth of any higher development of Pueblo culture. It was, rather, in the later stages at least a meeting place for Pueblo cultures which found here their extreme limit; no single culture traverses the entire area. Since Pueblo culture is identified with village agriculture, its hearths normally might be expected to have been in somewhat isolated, but not too restricted bodies of land suitable for intensive agriculture, such as irrigable valleys of some size. The local possibilities of dependable farming on any important scale are limited to the flood plains of the terraced valleys of the Gila, San Pedro, Aravaipa, and San Bernardino. Here the major populations would be expected and here they appear to be found.

There are, however, many more Pueblo remains in the steppe country than we expected to see, and some of the later settlements may have been nearly as large as the oases of the flood plains. Farmers could utilize these high smooth basins only by selecting the most advantageously situated surfaces and soils so as to benefit from the brief period of the summer rains. It appears in this connection that the number of sites thus available was quite large, and that, with sufficient pressure of population in the valley lands, numerous groups moved out onto pediment slopes and into mountain valleys and maintained themselves there. These are, however, considered in each case as the pioneer fringe of their culture, with the major hearth located outside of the steppe area.

LATE PUEBLO CULTURE ON THE
MIDDLE GILA AND THE ARAVAIPA

The latest and clearest scenes of the Pueblo occupation are on the Middle Gila and the Aravaipa, where the ware of the Middle Gila polychrome is associated with the most conspicuous surface ruins of the area. The Middle Gila is considered to be the hearth of a distinctive, late subculture. Figure 12 attempts a reconstruction of the limits of each culture as expressed in pottery remains.

The most impressive ruins associated with Middle Gila polychrome ware seen by us were the Curtis-Buena Vista site above San José on the Gila, and the Haby ranch site on the Aravaipa. This culture appears to have had its origin and center in that well defined part of the Gila Valley that forms the agricultural basin of Graham County, though it was scarcely less flourishing in the Aravaipa basin. The larger centers, however, already bear impress of decadence; when they were built it was no longer safe to live in open settlements. Walled towns held the population until such time as it migrated or was exterminated. The citadel site of the Haby ranch was a useless and arduous place until the people came to fear for the safety of their lives; then it may have been reared as the last protection of the inhabitants. It is only with the Middle Gila culture that the stronghold site becomes clearly developed.

THE SOUTHERN MARGIN OF MIDDLE GILA CULTURE

Flood-farming pediment sites south of the Gila give an extreme southeastern extension of this culture to the Maddox ranch

in the Animas, and to Mud Springs and Coryell ranch in the
Chiricahua margins. In the same class are the numerous remains
about Fort Grant, Hooker's ranch, Sunset, and the ruin below
Cochise Stronghold. None of these places enjoy any natural defenses, nor do they give evidence of artificial protection. They lay
far from the shelter of the larger settlements of the north and
seem to have been surrendered earlier, as an outlying fringe.
Middle Gila culture, one would surmise, antedated the walled-town
period in good part.

At a number of these places notable finds of Chihuahua polychrome occur, together with good black-on-red ware of the Little
Colorado type. Chiricahua Flat on the Coryell ranch, in particular,
yields interesting returns of the three types of pottery. The
beautiful Casas Grande ware has not been noted in the walled towns
of the Gila, and at the Haby site no Little Colorado ware was found.
These are implications that the outlying southern settlements of
the Middle Gila culture were occupied in the days of freely moving
trade, and that the walled valley towns without such trade objects
came late, when trade was largely checked by raids.

MARGINAL SITES OF CHIHUAHUA CULTURE

Persistent association of Middle Gila, Little Colorado, and
Chihuahua polychrome ware indicates their partial contemporaneity. The Chihuahua culture, centering upon the Casas Grandes
Valley of that Mexican State, however, may have had a long period
of independent existence. The normal type of polychrome, and a
cruder, presumably earlier, form have been identified. It appears
also that a very different ware of red clay, in part of fine clay,
that has been dotted with angular, usually triangular gougings, is
so closely associated with Chihuahua polychrome as to be considered part of the same culture. As is to be expected, the San
Bernardino Valley and the Animas country show the Chihuahua
influence most strongly. The irrigated section of the San
Bernardino Valley seems to have contained a number of villages
of this culture and the flanks of the Chiricahuas were similarly
dotted with small, non-defensive, and apparently rather sprawling,
villages. A time-differentiation between the gouged and normal
polychrome ware is suggested by the abundance of the former and
apparently complete absence of the latter at the Maddox ranch in
the Animas Valley. If our test pits mean anything the gouged ware
was the last pottery produced in our southeastern area. It is incidentally very common southward in Sonora. An interesting find
is that of poor quality (early?) Chihuahua ware in the remote
western Ramsey Canyon at the base of the Huachuca Mountains,
and its presence there in association with small-design, Red-on-
buff shards.

Whatever the presence or absence of those culture indicators in our record may be worth, the evidence bears to the effect
that an early Chihuahua culture had connections at the south with
the Red-on-buff culture of the west, that the climax Chihuahua

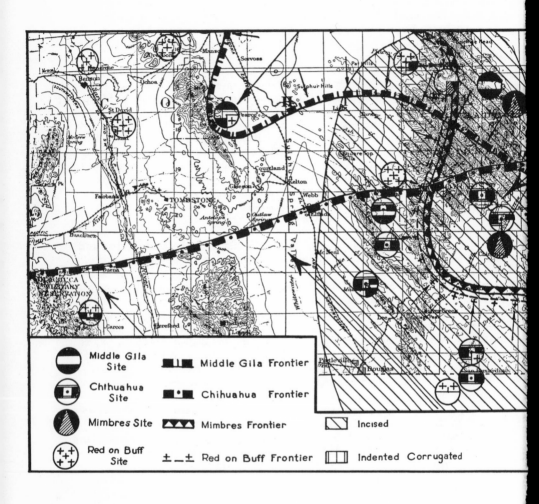

Fig. 12. Part of a map of "culture affiliations of the ruins, and attempted reconstruction of the limits of the several culture areas", showing sites of Gila culture
in the northeast spreading from a culture hearth outside the area to a frontier
toward the southwest, and sites of Red on Buff culture in the west spreading
to a frontier toward the east. Scale: 1 inch to 12.5 miles.

culture took possession of the irrigable San Bernardino Valley, and that a later culture, characterized by gouged ware and forsaking entirely the beautiful decorations of Casas Grandes—by this contrast under suspicion as produced by a different people—came in and occupied the same area for a time. These are hazardous conclusions on meager bits of testimony. A rough equation in time of a part of the culture with Middle Gila and Little Colorado can be hazarded. The defenselessness in general of the Chihuahuan sites indicates that they lie farther back toward the golden period of country-wide peace than do the dominant town sites of the Middle Gila. The commonly supposed lateness of this great southeastern culture center is based after all only on cross-finds of its pottery with Middle Gila, which means precisely nothing as to the length of time a distinctive culture may have taken to develop and be dominant in the hem of the Mexican Sierra Madre.

A small amount of incised ware found in the far western part of the local Chihuahuan culture area was probably traded in from the south, Sonora, during the late prehistoric Pueblo time. It resembles ware still in use on the western flanks of the Sierra Madre.

MIMBRES CULTURE FROM THE NORTHEAST

A smoothed corrugated ware is found characteristically associated with the finely drawn black-on-white of the Mimbres, and because of the correspondence in distribution is assumed to be an expression of the same culture. One site, that at the Whitlock Cienega, gave an almost pure Mimbres culture, which also appears to have been established about the Artesia Cienega. The western limit of Mimbres settlement extended well into Arizona. Verbal accounts indicate that the San Simon Cienega settlement was also a Mimbres settlement. The curious southwestern occurrence of Mimbres potsherds about the Chiricahua Range can hardly represent merely traded ware, for both the Cave Area and Weber ranch sites are pure Mimbres sites, if the smoothed corrugated ware is correctly correlated with Mimbres culture, and indicate at two well separated places the existence of outlying settlements of this culture at the base of the Chiricahua Mountains.

The cumulative variety of the pottery types in and along the base of the Chiricahua and Guadalupe mountains may be merely accidental better fortune in finding pottery here than elsewhere. This great variety, however, suggests two other explanations: (1) that this passageway from the north to the Bavispe and thus to the Yaqui Valley was a route of active trade, and (2) that thus at various times various cultures extended outpost settlements into this most eligible of corridors between the north and south.

The prevalence of small cross-fields of Mimbres and Red-on-buff suggests their contemporaneity. On Stewart ranch, near Guadalupe Pass, a Mimbres-smoothed-corrugated site yields a few shards of Red-on-buff. The Whitlock Cienega, an almost straight Mimbres site, yields a little Red-on-buff ware. At Artesia the proportions are more nearly even. In the ruins along the western margin of the Chiricahuas, which are Red-on-buff sites, a minor number of Mimbres shards are found. In general, the distribution of Mimbres and Red-on-buff is complementary, there being but slight overlaps, Mimbres culture holding the more easterly area, Red-on-buff the more westerly.

THE RED-ON-BUFF CULTURE

The type of pottery is well described by Kidder. This is the culture that came into the area from the west, and perhaps from the southwest. Apparently dominant in the habitable parts of the Santa Cruz Valley, it had nearly exclusive control of the San Pedro Valley, the two most interesting developments there seen being at Redington Mesa and in the Little Dragoons at the Westfall ranch. On the western margin of the Chiricahuas and even in the San Bernardino Valley there are important remnants of this culture. It was also spread all through the Middle Gila Valley, and had there a wider range than did the Middle Gila polychrome. Here it is characteristic to find one site containing Red-on-buff ware but no Middle Gila polychrome, with conditions reversed at the next site. The two cultures are considered therefore as not contemporaneous, with the probability that the Red-on-buff is the older. Without clear stratigraphic proof there are local indications, where it occurs with Middle Gila polychrome, of being subjacent. The ware with which it is most commonly associated is Mimbres. At Ramsey Canyon it is found with peripheral, supposedly early, Casas Grandes. Suggestive of greater age is the non-defensive character of the sites and their prevalent lack of enclosing walls or central structure as against those of the Middle Gila culture. The Redington vicinity, however, in the apparent development of defensive structures at that place and by its compactness of settlement, supplies a suggestion that there the culture may have lingered late. Kidder expressed especial interest in this ware, because "it is so radically unlike the polychrome, and, indeed, so unlike all other Southwestern pottery, that it gives rise to the suspicion that it may be the result of an intrusion from some hitherto unlocated culture centre". In this connection attention may be called to the association of this ware with supposed Mexican trade items, figurines of animals (crocodile at Westfall ranch, anteater at Fort Thomas), human figurines (obese leg at Miller ranch, coffee-bean figure at San Jose), and the curiously and carefully carved stone trays (basalt) that are rather widely distributed (Westfall, Riggs ranches). Is there implied here an early trade route along the San Pedro and Sonora valleys southward into modern Sinaloa, or is this culture itself the product of a migration out of the south, which blended with Pueblo elements?

EARLIER PUEBLO CULTURES

The greater part of the local settlements antedated the planned citadel pueblos. If the latter are late Pueblo 3 (dominantly Middle Gila), the majority of the ruins would be early Pueblo 3 (also partly Middle Gila, but more especially Chihuahua, and in part Mimbres and Red-on-buff). Throughout we were greatly impressed by the complete disregard of defenses in the ordinary site encountered, and the apparent dominance of one-room structures aggregated into straight rows of some length, but apparently of incidental plan. So remote are many of these habitations from refuge places, so far from drinking water, so openly placed, and so utterly lacking in thickened walls, that it is hard to conceive of them as having been built at any time when enemies were abroad in the land. We are inclined to regard the trade with Mexican centers and with the north as having been intercepted in the later stages.

The Armadillo ware may possibly represent a separate and earlier culture. Its distribution does not agree with that of any other ware. It seems to have occupied the Middle Gila Valley and thence to have extended southward about the margins of the Pinaleno Mountains. Some of this ware, especially that about Artesia, was basket-molded, the weave being diagonal platting, such as is found in splint baskets. Other ware was apparently in imitation thereof. Are these primitive processes ill in accord with the finer pottery that is found in the same sites, or were they local whims of no diagnostic significance? In so far as our information goes the ware was of quite restricted distribution. In view of the limited attention paid thus far to non-painted ware, we can hazard nothing further than a surmise as to the greater antiquity of the Armadillo pattern and its apparent association with small settlements.

On the Grantham farm, near Light, in Sulphur Spring Valley, there is a small cluster of house ruins. One of these houses was excavated by E. J. Hands. It is small, rectangular, with a floor about three feet deep. The walls are bowlder-lined and were plastered. On the floors are the remains of a burned and collapsed clay-thatched roof, in which the burned clay contains the impressions of branches, twigs, and rushes. Apparently it was a pit house, roofed with branches, clay daubed. In it were found only plain coarse pottery, and crude, apparently neck-coiled, corrugated ware. We seem to have here primitive pit-house construction of a very small settlement with scattered houses. It lies in the midst of an open, waterless, featureless plain, for which agricultural advantages are hard to imagine, in as featureless and unpromising a site as might be selected. Only occasionally does Turkey Creek flood into the basin beyond this site. Agriculture however seems to have been practiced, for not only are mortars found which might have been used to grind wild seeds, but also metates such as are thought to denote the grinding of the softer maize. Apparently other small settlements of similar sort are scattered far out into the Sulphur Spring Valley in this section. Until further information is secured these may be regarded either as indigent outposts of more advanced settlements or as remnants of earlier habitations.

A curious fact concerning the various test pits we sank, which is further corroborated by the much wider experience of Hands, is that many of the settlements viewed by us were composed of pit houses, of a sort, with this marked characteristic, that at a depth of a foot and a half to three feet, each was found to have a floor. The surmise presents itself, that except in the compact pueblos it was customary to begin house-building by excavating. The condition cannot be assigned to subsequent filling of the surface, for the sites normally are subject to denudation. What appears at first sight to be foundation stones are normally exposed bowlders, imbedded in walls that extend to some depth beneath the surface of the ground. Whether in this construction there is an implication of greater age, we cannot undertake to answer.

The impression that this area represents authentic ancient and medieval phases of Pueblo culture rather than late-lingering elements is based on two assumptions: (1) that the given elements of material culture, such as house form, structural grouping, and pottery design, are essentially synchronous wherever they appear, and (2) that a general ancestral hearth for the whole Pueblo culture in the San Juan and upper Rio Grande country is unproved. The first assumption runs counter to Waterman's conclusion of the probable contemporaneous existence of all "stages" of Pueblo culture. All the records we have presented are those of agricultural peoples and have rather convincing areal continuity. It is not apparent to us why at one and the same time there should have been employed widely differing structural forms and pottery techniques in closely adjacent sites that do not correlate with subsistence differentiations of these sites, but which seem to show radial distributions. Again, we have difficulty in accepting without reserve the San Juan-culture hearth concept together with a southern, apparently Central American source of agricultural practices and crops, and with a continuous belt of oases of high quality and large size extending down the west coast from Arizona to the Mexican Plateau. These river oases constitute as far north as the base of the Colorado Plateau a country of far more obvious agricultural attractions and favorable seasons than is the San Juan country. Our curiosity concerning the source of the Red-on-buff culture in particular is unabated. May the possibility of early, southern-culture connections, later detachment of the Pueblo country by hostile intrusions between the as yet only partly differentiated Pueblo land and Mexico, and the still later final evolution of Pueblo culture under isolation not be considered as an alternate working hypothesis? We may be guilty of <u>a prioristic</u> reasoning in disliking to accept an inclement, meager northern source for a great culture hearth in preference to the subtropical valleys of western Mexico and even of Arizona south of the Mogollon Plateau. Perhaps, however, evidence is not yet sufficiently conclusive to assert an essentially autochthonous Pueblo culture with its southern periphery in the vicinity of the international border.

PART II.

DERIVATIVES

CHAPTER 9

Derivatives of
Type 1 (Exploratory Traverse)

Exploratory traverses and the reports on them continue to be useful both in and out of geography. They serve as a short cut to regional coverage, by sampling along a line transecting areas. They range in variety and purpose from specialized technical surveys to popular travelogues.

From almost innumerable possibilities two samples in geography are included here. As already indicated, the so-called "derivatives" in this and following chapters do not follow simply the headings under which they are grouped but derive their viewpoints and methods from any or all of the types previously recognized. The two studies in this chapter were both made in full view not only of the first type but of the first six types at least, of those previously described.

"The Railway Traverse as an Aid in Reconnaissance" by C. C. Colby, 1933, is particularly a sequel to type 6 (Areal Uniformity) in a conscious effort to extend the use of surveys based on areal uniformity and diversity from details of small areas, as at Hennepin and Montfort[1], to generalizations over larger regions. The innovation in field method is a short-hand

1. *pp. 99 - 114 above.*

system of recording from observation under circumstances of rapid transportation.

"An Air Traverse of Central America" by R. S. Platt, 1934, is a sequel to type 6 (Areal Uniformity) and was made in view of type 7 (Areal Organization) in an effort to extend the use of surveys based on uniformity of occupance over larger regions through use of the newly available means of commercial air transport, and to test the use of photography from the air by geographers as a supplement to observation.

The field method includes observation of uniformity and diversity as in Type 6, but obviously cannot include emphasis on field inquiry as in type 7 (Areal Organization), except by supplementary reconnaissance on the ground. But the uniformities in this case are various densities and forms of occupance, and therefore are in accordance with Mark Jefferson's advice which preceded areal organization in type 7. In fact this study recognizing primarily uniformities of occupance was connected more immediately with Jefferson's idea than were the areal pattern studies of type 7 (Areal Organization), as indicated by personal correspondence from Jefferson on this study.

Obviously both the studies in this chapter, as well as most of those in the following chapters (except as specifically noted) are addressed to the ever-increasing audience of professional geographers interested in substantive findings or field methods.

THE RAILWAY TRAVERSE AS AN AID IN RECONNAISSANCE[1]

by C. C. Colby

The railway traverse, as illustrated by the accompanying examples, represents an attempt to secure quantitative data in regional reconnaissance. The underlying idea is to record on a base map of the area traversed, what one sees from the car window and thus to provide tangible materials for future study. It is hoped that such traverses may prove to be a step in the solution of the dual problem inherent in regional work, namely, accuracy on the one hand, and reasonable coverage on the other.

The accompanying traverses, [of which one is reproduced here, Fig. 13] are small sections of a railway traverse from Winnipeg, Manitoba, westward via Prince Albert, Saskatoon and Edmonton to Grande Prairie in the Peace River section of Alberta. They were made in August 1929 by a graduate field party from the University of Chicago. The traverse [not reproduced here] lies in a well-settled area long the Neepawa–Riding Mountain division of the Canadian National Railways. Its eastern end is about 80 miles west of Winnipeg. The one in Fig. 13 is in the Peace River country, a pioneer area about 250 miles northwest of Edmonton. The observations recorded in these traverses were preceded by some preparatory ground study in which the party became familiar with the base maps with which they were to work, with the size and shape of the fields and other features of the cultural pattern not shown on the maps, and with the appearance of the major crops in August.

Traverse records in Western Canada are facilitated by excellent base maps. Practically the entire settled area is mapped on the scale of 1 to 190,080 or 1 inch to 3 miles. The maps are of recent date and the cartographic work is of high order. This means that the maps present the major items in the landscape pattern as it is today. As each map covers an east–west distance of approximately 95 miles, and as the scale is relatively small, frequent changes of maps in making a railway traverse are not necessary. For the sake of clarity in reduction, most of the features shown on the maps were omitted in making the drawings for these traverses. To get the full setting for the traverses, readers should consult the sheets indicated. . . .

In making these traverses the party worked in teams of two, two teams working at a time. One of the teams made a record from the right-hand windows, while the other team worked the left-hand side. As the work requires a high degree of concentration, better results were obtained when the teams worked for intervals of about an hour rather than for longer periods. In order that each team begin its work at a known point, team changes were made at stations. The precise method of work varied with the teams.

1. _Annals AAG_, vol. 23 (1933), pp. 157-164.

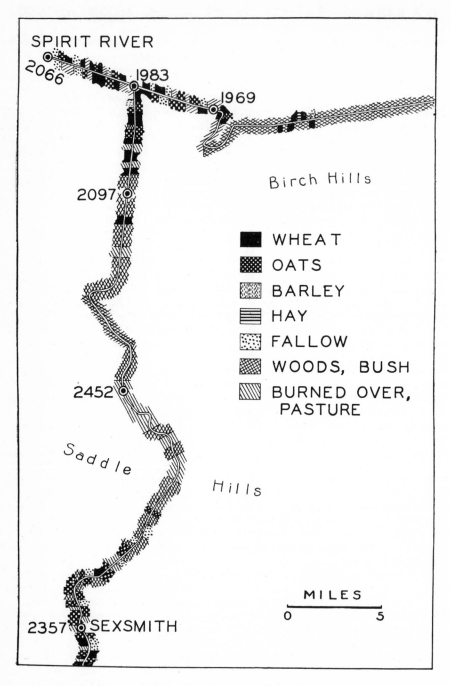

Fig. 13. Railway traverse map, Peace River country.

Commonly, however, one member of a team made the observations while the other member recorded them on the map. The observer identified the crops or other items of the cover and measured the frontages occupied by each crop or item along the railway. Distance was measured by counting the telephone poles, the count being made with a pocket tallying machine, such as is used in ground pacing. In the prairie sections of Canada, the telephone poles are spaced regularly and give a fairly accurate means of measuring distance. The task of recording the frontage occupied by a particular crop was facilitated by the fact that the section lines appear on the base maps, and that the fields in most places are even divisions of the section. The record on the map was made in a color code. As stations are spaced about every five miles along the railways, the spacing could be checked before errors became serious. During the pause at a station, notes covering points of special interest in the preceding miles were recorded on the map. Briefer notes were made en route as striking changes in slope, drainage, and the like appeared.

The first traverse reveals three distinct cover combinations, or, in fact, three types of land use. The first cover combination is characteristic of the 14 miles of the traverse extending from A to B. In this section each item of the cover is of considerable importance. Thus wheat, for example, occupies 18 per cent, oats 18 per cent, and barley 5 per cent of the frontage along the railroad in this section of the traverse. Such a linear balance in the crop frontages suggests a mixed type of farming with wheat and oats predominating. The second cover combination occupies the 15 miles of the traverse from B to C. In this section crops are conspicuous by their absence. In fact, in this section woods and bush occupied 56 per cent and pasture 19 per cent of the railway frontage. This woods-pasture combination stands in marked contrast to the combinations in the other sections. The third cover combination extends over the section of the traverse between C and D. In this 14 miles most of the land is cropped, with wheat strikingly predominant and oats and fallow conspicuous. This combination is the one commonly associated with the Canadian Prairies.

The first combination lies in a broadly level area below 1000 feet, the second lies in terrain which rises nearly 300 feet in the 16 miles, while the third lies in an area which slopes less than 20 feet in the 15 miles. These facts of slope are shown more clearly on the base map. Examination of this map shows that each of the three sections of the traverse is a distinctive terrain. Thus the first combination lies on the "first prairie level" or the Plain of Manitoba, the second traverses the hilly slope of the east-facing Manitoba escarpment, and the third is on the "second prairie level" or the Plain of Saskatchewan.

The traverse in Fig. 13 gives concrete evidence of the character of the Peace River country, with small cleared prairies set like oases in a vast wilderness of uncleared bush. In the section covered by the upper left hand corner of the figure, most of the

land is under cultivation. This section of the traverse lies in
Spirit River Prairie -- a cleared area of about 170 square miles.
Originally some of the cleared area was mantled with grass while
other parts were covered with low bush or light timber. In 1929
the cover combination in this area was made up in large measure
of four items, namely, wheat, oats, fallow and bush. Spirit River
Prairie is surrounded on all sides with typical Canadian bush.
Neither the land nor the timber is of good enough quality to warrant
the cost and effort of clearing most of these bush covered areas.
The continuity of the bush is illustrated by the Birch Hills and the
Saddle Hills section of the traverse. This section of the traverse
lies transverse to the Saddle Hills cuesta, the north-facing excarp-
ment of which limits the Spirit River area on the south. In the
Saddle Hills area, the land is high and rough, the soils are poor
and the few clearings only emphasize the continuity of the bush.
Back from the railroad little or no land is cleared in either the
Birch Hills or Saddle Hills sections.

Obviously a traverse or log made from a moving train will
contain errors. Obviously, also, better results may be expected
from slow moving trains which make many stops than from fast
moving expresses stopping only at the larger places. In the traverse under discussion it is to be expected that mistakes were
made in identifying cover items, for barley and certain types of
wheat look much alike in their mid-summer phases and the criteria used in distinguishing pastured area were not altogether
satisfactory. Errors in spacing also are inevitable, both from
mistakes in measuring the frontage occupied by the various items
and in plotting a given frontage on the map. Experimentation and
checking, however, have demonstrated that such errors are not
serious where the preparatory study is adequate and the work is
done carefully. In any case the results should prove far more
accurate than conclusions based on uncharted observations of even
the most careful and experienced travelers.

The railway traverse has proved its worth in numerous
ways. Study of such traverses, for example, raises questions for
subsequent detailed work in the field. It leads to the formulation
of preliminary ideas of crop and cover combinations. It directs
attention to areas of unusual interest or perplexity. It offers
visual and statistical support to regional generalizations. The
traverse may be useful, moreover, in applying the results of a
detailed examination of a small part of an area to the whole area.
It gives a chance to compare field records, however fragmentary,
with statistical materials derived from census or other sources.
In short, it is a means, and an effective one, of launching a regional study.

AN AIR TRAVERSE OF CENTRAL AMERICA[1]

_ by R. S. Platt

PROJECT

A reconnaissance traverse of Central America from Mexico to Colombia was made in five days of January 1933 (Fig. 14). The project was a by-product of a field trip in the northern Andes and was carried out en route to the field in regular planes on air lines. The traverse had a twofold purpose: first, to test possibilities and limitations of reconnaissance under such circumstances and to consider appropriate technique; secondly, to gather new material on Central America.

PRACTICABLE ACCOMPLISHMENT

It was not practicable to cover the traverse with a continuous strip of photographs nor to construct a map. Under pressure of observing, writing and photographing it was not even practicable to follow the course closely on the available map sheets and identify all landmarks. The location of every photograph and recorded observation along the route was more efficiently calculated after the flight, by a time notation for every item, occasional notice of the speed of the plane, and observation of a few landmarks to check the route.

By intensive concentration it was found practicable to take pictures with accompanying notes at an average rate of one every two minutes, equivalent to about one every four miles. These were close enough together to overlap in some cases when taken from high altitudes, but it was not found so important to have them overlap or even to take them at regularly spaced intervals as to select views showing typical associations of landscape features, or forms and variations of the pattern of terrene occupance. In some cases four or five pictures were taken in one minute without the writing of notes intervening. Most of the pictures were taken almost vertically to include the nearest part of the pattern. Even through glass at a high angle these were generally successful. Oblique pictures showing the horizon line along the upper edge turned out to be less satisfactory in most cases, because of loss of detail with increased distance.

There were variations in altitude according to weather conditions, the maximum being about 10,000 feet above the land surface. Since at all times the distance was less than two miles it was possible to distinguish below not only forest, grass, and cultivated lands, but also various kinds of crops, and types of buildings. There appeared a striking repetition of similar features

1. Annals AAG, vol. 24 (1934), pp. 29-39.

similarly arranged with reference to each other and to the natural background, clear-cut variations from place to place and from these readily established generalizations on the pattern of terrene occupance district by district. Both photographs and notes were directed to the recognition, description and delimitation of the types of occupance in their natural setting.

FINDINGS

There was confirmation in a broad way of a general composite similarity through the whole traverse area as a part of a major region, Caribbean America, a tropical symphysis of land and sea, of hot lowlands and cool highlands, of wet forest and dry scrub, of populous communities scattered in a wilderness.

There was confirmation also in a broad way of certain larger subdivisions of this region: the moist forested lowlands of the Caribbean margin, the rugged highland backbone of Central American bordered by volcanoes on its southwestern edge, the narrow semi-arid lowlands of the Pacific margin, and the mountain masses of the northern Andes.

But such general concepts seemed elementary and dim, of substance thinly spread, in the presence of the vivid landscape types appearing within and across the larger divisions.

The variety was not chaotic but fitted readily into a few types, distinguished primarily according to intensity of land occupance. Four grades of occupance emerged: at one extreme complete occupance where all the land was occupied to a point of visible improvement (Fig. 15); at the other extreme blank occupance where none of the land was visibly occupied; between these close occupance where more than half of the land and sparse occupance where less than half was occupied (Fig. 16).

In the recognition of a grade of occupance the minimum unit of area did not include all the land in sight but at least several square miles clearly seen below. Exact measurement of the proportion of occupance was impossible, but direct estimate seemed sufficient, since the distinction between grades was not merely quantitative but generally qualitative as well, representing stable differences of development under different circumstances. There were indeed qualitative differences within each grade, but these were for the most part obvious modifications fitting likewise into a few simple types.

COMPLETE OCCUPANCE

Of complete occupance only small spots appear on the map (Fig. 14). Many of the these are cities -- Merida, Guatemala, San Salvador, Managua, San José, Panama, Medellín.

Rural areas of this grade are confined to exceptionally uniform tracts of land in highly productive agricultural districts. These are in the higher plateau of Guatemala, the lower plateau of southeastern Guatemala and Salvador, (Fig. 15), the lake basin

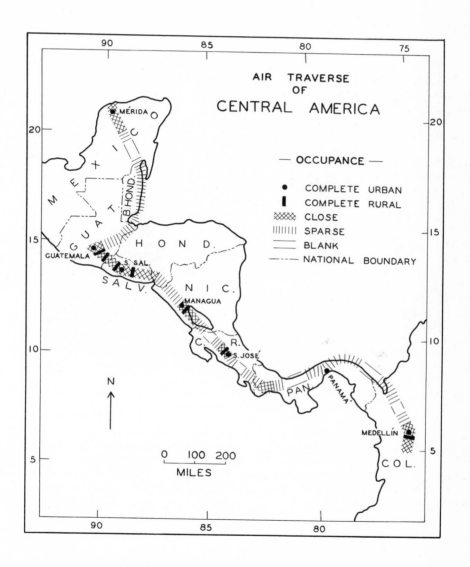

Fig. 14. Air traverse map: "The Route and the Intensity of Occupance".

Fig. 15. "Complete Occupance in a smooth plateau area in Salvador. Cornfields and pastures predominating; coffee in shady groves, a plantation in the right foreground; fields bordered by trees and bushes and some of them by lanes; small scattered houses barely visible".

Figs. 15 and 16 are included as examples of photographs taken from an airliner by geographers in connection with field study. They show some features of a pattern of occupance as in a map of areal organization and some elements of a pattern of uniformity and diversity as in a landscape mosaic map. They represent characteristic features of pattern selected from observation and not a coverage of area as in an aerial photographic survey.

Fig. 16. *"Sparse occupance in a valley of southeastern Costa Rica. Irregular and impermanent agricultural clearings in a forest along a stream; a master stream across the upper part of the picture".*

plain of Nicaragua, the plateau of Costa Rica, and the Central Andes of northern Colombia. In these districts spots of smooth land are covered by a pattern of rectangular fields, fairly small, outlined by walls or bushes. In each district a considerable number of the fields are occupied by corn, and others are in pasture or fallow. Small houses are numerous, scattered or clustered among the fields here and there; large buildings are relatively few. Lanes between fields are numerous; highways and railways few.

In other respects there are differences among the districts. The highest, in Guatemala, has fields of wheat or other small grain, as well as corn, while the others have sugar-cane, plantains, cassava and other root crops, and tropical fruits. The districts of medium elevation, in Guatemala, Salvador, Costa Rica and Colombia, have coffee groves among the open fields or grouped around drying floors and buildings (Fig. 15). Costa Rica has fields of upland rice. The lowland area in Nicaragua has a higher proportion of pasture.

CLOSE OCCUPANCE

Areas of close occupance, more extensive than the spots of complete occupance, appear in all the districts mentioned above and in some others. Close occupance in the plateau of southeastern Guatemala and Salvador extends on into Honduras declining in elevation almost to the Pacific coast. Another lowland district, similar but detached, appears on the Pacific slope of western Panamá. In all these areas the elements of the pattern are like those in the rural spots of complete occupance -- cornfields, pastures and small houses, and, in their respective districts, coffee and other special crops. But the field pattern is irregularly broken, generally by steep and rocky slopes, canyon walls below or lava flows above, wooded in some cases, barren in others.

One area, of close occupance at the northern end of the traverse in Yucatán, far from the others and including no rural spot of complete occupance, is distinct in character. In this district the pattern is not broken by irregularities of the land surface. Here a homogeneous lowland plain is occupied in part by large, rectangular fields of sisal grouped around drying yards and buildings; in part by small subangular fields of corn; and in part by scrubby woods.

The scrub growth occupies about half of the land surface and a question might arise as to whether the occupance is close or sparse. The former classification seems proper especially since most of the wooded land shows signs of occupance, having been recently cultivated and then abandoned for a period of years in a sort of fallow rotation revealed by field patches in various stages of reforestation.

SPARSE OCCUPANCE

Areas of sparse occupance lie between and beyond those of close occupance. In some cases they are fringes of the same pattern containing the same items as the more densely occupied areas near-by. But in most places they are distinctive settlements of a different sort. Thus between the close occupance in the lake basin of Nicaragua and that on smooth slopes near the Honduran-Salvadorean boundary there is sparse occupance in the Honduran-Nicaraguan boundary zone -- a predominance of dissected brush covered hills, a few small groups of buildings with cattle corrals among the hills, and patches of corn, cane and plantains along stream valleys.

Likewise between the Costa Rican plateau and the neighboring districts of close occupance, to the northwest and to the southeast there is sparse occupance among rugged forested slopes, irregular patches of corn, cane and plantains in mountain valleys (Fig. 16), and irregular patches of fire-cleared pasture on ridges in lower drier areas. In Colombia there is similar sparse occupance in eastern valleys of the Western Andes not far from closely occupied basins in the Central Andes.

Even in the uniform plain of Yucatán the transition from close to sparse occupance is marked by a qualitative change -- the disappearance of sisal plantations and the appearance of isolated huts with their clearings in more luxuriant forest.

Other areas of sparse occupance are not associated with those of denser settlement even by proximity. The coastal margin of British Honduras with a bit of Mexico to the north and Guatemala to the south appears as an area of sparse occupance distinct from other settled areas along the traverse. Here are huts and clearings in the forest, each showing signs of the sort of fallow rotation already mentioned, patches of newly cleared ground, of corn, cane and plantains, and of young forest growth. In a few places along valleys there are larger clearings occupied by banana plantations, and along the coast fringes of coconuts.

Another separate area of sparse occupance is centered on the Panamá Canal. Huts and patch clearings in the forest like those in other districts, here most numerous near the artificial lakes, contrast sharply with the exotic works of the canal. Probably rural settlement has been stimulated at the historic crossing place, but close occupance does not appear among the dissected lateritic hills of the isthmus.

Sparse occupance east of the canal along the north coast of Panamá almost adjoins the Canal settlement, and yet is distinct from it. This is the San Blas district, where Indian villages occupy cays off shore, coconut groves fringe the beaches, and patch clearings of corn, cane and plantains are scattered through the forest on the mainland.

The string of cays comes to an end near the eastern boundary of Panamá and beyond this the scattered occupance near the coast in Colombia represents a separate settlement of patch clearings along valleys of the western slope of the Western Andes.

BLANK OCCUPANCE

There remain to be mentioned several blank areas between settled districts. Some of these are in lowlands and others in highlands. They include an interior area of the Yucatán peninsula, separated from the coast by no barrier but distance; rugged forested slopes of northwestern and southeastern Costa Rica; dissected forested mountains of western and eastern Panamá; and the bare crest of the western Andes.

A question might be raised as to the propriety of including a bit of the Andes in a Central American traverse. It is included in view of its affiliation with the Central American pattern of terrene occupance and as evidence against the sanctity of an orthodox boundary. Its inclusion is simpler than that of Yucatán. The traverse observations continued farther south, but here other factors appeared calling for discussion elsewhere.

CONCLUSION

It is evident that the traverse, following a zigzag course through Central America, touches various districts without indicating their extent or defining their relations to each other. The reconnaissance pattern is still to be completed. Yet from this one traverse a few generalizations may be suggested.

1. The grades of occupance, appearing like spectral bands along the traverse, may be thought to occur as segments of concentric rings centering in the principal separate communities of the region. But in this connection it is to be remembered that the distinction between grades generally is not only quantitative but qualitative and is based on local surface differences rather than on distance from a central nucleus.

2. The surface differences affecting habitability seem to be largely in distribution of precipitation, in ruggedness of land forms, and in maturity of soils. Areas of complete and close occupance appear only where there is evidence of both rainy and dry seasons and a preponderance of smooth land. With one exception they are in a belt of immature volcanic soils, high in some places and low in others. The one exception is in the limestone plain of Yucatán. In areas of sparse occupance there is conspicuous concentration of settlement in valleys on immature alluvial soils. Mature soils are conspicuously unoccupied except for pasturage in a few places.

3. The areas of complete and close occupance show marks of European culture in their towns and farms. In some areas of sparse occupance there is a European touch in plantations or grazing lands, but in most places there are marks of primitive culture in hut villages and forest clearings. In most of the areas of complete and close as well as in those of sparse occupance small-scale subsistence farming is more in evidence than large-scale commercial farming. Signs of productive activity other than farming are few and minute.

4. The distribution of the types of occupance along the traverse suggests the divisions of a political rather than of a physical
map. In general the pattern accords with a concept of the Central
American nations as separate groups of people isolated from each
other. But it does not substantiate the idea of the separation of
these nations by natural barriers. National boundaries do not coincide with natural boundaries nor follow uninhabited zones, but cut
through outlying communities. Therefore between these nations,
based on major concentrations of population, boundaries apparently
have not been set with respect to local barriers or population
groups in the boundary zones, but have crystallized according to
the relative political influence extending into these zones from
more or less distant major centers.

C H A P T E R   10

Derivatives of
Type 2 (Area Survey)

Area survey and description of the lands surveyed, along with classification of land-use types,
continues to be useful. After the great western
surveys of the 1870's land classification for
settlement and use was dropped from the topographic mapping program of the U.S. Geological
Survey.   But later it was taken up again and
has been carried on in various places by various
agencies, partly under geographic auspices.

The Michigan Land Economic Survey is an outstanding example.   A part of "Farmsteads and
Land Types in Emmet County, Michigan", by
F. W. Foster, 1941, made within the framework
of the state survey, is taken here as a sample
study.

Aside from its relation to type 2 (Area Survey)
this study has been made in view of some of the
other stages previously described, particularly
type 6 (Areal Uniformity). The field method is
directly connected with that of the Hennepin and
Montfort studies.[1]

Generally, though not in this study, the survey
method of the Michigan Land Economic Survey
deviates from that of the fractional complex

1. *pp. 99-114 above.*

code in the production of two maps instead of one – a map of the land and another of the land-cover – thus following one of the three alternatives mentioned by Jones and Finch in the Hennepin study.[1]

FARMSTEADS AND LAND TYPES IN EMMET COUNTY, MICHIGAN[2]

by F. W. Foster

INTRODUCTION

A method of land classification in which the unit of inventory is the land type has been proposed and applied in the field. The basic land types for Emmet County were established by J.O. Veatch after reconnaissance in the early summer of 1937. By the close of the field season the northern two thirds of the county had been mapped. The work was completed during the summers of 1938 and 1939. With aerial photographs it was possible to revise and refine the land types outlined in the first summer. New ones were added, and some were dropped to achieve the same degree of detail.

If the land types as established are valid entities, there should be some relationship between the physical conditions they represent and the cultural patterns that develop as they are used by man. Such connections will be best expressed in terms of productivity. A complex of conditions in addition to the productivity of his land influences the ultimate success or failure of any farmer. These include ambition, alertness, available markets, and the cost of transportation. In a small area where the same general advantages and disadvantages prevail marked variations in the character of farms and farmsteads from place to place will, however, reflect the quality of the land. On the basis of this idea correlations have been made between the land types and the farms and farmsteads in Emmet County.

DESCRIPTION OF THE LAND TYPES (SEE FIG. 17)

As Emmet County is approached from the north the land rises in a series of terraces retreating from the shore of Lake Michigan.

1. *p. 99 above.*
2. *Papers of Mich. Acad. Science, Arts and Letters, vol. 27 (1941), pp. 351-367*

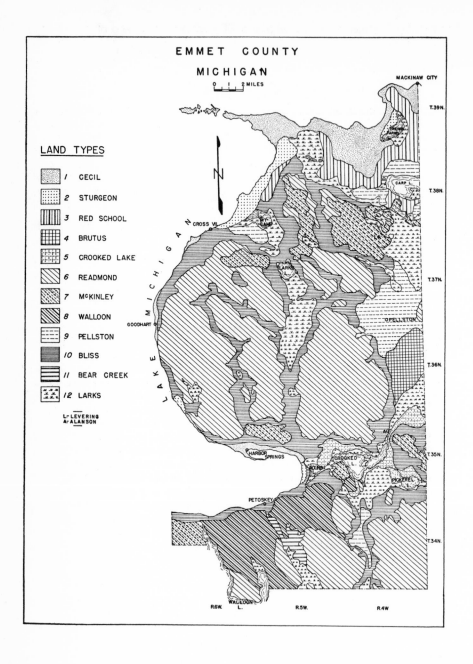

Fig. 17. Land classification for occupance, based on soil types.

These terraces are level or slightly inclined and are marked by relict shorelines along the lakeward margins. The nature of the drainage is dependent upon the position of the terrace and the character of the soil material. South of the benches a morainic mass stands high above a surrounding lowland area of diverse composition. The lowland is particularly evident along the east side of the county and is terraced after the manner of the benches in the north. The morainic material is shaped into drumlin-like ridges or deposited as sandy plateaus that are cut by numerous dry valleys. The plateau surface and its margins exhibit occasional kamic deposits. A number of broad flat-floored valleys transect the moraines. Their location is such that they separate the upland into a series of poorly defined ranges with a north-south trend. In the southern part of the county the eastern lowland swings to meet Little Traverse Bay. South of the depression thus formed the elevated area continues -- the drumlins in the west and the sandy moraines in the east. On the varied surface described, with its complex associations of soil, slope, vegetation, and drainage, the land types are developed.

OUTLINE OF THE LAND TYPES

1. Land Types with Small Local Relief and Slow or Poor Drainage. . . .

RED SCHOOL
  Vegetation: Cedar, white spruce, balsam fir, aspen, elm, ash, red maple, yellow birch, basswood, tamarack.
  Surface: Gently sloping toward the lake; broken by old sandy beach ridges.
  Soil
    Major – Ogemaw sandy loam, Munuscong sandy loam
    Minor – Saugatuck sand, Newton sand and Rubicon sand
  Drainage: Slow; water has a tendency to stand on surface. . . .

2. Land Types with Small Relief and Rapid Drainage. . . .

3. Land Types with Considerable Local Relief

WALLOON
  Vegetation
    Major – Hard maple, beech, elm, basswood, yellow birch
    Minor – Aspen, cherry, with cedar, balsam fir, red maple, ash, alder, and willow in depressions
  Surface: Pronounced drumlin-like topography with a northwest-southeast trend, steep marginal slopes
  Soil
    Major – Onaway sandy loam
    Minor – Onaway loam, Emmet sandy loam, Granby sand, Newton sand, Lupton muck, Rifle peat
  Drainage: Poor in depressions. . . .

Walloon agriculture. -- Farming on the Walloon land type is
the most successful in the county. The appearance of the farmsteads is generally prosperous. Fields, fences, yards, and orchards
give an impression of being well cared for. Crops are vigorous,
and the signs of a successful economy are seen everywhere.

A greater part of the surface has been cleared of vegetation.
Trees grow in the steep-sided valleys that occasionally cut back
into the hills and along the bottoms of the poorly drained depressions. Portions of the lowland areas have been cleared and are
used for pasture. Fields are large, and the fence lines are straight.
Farm economy is based upon the production of potatoes and animal
products. Some acreage is devoted to alfalfa and other hay crops,
as well as to corn and small grains, particularly oats and wheat.
A fair percentage of the cropland is in pasture.

Despite the fact that farming here is general in character
three types of specialization have developed -- dairying, potato
raising, and flower growing. Dairy farming, common over the
land type, is most prevalent in the vicinity of Petoskey. These
farms are among the best in the county. Other farmers raise
quantities of potatoes. The extreme specialization is indicated
by emphasis on the production of certified seed. A few agricul-
turalists concentrate on flowers, bulbs, and seeds. The flowers
are sold in the resort market and in Chicago. Seeds and bulbs
are disposed of through the various seed farms. . . .

Red School agriculture. -- Large parts of the Red School
land type are not used for agriculture. The area under cultivation
appears, however, to be expanding. Here and there fields are being
cleared of stumps. A stony surface and slow drainage contribute
to the difficulties of farming. Though farmsteads are not prosper-
ous-looking, continual improvement has been noted over a period
of three years. The local markets at Mackinaw City and Mackinac
Island may appreciably encourage the expansion of the farm area
and the improvement of the farms. . . .

If the land types with small local relief and slow or poor
drainage are considered, a marked difference in farmstead density
is noted (Table I). The Cecil type, with 11.94 square miles for
each farm home, stands lowest. The Larks is next, with all its
farmsteads on the higher ground included within the complex. The
Crooked Lake is third. Here a considerable part of the surface has
been cleared, but a well-rounded farm program is apparently impossible. The Red School is fourth. This relationship may be expected to change in the near future since the process of clearing is
still under way. . . .

The Walloon, the McKinley, the Readmond, and the Sturgeon
are the land types with considerable local relief. The Walloon has
the smallest average area per farmstead of any type in the county
(Table I). . . .

The Walloon, with 15.7 per cent of the units in Class 4, 60.3
per cent in Class 3 and 21.5 per cent in Class 2, is obviously the
best land type for agricultural use. . . .

TABLE I

CORRELATION OF LAND TYPES AND FARMSTEAD TYPES

In the first four [items] the second figure is the
percentage.

Land Type	Red School	Walloon . . .
Farmstead type:		
Class 2 – inferior	24	52
	61.6	21.5
Class 3 – ordinary	14	146
	36	60.3
Class 4 – excellent	0	38
	0	15.7
Class 5 – superior	1	6
	2.5	2.48
Total number of occupied farmsteads	39	242
Total number of non–farms	8	35
Number of square miles in each land type	18.48	29.68
Average number of square miles per occupied farmstead	0.473	0.123

CONCLUSION

Land types have been established with reference only to their
physical characteristics. If we make allowances for the personal
attributes of ambition, superior training, and home background,
and if we discount the advantages that accrue from superior location with respect to market and transportation, then we may expect
that the quality and number of farmsteads and the general character
of farming will reflect, in some degree, the productive quality of
the land type. Such a relationship is well expressed in Emmet
County, where no area is at a marked disadvantage with respect
to transportation and national markets. It is felt that the analysis
of farming, the figures and discussion pertaining to the density of
farmsteads, and the correlation between farmstead quality and the
land types have indicated the connections that exist. A more detailed investigation would probably reveal closer relationships.

CHAPTER 11

Derivatives of
Type 3 (Explanatory Physical)

Explanatory physical geography has been carried on by scientists variously connected, many of them less directly associated with geography than were R. D. Salisbury and W. M. Davis.[1] Major contributors are geomorphologists associated with geology, and major contributions are made in laboratory experimentation on physical processes instead of in field study, and so are in the realm of geophysics. Scientific intercourse is through the American Geophysical Union rather than the Association of American Geographers.

From the outset physical geography has included work by meteorologists and climatologists. Naturally this has not involved field study in the same way as has the old familiar work of physiographers or geomorphologists.

"Hurricanes into New England: Meteorology of the Storm of September 21, 1938" by C. F. Brooks, 1939, may be considered a field study in physical geography in a broad sense. As Director of the Blue Hill Observatory the author observed the storm and the resulting destruction in New England. For many years he associated himself with geography and was Presi-

1. pp. 35, 37 above.

dent of the Association of American Geographers in 1947.

This hurricane study may be considered also as representing a valid and continuing line of thought in explanatory human geography, type 4, even though presumably it was not intended to do so.

Natural calamities, direct destruction by the forces of nature, acts of God, are obvious instances of the influence of natural environment on human life. Storms, floods, earthquakes and volcanic eruptions are causal factors not to be denied and can be studied as such. This is not anthropogeography but physical geography in its point of view.

"A Permanent Loss to New England: Soil Erosion Resulting from the Hurricane", by H. H. Bennett, 1939, is a related study. It is a field study only in a similar broad sense, that the author observed these results in the field. He associated himself with geography and was President of the Association of American Geographers in 1943. He was organizer and Director of the U.S. Soil Conservation Service. The article is addressed to geographers and conservationists in general.

This soil erosion study likewise is a derivative of type 3 (Explanatory Physical) and type 4 (Explanatory Human). It is concerned with physical processes of nature in the storm, and with the direct influence of nature on man in soil erosion. In addition it is still more concerned with the influence of man on nature as an agent in physical process, through adoption of special farm practices. This introduces a sequel to physical geography which has been of great importance in human geography: the conservation of natural resources. Ideas of proper use or misuse of resources were implied in exploratory reports and land classification in the 19th century. But they were most explicitly expressed in that period by G. P. Marsh. In Man and Nature or Physical Geography as Modified by Human Action, 1867, Marsh gave as an objective in social science ''to indicate the character and approximately the extent of the changes produced by human action in the physical conditions of the globe we inherit; to point out the dangers of imprudence and the necessity of caution in all operations which, on a large scale, interfere with the spontaneous arrangements of the organic or the inorganic world, to suggest the possibility and the importance of the restoration of disturbed harmonies and the material improvement of waste and exhausted regions.''[1]

The plea for conservation of natural resources was taken up in earnest after the turn of the century by other non-geographers, notably Gifford Pinchot with the support of President Theodore Roosevelt. These have been succeeded by many

1. G. P. Marsh: "Man and Nature or Physical Geography as Modified by Human Action", (N.Y.: Chas. Scribner & Co., 1867), p. III.

conservationists in geography, notably by H. H.
Barrows, and now more recently by geographers
working on resource management and including
specialized field study in a program of geography allied with engineering and planning.

HURRICANES INTO NEW ENGLAND:
METEROLOGY OF THE STORM OF SEPTEMBER 21, 1938[1]

by C. F. Brooks

The hurricane of September last was a whirling, circular
storm with very destructive winds spread over a diameter of 200
miles. At its center was the usual calm eye, some 40 miles in
breadth. This vortex rushed northward to Long Island and New
England with the speed of an express train, augmenting wind velocities to extremes of about 120 miles an hour on the east of the
path of the center. The wind drove the sea water with such force
that, when added to the rise in sea level due to the low pressure
and thrown against the coast, the sea rose 10 to 15 feet above the
expected level, in itself high water, the time being high tide.
Towering surges on this combined astronomical tide and storm
wave threw the sea to such heights that demolition was general
along the exposed coast and hundreds of persons were engulfed and
drowned. Flying spray incrusted windows and salt killed vegetation
20 miles inland, and traces were found even 50 miles from the
raging sea. Inland, the rivers, already flooded by four days of
tropical rains, added to the destruction.
The gale, roaring in great gusts over the countryside, broke
off or uprooted millions of trees, damaged or destroyed thousands
of buildings, and, directly or indirectly, downed nearly 20,000 miles
of electric-power and telephone lines. Many people were killed or
injured by falling trees, chimneys, or flying debris. The damage
was most extensive on the tops and sides of hills. There were also
lanes of destruction where particularly vicious gusts, attended perhaps by eddies, had plowed through the woods, breaking off trees or
uprooting them from the sodden ground. More than five billion
board feet of timber were thrown down, leaf pulp turned white
houses green, and leaves that were not blown to pieces were
"scorched" by the beating, desiccating gale.

1. _Geog. Rev._, vol. 29 (1939), pp. 119-127.

There were some 600 lives lost. The American Red Cross places the deaths at 488, with 100 additional missing, and 1754 more or less injured. The WPA survey places the loss of human life at 682. The Red Cross also finds that 93,122 families suffered more or less serious property losses, that 6933 summer dwellings, 1991 other dwellings, and 2605 boats were destroyed, also 2369 barns and 7438 other buildings. The total economic loss is estimated at $250,000,000 to $330,000,000. Although the loss of life has been greater in a few other hurricanes, the damage to property in this storm was the greatest that ever occurred in a single storm anywhere in the world.

Such things had happened before—in 1815 and 1635—and had been vividly recorded in newspapers, meteorological records, and town chronicles and in Sidney Perley's "Historic Storms of New England". In fact, Perley describes ten storms of hurricane intensity in two and a half centuries, and Tannehill lists eight more, and there have been four more in the last fifty years, which makes five or ten New England hurricanes to a century and one that is especially fierce and widespread in each century and a half.

ORIGIN OF THE STORM

The hurricane that devastated Long Island and New England on September 21 had its origin in the tropical Atlantic, far east of Puerto Rico. On the morning of the 16th it was already of full hurricane strength; in fact, as early as the 13th a cyclonic circulation was in evidence in 37° W., 19° N. Presumably, therefore, the hurricane formed near the Cape Verde Islands, where other such storms have been known to originate, between the northeast trade and the southwest monsoon. Indeed, it is not improbable that the disturbance initiating the hurricane came out of monsoon Africa—one of the "tornadoes", which are not twisters but large, heavy thunderstorms that form in the interior and move westward to the coast.

The direction (W. by N.) and speed (15-20 miles an hour) of progression of the hurricane as a whole were practically the same as the gradient wind in the general pressure field at the southern and western margins of the North Atlantic high. This high, centered south of Newfoundland, was attended by a broad stream of tropical air, which curved northward east of Florida. The hurricane moved along (Fig. 18) in this stream more or less as would have a floating balloon. Its entry into the stream may be considered, in the absence of further knowledge regarding its origin and early history, as essentially accidental. But once in the stream, the effect of the hurricane was marked. The storm became a great whirl that sucked air into itself from a belt about 300 miles wide and discharged it upward, thereby putting it through the cyclonic wringer. Within the tropics this process did not alter the warm, moist character of the tropical-air stream—the supply of moist tropical air was ample for long distances on each side.

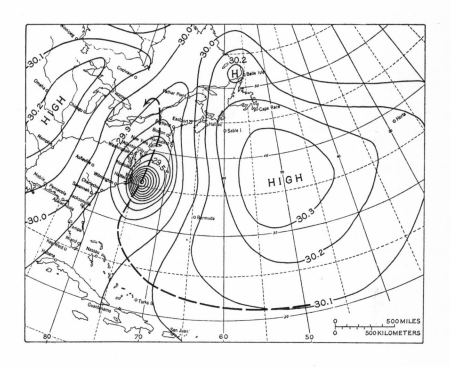

Fig. 18. "Pressure map for September 21, 1938, at 7:10 A.M., and track of
hurricane".

Once the storm left the tropics, however, it no longer had an unlimited supply of tropical air on its left. Polar air reached the southeastern states as the hurricane recurved. In fact, the arrival of this air probably helped the recurving; for its lower temperature increased the density of the atmosphere and thereby favored a slope in the upper-air pressure surfaces from east to west, a direction of slope that calls for a northward movement of the upper air.

The drawing of cool, dense air into the storm from the northwest and west favored a more and more rapid rise in pressure south of it as the incoming air got cooler and cooler with higher and higher latitudes--pressure at Hartford, for example, fell 0.4 inch one hour and rose 0.75 inch the next. This raising of the pressure on the south should have accelerated the northward movement of the center of lowest pressure, even making it go faster than the general current. Moreover, the cool, dry air could not furnish more than half as much latent heat, the lifeblood of a tropical storm, as the warm, moist air had been providing. On the other hand, the contrast in temperature between the east and west sides of the storm created potential energy that made up in part for the loss of latent heat, so that the rate of decrease in intensity was not rapid. Also, the storm moved northward so fast that the reduced energy had little time to make itself felt. . . .

Where descending blasts of wind impinged on steep hill slopes and were concentrated by the topographical configuration, their velocity was greatly increased locally, and trees and structures on exposed slopes or shoulders of hills or cliffs or just beyond were blown down or greatly damaged. At the Blue Hill Observatory, where such gusts might have been expected to show about their maximum increase, velocities of more than 150 miles an hour were almost certainly indicated by the record from a 3-cup anemometer: the velocity, as read from the record, was 186 miles an hour, with an uncertainty, however, of 30 or 40 miles an hour each way. . . .

The hurricane had a central eye of considerable diameter. Over Long Island it extended from a point west of Brentwood, where for 50 minutes there was a period of calm without enough wind to blow out a match, to Mattituck, where a calm of five minutes was reported. However, as the storm was moving in a direction east of north in this area, the diameter of the eye was not necessarily as great as the distance--43 miles--between these points. A conservative figure is perhaps 40 miles. As the eye moved over the Connecticut coast, there was a decrease in wind velocity extending from somewhere west of Fairfield to Saybrook, a distance of 48 miles. Friction with the ground, increased by the rough topography of central Connecticut, seems to have reduced the whirling velocity in the vicinity of the eye so greatly that the diameter of the calm, sunny eye had decreased to 12 or 14 miles as its eastern edge brushed Hartford. How much farther north it lasted I do not known, but Northfield, Vt.--in a deep valley, to be sure--had a light wind for 18 minutes as the direction shifted from northeast to south.

As the hurricane entered the trough, it traveled along the general north-south front between the tropical air on the east and the modified polar air, 20° F. cooler, on the west. The rapid rotation began to turn the fronts: the warm front, originally toward the northeast, turned toward the north; the cold front, originally toward the south, turned toward the east as the storm passed over southern New England. As the tropical air passed up the warm-front slope, its fairly stable lapse rate was increased, and the increased rate resulted in deep convective overturning and extraordinarily heavy rains, amounting to 4 to 6 inches or more over the central and western highlands of New England. These amounts added to the 8 to 11 inches that had fallen in the preceding four days gave 5-day totals of as much as 17 inches and resulted in record floods.

The lowest pressure reported from a land station was 27.94, shown at a Coast Guard station, Bellport, on the south shore of Long Island. At New Haven the sea-level pressure fell to 28.11 and at Hartford to 28.04. It seems that the center went closer to Hartford than to New Haven and that there was relatively little filling up of the storm during the first half hour after it struck land. Thereafter the successive low pressures observed at stations in Massachusetts and Vermont were appreciably higher, though the lowest pressures were not represented by the distribution of the observing stations.

HURRICANE HAZARD IN NEW YORK AND NEW ENGLAND

The conditions under which a West Indian hurricane will strike our North Atlantic coast with full vigor are that (1) the general pressure gradient from east to west must be great throughout the troposphere; (2) the terrain in front of the storm must be well bathed in moist tropical air; and (3) the storm remains over the open sea all the way from the West Indies to its northern landfall. Without the rapid progressive movement the storm would have a chance to lose much of its whirling velocity over the cooler waters north of the Gulf Stream: The presence of moist tropical air over the region helps to prevent a too rapid reduction in energy. Friction with the land is a quick reducer of the velocity of the wind at the surface, causing a decrease in both the deflective effect of the earth's rotation and the centrifugal force of the whirling wind. This results in a considerable flow of air across the isobars into the low-pressure center and, consequently, in a marked reduction of the pressure gradient, which is immediately felt on all sides of the storm. In order to have one of these hurricanes strike the North Atlantic coast from the open sea it is, of course, first necessary that the general winds in the middle levels of the troposphere shall be directed essentially northward or perhaps northwestward, so as to give the storm a movement from the south or from the southeast.

In terms of the hazards to New York City this is a very fortunate circumstance; for not only is New York protected by the New

Jersey coast on the one side and by Long Island on the other but the chances of the storm's coming from the southeast are slender. Nevertheless, a high storm tide can reach New York, even if surf and the strongest winds from the open ocean cannot. If such a storm tide should coincide with high spring tide and the Hudson in flood, lower Manhattan and its subway entrances might be inundated suddenly. In 1821, the tide rose 13 feet in one hour as a hurricane center passed over New York; in 1938 it rose about 6.9 feet in half an hour when the storm center passed into central Long Island.

Other lessons taught by this catastrophe are: that the North Atlantic states should have a hurricane observing and warning service equal to that of the South; that especial attention should be paid to cloud motions to be observed and reported whenever visible, as indicators of the direction and velocity of the middle and upper levels of the air stream in which a hurricane may be travelling; that the network of radiometeorograph stations for deep soundings of the temperature and humidity of the atmosphere be extended to include the northeastern states, so that the potential energy available for the storm can be computed and weather maps for levels aloft can be drawn and winds computed when not observable through low clouds; and that reports be made of the tide levels relative to those predicted and to the occurrence of storm swells all along the coasts where a hurricane might come ashore, by using the valuable rules worked out by Cline for predicting the landfalls of hurricanes in the Gulf states. A teletype, or equivalent intercommunicating system, under the control of the Weather Bureau is required for directing the observers to make the special observations needed at times of threat, for the rapid and sure collection of the observations, and for the dissemination of forecasts to distributing points.

A PERMANENT LOSS TO NEW ENGLAND:
SOIL EROSION RESULTING FROM THE HURRICANE[1]

by H. H. Bennett

The tropical hurricane that swept across New England on September 21, 1938, caused damage and destruction variously estimated at from a quarter to a half billion dollars. Appraisals of the loss have been dramatized largely in terms of human suffering and damage to buildings, telephone and telegraph lines, highways, forests, and crops. Less dramatic, but even more destructive, was the damage done to the land itself.

1. Geog. Rev., vol. 29 (1939), pp. 196-204.

Throughout the storm-swept area thousands of acres of rich farmland was literally ripped apart by the force of the rains and floodwaters. In the states most seriously affected--Connecticut, Massachusetts, Rhode Island, Vermont, and, of the Middle Atlantic States, New Jersey--it is estimated that about five million acres of cropland was exposed to the full force of the storm. Because the rains and floodwaters struck at a time when many fields had been bared by harvest or for the fall seeding, there were few impediments to the wholesale removal of surface soil. All sloping fields suffered severe soil losses except where adequately protected by vegetation.

Surveys of damage done to harvested and growing crops have placed the loss of tobacco at about 6,000,000 pounds, or almost 25 per cent of the total production forecast for the area. Some 150,000 bushels of onions were destroyed or seriously damaged. About 4,000,000 bushels of applies, more than half of the estimated New England crop, were blown from the trees, at heavy loss to the owners. About a fourth of the apple trees were damaged to some extent, and 10 per cent are considered a total loss.

Damage to forests was even more severe. According to the latest revised estimates of state and federal forestry officials, from 3 to 4 billion board feet of timber, or about one-eighth of the total annual cut of the whole country, was leveled by the force of the hurricane.

In terms of permanent loss to the region, the wholesale removal of productive soil may equal the total of all other costs imposed by the storm. Buildings, telephone and telegraph lines, highways, bridges, and even the forests can be restored or the damage minimized by salvage. But the thousands of tons of productive topsoil, sluiced into the streams and rivers, are gone forever. This cream of fertile farmlands not only was removed from upland fields but was deposited on lower cultivated lands and in and along drainageways. The future well-being of numerous farms and orchards throughout the seriously affected areas has been permanently impaired.

THE RAINFALL

The general meteorology of the storm has already been described.[1] Some further discussion of precipitation is necessary here. Use will be made of records of the automatic rain gauges maintained by the Soil Conservation Service in connection with its demonstration projects. At Moorestown, N.J., rain started on September 18 and continued through September 22. The heaviest rainfalls occurred on the 20th (3.45 inches), the 21st (1.41 inches), and the 22nd (2.51 inches); the total rainfall during the five days of the storm was 7.94 inches. The greatest intensity occurred on September 20, when 1 1/2 inches of rain fell in 45 minutes just

---

1. *pp. 187 - 192 above.*

before noon. The rain on September 21 and 22 was nearly continuous, but there was only one period of marked intensity, when 0.35 inch fell in about 20 minutes.

The most serious erosion in west-central New Jersey occurred on September 22, under a rainfall of 2 1/2 inches in about six hours. As the surface soil was already very wet, locally almost semifluid, the sudden downpour was able to remove a larger amount of material than would normally be expected with this intensity of precipitation.

Precipitation records maintained in connection with the soil-and-water-conservation project at Freehold, N.J., show that excessive rainfall began on September 19 and continued with few interruptions until 4:15 p.m. on the 21st. Periods of great intensity occurred on the 19th and on the afternoon of the 20th. The heaviest continuous rainfall lasted from 5:00 to 9:00 p.m. on the 20th, when a total of 1.47 inches fell. On September 21 rain fell almost continuously between 9:00 a.m. and 4:30 p.m.; the total fall was 3.9 inches. It was during this period of heavy rainfall that the highest wind velocity occurred, beginning at about 2:00 p.m. and continuing until about 6:00 p.m.

Observers who were in the field at the time state that wind, water, and soil all traveled together and that in some places soil was actually moved uphill over gentle slopes and across divides, to be washed away into streams on the leeward side of the crest. In many places grooving or striation of the surface soil, in the direction of the wind, was observable. It is estimated that figures which ordinarily would be used to indicate intensity of precipitation should be at least doubled in order to express the force of this wind-driven sheet of water. In this locality the rainfall from September 19 to 22 inclusive was heavy enough to saturate the surface soil on all but the sandiest lands. This rainfall together with the high wind velocity created conditions favorable to extreme soil erosion. It was also noticeable that normal differences in the capacity of soils to absorb water were almost obliterated and that sandy soils and loam soils were about equally affected by immediate runoff. Possibly this unusual soil behavior was partly due to the spreading of fine earth by the storm in such a way as to seal the surface pores of both sandy-loam and loam soils; but probably it was also partly due to the added erosive action of the wind-driven rain. Water and sand were both carried with the wind. Large amounts of sand and some gravel were washed into numerous hollows and across roadways.

On the Scantic River soil-and-water-conservation demonstration project, along the boundary between Connecticut and Massachusetts and immediately east of the Connecticut River, the precipitation record showed a rainfall of 0.5 inches on the afternoon of September 17, 0.6 on September 18, 2.5 inches on September 19, 6.9 inches on September 20, and 4.6 inches on September 21, when the hurricane swept with full force up the Connecticut valley. The total rainfall for the five days before and during the hurricane was slightly more than 15 inches, as compared with a normal average for the month of 3 1/2 inches. As in the New Jersey areas, the soil was already saturated, or almost saturated, before the greatest intensity of rainfall and wind velocity occurred.

The greatest intensities occurred on September 20, when 1.7 inches of rain fell in 80 minutes, and on September 21, when 1.2 inches fell in 60 minutes. Soil-erosion damage, therefore, was primarily due to the continuous downpours and high wind velocity rather than to extreme intensity.

EROSION DAMAGE

Damage to fields ranged all the way from deep gullying to the removal of an inch or more of topsoil more or less evenly from entire fields. On hundreds of acres of potato land, erosion of the latter type--sheet washing--was so severe that fields seemed to be in the stage of harvest. Potatoes were scattered over the ground surface much as if they had been freshly dug. Over large areas, growing crops of all kinds were washed out of the ground and carried along with the soil. In other places, crops were buried under deposits of mud, sand, and gravel that were spread out over lower slopes and bottom lands by runoff from the adjacent slopes or by floodwater from the unconfined streams.

Soil losses were particularly heavy in the Connecticut Valley, in Massachusetts, Vermont, and the coastal-plain and piedmont areas of New Jersey. Near Hartford, Conn., rainfall center of the storm, gullying and the less spectacular sheet erosion took a heavy toll. On one farm, typical of hundreds in the Connecticut Valley and adjacent areas torrential rains falling before and during the hurricane cut a gully more than 1000 feet long across a field of potatoes and tobacco. On the same farm about an inch of topsoil was swept more or less cleanly from a 7-acre tobacco field. This and the soil removed by gullying possibly amounted together to more than 1000 tons.

The intensively farmed areas along the Connecticut Valley were most severely eroded. About 175,000 acres in Connecticut and 125,000 acres in Massachusetts are under continuous cultivation of tobacco, onions, potatoes, and a variety of truck crops. These special-crop lands have an estimated value in Connecticut of at least $50,000,000 and in Massachusetts of more than $30,000,000. It is believed that these valley areas lost at least $3,000,000 by the removal of surface soil from upland fields (Fig. 19) and its deposition over lower areas and in stream channels. In the rest of the two states stream-bank erosion constituted the chief damage, probably amounting to about $500,000 in terms of soil loss. The cost of soil losses in Rhode Island has not been estimated, since only scattered portions of the cultivated land were bare during the storm and erosion was severe only locally.

Like the Connecticut Valley, the area of intensive agriculture in central New Jersey, from Raritan Bay to the Delaware River and down its estuary to Delaware Bay, suffered severe soil losses. Potatoes constitute the chief crop, but some 40 other truck crops

Fig. 19. "Severe erosion damage to bare cropland, near Hartford, Conn. This field of highly productive loam soil had been plowed downhill instead of on the contour". The author of the study in the field.

Fig. 19 is included as an example of photographs showing the texture of landscape elements at the scale of human sight and occupance.

are grown for the near-by metropolitan markets, and the area also has an intensively farmed orchard belt. Probably more than 150,000 acres in this area lost on an average half an inch of topsoil or more an acre. A conservative estimate of the cost of this soil loss would be at least 15 dollars an acre; hence the cost of the direct loss from sheet and rill erosion in New Jersey can be placed at $2,250,000. In addition, many fields and orchards were so badly gullied that they cannot be reclaimed on a practical basis for any intensive form of agriculture. If the damage caused by gullying is added to that caused by sheet and rill erosion, it is probable that the total soil loss in central New Jersey amounts to more than $3,000,000. In some of the orchard lands the surface soil and the subsoil were completely cut away and the underlying beds of gravel left exposed. Trees were deprived of their support, and hundreds were blown over.

The greatest soil losses in the New England areas occurred on unprotected fields with slopes of about 2 to 10 per cent. Slopes of 15 per cent or more are rarely cultivated intensively but are grass-covered or in brush or timber. Consequently they did not suffer severe soil losses as a result of the storm. In the New Jersey area practically all slopes of more than 5 per cent and many slopes of 2 to 5 per cent were seriously damaged wherever the soil was completely exposed through the harvesting of crops, and it has been estimated that at least two-thirds of the cultivated land in the central New Jersey area was thus exposed.

Erosion was not confined to farmlands. Hundreds of miles of surfaced and nonsurfaced highways were seriously damaged by the cutting away of embankments, the undermining of roadbeds, and the overwash of debris. Highway engineers have estimated that it will require six to seven months to clear the Mohawk Trail alone of erosional debris and to restore it properly for traffic. Railroad right of ways were also badly eroded.

Although in the past New England farmers generally have not considered soil erosion a major agricultural problem, the September storm showed clearly that soil wastage is becoming increasingly serious throughout the region. Soil surveys made in the Connecticut Valley thirty years ago revealed not a single gullied or soil-stripped field. Hundreds of such fields exist today, and soil removal is proceeding at an accelerating rate. The same thing is true of the coastal-plain area of New Jersey and other areas in the Northeast.

SOIL CONSERVATION IN THE NORTHEAST

Data gathered over several years at soil-and-water-conservation experiment stations show clearly that eroded land is subject to greater soil and water losses than land with all or most of its original surface soil in place. Continuous planting of open-tilled crops, regardless of the condition of the soil, is ruinous. Constant stirring of the soil, in addition to exposing it to erosion, causes a loss of the organic matter necessary to keep it porous and absorptive.

Observations made on the demonstration projects of the Soil Conservation Service at Moorestown and Freehold, N.J., and in the Scantic River Valley of Connecticut and Massachusetts revealed sharp contrasts with the heavy soil losses suffered elsewhere in the storm area. Within these project areas, where farmers have adopted modern soil-and-water-conservation practices, the fields either were wholly undamaged or were only slightly eroded. Practically no fields having a surface slope of 5 per cent or less were materially affected where such practices as contour strip cropping and terracing had been adopted and where damage by off-flowage from higher lands was prevented by diversion terraces. Soil movement was restricted to a very small amount within the limits of the strips or terrace intervals, and practically no completed structures were damaged to any important extent.

In the Winooski River project in northern Vermont, where stream-bank erosion has been one of the chief problems confronting the farmers, no new riverbank washouts were discovered where protective devices had been installed on the lands of cooperating farmers. Not a single case of riverbank loss was discovered on the farms of cooperators where stream banks were protected by mats and small willows. Riprap structures were intact. On one farm tree barricades more than 1000 feet long held the stream within the channel. There was no evidence of deposition of silt on the bottom lands of this farm, though gravel and sand had been deposited there in previous high-water stages. Where gully structures had been installed and trees planted, gullies had not spread or deepened. Even river-bottom fields that had been planted in crop strips at right angles to the usual flow of the current did not show any cutting or erosion. Thus, under widely differing conditions of storm attack on the uplands, on slopes to streams, and on the stream banks themselves, these farming practices and engineering structures proved their efficiency under the severest of tests.

Broad-base, wide-channel terraces were particularly effective in retarding surface runoff and disposing of large volumes of water which otherwise would have caused enormous soil losses. In the demonstration area near Rockville, Conn., farmers reported that field terraces supported by contour cultivation and strip cropping on a rotation basis had reduced soil losses to a minimum. Only in a few places, usually where terrace systems were incomplete or where the structures had not had time enough to settle and become stable, was even slight erosion damage reported. Where crop rows had been run across fields, on the contour, soil losses were negligible, though the grooves between the rows were silted, in some places almost to capacity. Strips of close-growing crops planted between strips of tobacco, corn, and other open-tilled crops likewise checked surface runoff and caught large quantities of topsoil washed from the open-tilled strip immediately above. In many places water moved slowly and evenly in terrace channels for two to ten hours after rainfall had ceased. The safe and orderly movement of the surface water permitted maximum absorption by the soil and at the same time wihheld enormous quantities that would otherwise have been dumped into streams at a time when they were nearing flood stage.

During the September storm countless secondary streams in New England went on flood rampages. To some degree, future flood hazards along these streams have been increased by erosion resulting from the storm. Each new gully is now a "wet-weather" tributary of the nearest creek or stream. Land from which the absorptive surface soil has been stripped away will shed more rain water.

Near Freehold, N.J., where some 150 farmers in the watershed of Manalapan Brook are cooperating with the Soil Conservation Service in demonstrating practical soil-and-water-conservation measures on about 15,000 acres, work already completed was remarkably effective in reducing soil losses and retarding surface runoff. As in Connecticut, completed work in this area emphasized the importance of upstream water retardation in comprehensive flood-control operations.

C H A P T E R   12

Derivatives of
Type 4 (Explanatory Human)

Explanatory human geography has not developed
into a science as was hoped by its proponents
fifty years ago.   But it has been followed by
derivatives of continuing significance.

The   undeniable,   overwhelming   influence   of
forces of nature on human life in natural catas-
trophes has been mentioned as a continuing subject of study in geography, particularly from a
physical geographical viewpoint.   This has been
illustrated in the studies of a New England
hurricane and soil erosion by Brooks and Bennett
in the preceding chapter. (Derivatives of type 3,
Explanatory Physical).[1]

A more direct sequel to anthropogeography as
a study of environmental influence on human life
(type 4) appears in physiographic climatology
as carried on by the Environmental Protection
Research Division of the U.S. Quartermaster
Corps[2] in testing the influence of different climatic conditions on soldiers variously equipped.
This seems to follow a suggestion made by C.
O. Sauer in 1925 implying that environmentalism or human ecology as a study of human
tropisms might have a respectable place in bio-
physics.[3]   The work is mainly biological lab-

1. *187-199 above.*
2. *Research & Engineering Center, Natick, Mass.*
3. *C.O. Sauer: "The Morphology of Landscape", in* <u>*Univ. of Calif. Publ. in Geog.,*</u>
    vol. 2 (1925), p. 52.

oratory research, and no geographical field study has been found available for inclusion here.

Another line of study traceable back to environmental interpretation (type 4) is that of sequent occupance, defined and pursued by D. S. Whittlesey, who was inspired by the anthropogeography of Miss Semple and the historical geography and human ecological adjustment of H. H. Barrows.[1] The clear and timely purpose of sequent occupance is to bring the time–differences of history into a static areal frame of geography. Semple, Barrows and Whittlesey were all students of history, and in studies of sequent occupance the concept of culture and historical culture process is that of history rather than that of anthropology.

"The Kankakee 'Marsh' of Northern Indiana and Illinois" by A. H. Meyer, 1935, is taken as representative of studies in sequent occupance. This was made in full view of the first six types before 1930. It reflects ideas of direct environmental relations (type 4) in their least deterministic form, as human adjustment to and of the environment. In addition it has a background of physical geography (type 3) and economic analysis (type 5), and makes good use of areal uniformity and diversity (type 6).

The field method is one of comprehensive and well prepared reconnaissance using devices

1. *"Geography as Human Ecology"* in Annals A.A.G., vol. 13 (1923), pp. 1-14.

from any of the stages before the last two. The
writing is addressed to an audience of scholars
interested in geography and the social sciences.

THE KANKAKEE "MARSH" OF
NORTHERN INDIANA AND ILLINOIS [1]
by A. H. Meyer

SEQUENT OCCUPANCE FORMS AND FUNCTIONS

The transformation of the Kankakee "haven of wild life" into a "modern home for man" may be treated under four stages of
settlement: (1) the period of the Indian hunter and the French
trader; (2) the immigration of the pioneer trapper and the frontier
farmer; (3) the epoch of the stock farmer and the sportsman fowl-
er; and, finally, (4) the present joint occupancy by the Corn Belt
farmer and the river resorter. These stages have been graphically synthesized in the Silhouette Study (Fig. 20).

The first two stages are characterized essentially by human
adjustment to the environment. The last one dominantly exhibits
human adjustment of the environment. The third is characteristically expressive of a transitional condition in which the hitherto
dictating influences of the marsh-swamp fundament became progressively weaker as the drainage net was perfected, leaving only
remnants of the naturally induced culture forms reminiscent of an
older and much more romantic period.

The Pottawatomie's Kankakee
(--1840)

The French explorers, Charlevoix, La Salle, Tonti, and
Father Hennepin, were the first to give an account of the characteristics of the Kankakee region. This valley they entered at
its source near South Bend, Indiana, after experiencing much difficulty in locating the portage between the St. Joseph River, up
which they had ascended from Lake Michigan, and the source of
the Kankakee, which they regarded as the headwaters of the Illinois River. Here they came into contact with the Pottawatomie
Indian, who found the marsh a refuge against the ferocious Ire-
quois of the East.

1. _Papers of Mich. Acad. Science, Arts & Letters_, vol. 21 (1935), pp. 366-395.

THE POTTAWATOMIE'S KANKAKEE (–1840)

THE PIONEER'S KANKAKEE (1840–80)

THE RANCHER'S AND THE RECREATIONIST'S KANKAKEE (1880–1910)

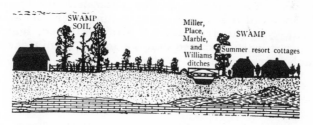

THE RECLAMATIONIST'S AND THE RESORTER'S KANKAKEE of the twentieth century (1910–)

Fig. 20 Part of "a Silhouette Study in Sequent Occupance of the Kankakee Marsh".

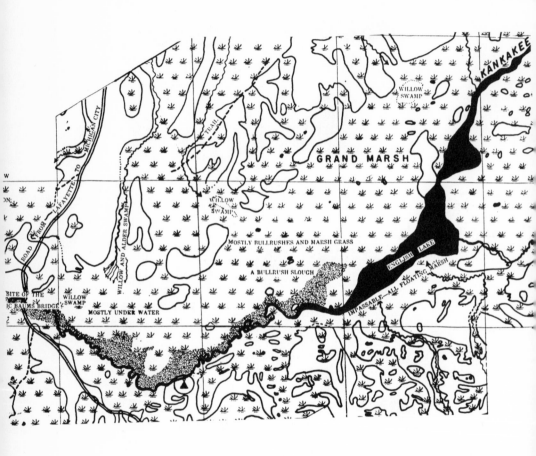

Fig. 21. Part of a map of "Fundament of the Kankakee Marsh". Uplands (white), water (black), swamp timber (grey), marsh (herb symbol). Scale: 1 inch to 4 miles.

While some of the Indians appear to have settled more or less permanently on the marsh margin or on islands within the marsh or swamp, the majority seem to have migrated back and forth, in summer occupying the marginal moraine or Lake Michigan plain, and in winter retiring to the swamp (or marsh) island, (Fig. 20).

At least six river, or near-river, island encampments are shown on the original Federal surveyors' plats.

Besides transportation, the river situation, like that of the Lake Michigan trading posts, favored communication with the French fur traders, who likewise came to use the swamp island sites as home and headquarters for carrying on their own trapping as well as for trafficking with the natives.

Encampments

Ball reports a number of camps of Indians: "In the winter of 1835-36 about 600 had an encampment in the West Creek woodlands, where deer were abundant, and an encampment was there again the next winter." Another Indian camping ground was located south of the present Lowell. These would classify as marginal marsh situations, though the exact sites are not given. Among marsh island sites the author mentions Red Oak Island, where in 1837-38 two hundred Indians had a garden and where there were two stores kept by French traders; also Big White Oak Island, south of Orchard Grove, where there was an Indian cemetery. Among the swamp island sites next to the river Werich reports an "Indian Garden" at the mouth of Sandy Hook branch, tributary of the Kankakee (in Porter County), and another "Indian Island" a few miles farther down the river.

Trails and Roads

The trail routes, or pioneer roads, like the camp sites, clearly reflect the influence of the terrain. Three main lines of communication crossed the marsh. Two of the routes, the central and the eastern, followed the sinuous trend of the ridges, where they most nearly approached the river; the one skirting the marsh on the west took advantage of an anticlinal ledge of limestone in the river bed which made fording easy.

The route through the heart of the marsh crossed at the Pottawatomie Ford (Site of Bridge, Fig. 21), which was destined to become the most historic spot along the Kankakee River in the marsh proper. Here was established in 1836 the Eaton Ferry, which transferred the early travelers across the one and one-half mile marsh between the Porter County sandy upland area and the sand-ridge landing in Jasper County on the side of the river opposite.

The epoch of Indian occupation may be said to close with 1840. By the treaties of 1832 and 1836 with the Federal Government the Pottawatomies relinquished their claims to the lands of

northwest Indiana. A few were permitted to remain, those that
had been especially friendly to the authorities, but these were
absorbed in the pioneer trapper group of the next epoch, which
we have dated from 1840 to 1880.

The Pioneer's Kankakee
(1840-80)

We are told that, after the initial marsh invasion by a sprink-
ling of French trappers and traders, the "upper basin of the Kankakee River was slowly taken over by the Danish and Swedish,
and the lower by the English and some Germans". Ball, in speaking of the settlement of northwest Indiana, especially of the latitude
of the Kankakee and north thereof, designates as the chief sources
of immigration New England, New York, Pennsylvania, Ohio, Canada,
the British Isles, Germany, Holland, and Scandinavian countries,
with a few from south and central Indiana. Werich refers specifically to the year 1833 as the time of the advent of the first white
families from the East, the Morgans and the Dyes of Ohio, who
settled in the neighborhood of Sandy Hook, referred to above
(Fig. 21). By the early 'fifties a number of pioneers had settled
north of Knox, Starke County.

Though the immigrant farmer had a more or less fixed habitat, the pioneer squatter commonly practiced seasonal migration. He lived in a shanty on an island in the marsh or swamp
during the winter trapping and hunting season (Fig. 20) and removed to the margin of the marsh in the summer, where he
might "hire out" as a "farm hand" or find some kind of job in
town.

The island, though lonely, served its homesite function well.
The sand base insured perfect drainage at all times; its vegetation,
consisting of an upper story of oaks, a lower scrub growth, and a
ground cover of bush and herb, prevented the island from being
blown away; the formation, a natural aquifer, provided a whole-
some and abundant supply of water, naturally filtered; the timber furnished shelter and firewood; the ground cover often included dense growths of huckleberry and blueberry. As previously
pointed out, this site had every advantage for exploiting game,
fur, and subsistence food products.

Home of the Squatter Trapper

The typical trapper of the Kankakee occupied a shanty of
one or two rooms most simply constructed of unfinished lumber
and usually with a single entrance. It appears to have been a
common practice for trappers to move about, remaining on one
spot for only a few years, then going to another island, where a
new shanty would be erected. Occasionally a more substantial
structure would be built in the form of the familiar frontier log
cabin.

The distribution of such primitive shelters was of the most scattered type, a pattern definitely related to the dispersion of the island sites themselves. In the early days the population was exceedingly sparse; later on, when the trapping business assumed greater commercial importance, more trappers were attracted, until restrictive measures were adopted, including separate "trapping claims" laid out at right angles to the river.

The revenue derived from game resources during this period can be only roughly estimated, on the basis of hunters' reports. Muskrats supplied by far the greatest bulk of fur marketed, but brought the low price of from 3 to 15 cents per pelt. However, what the pelts lacked in individual value was offset by their overwhelming numbers and ease of exploitation. It is reported that a trapper found muskrat houses so numerous that three or four could be speared from one position of the boat. Another trapper states that, after the great marsh fire in 1871, (incidentally the year of the great Chicago fire), he sometimes caught in a single night more than 80 "rats" in a line of 100 traps. In Lake County alone the annual catch during the period from 1834 to 1884 is said to have averaged between 20,000 and 40,000.

Farm Economy of the Frontier

Farm economy, such as there was, and fur exploitation went hand in hand during the frontier occupance of the Kankakee. So closely were they associated that the form and function of the settlement of one were only a slight modification of the form and function of the other. The typical frontier farmer was also a hunter, and in no small measure supplemented his income and diet with the wild products of the marsh and swamp.

Though the ideal site of the trapper seems to have been a rather heavily wooded dune island in close proximity to marsh, swamp, and river, that of the farmer probably was the marsh margin, or marsh islands near the margin, and particularly those with a somewhat heavier soil.

Perhaps the outstanding fact of sequent occupance and utilization of farm lands in the Kankakee from the earlier days down to the present is the progressive expansion from the higher and drier, though generally much poorer, island and ridge soils to the lower and generally increasingly fertile soil types as they became available by drainage. This does not mean that the general agricultural development necessarily involved the abandonment, by the early settlers, of the original, and in some respects still preferred, sites of settlement. It is, rather, expressive of the areal spread of occupation as related to the growing drainage net and the early island sites, which represent the original nuclear farmstead attachments in the area. "There was the usual tendency to occupy first the lighter and the forested soils, because they were easier to handle with the primitive instruments employed than the heavier soils and prairie lands, and in addition, the timbered areas furnished game, firewood, and building material."

Wild grasses and sedges figured very significantly in the simple farm economy. They constituted the chief, if not the only, source of hay as well as pasturage. If the season favored the farmer, he might without much difficulty harvest the hay by a hand scythe or a mower. But should it be a wet summer, sleds, drawn by horses shod with sandal-like shoes, had to be used to haul the hay out of the marsh; or it was carried out on a pair of poles by two individuals walking tandem fashion. If it was impossible to reach the farmstead, the hay was temporarily stacked on an island near by and removed later to the farm premises when conditions permitted. Sometimes it had to be cut on the ice, which resulted in forage of rather inferior quality.

The farm routine of pioneer days was characteristically built up around the seasonal offerings of nature: in spring and fall, wild-fowling; in summer, wild-haying, fishing, and huckleberrying; in fall and winter, trapping, hunting, and chopping wood. The growing of corn, possibly supplemented by wheat and oats, and the planting of potatoes and other garden vegetables, together with a little ditching by hand in summer, and perhaps some timber clearing in the winter, rounded out the season's program. Ditching as a legally controlled enterprise received attention as early as 1852, and ditching by hand was reported in Lake County in 1854. But not until steam dredges had been brought into operation in 1884 was there any considerable progress made in drainage. So the ditch may be said to be the key to an understanding of the economy of the Kankakee, of its chronologically and chorographically integrated forms and functions, just as in most regions roads furnish the index to regional development. With systematic ditching came systematic road building and the development of a coordinated ditch-road settlement pattern, which chiefly characterizes the next two periods.

The Recreationist's and the Rancher's Kankakee
(1880-1910)

The erection of large clubhouses for sportsmen (1878-79); the introduction of large herds of cattle for range feeding by Nels Morris, the Chicago packer, and by others (1880); the use of the steam dredge for the first time in the Kankakee (1884) -- these may be taken as basic criteria for the recognition of a new epoch. By this time, we are told, nearly all old trappers had left the marsh. "Rats" and certain other fur-bearing animals were still abundant, but pelts were cheap, though some forms of animal life were becoming scarce if not actually exterminated, as in the case of deer (last one reported shot in 1880). But wild fowl and fish seemed as plentiful as ever and attracted large numbers of sportsmen from far and near, who found the marshes and river a veritable "hunter's and fisherman's paradise." Whereas this form of the recreation industry expressed itself in seasonal boom days for the otherwise thinly settled river territory, the stage was all set for a reclamation program of the marginal marshes. This involved at first ditch drainage, primarily to convert the wild-hay marshes into cattle ranges and grain fields to support a livestock industry.

Ditch digging, now expedited by the steam dredge, also facilitated road building, for the ditch spoil bank itself often served as an elevated roadbed of porous sands and gravel, excellently drained and passable throughout the year. Railroads which were constructed across the swamp and marshes as early as the 'fifties and the 'sixties merely to connect the older and more settled and better developed Hoosier communities downstate with the coming metropolis of Chicago now actually figured in the Kankakee development along agricultural and recreational lines.

The "Hunter's Paradise"

Railroads thus opened up the once-secluded frontier empire of "fur, fowl, and fin" to the sportsmen of distant cities as well as of communities near by. As individuals and as organized clubs they came in numbers from Boston, New York, Philadelphia, Washington, Chicago and other large cities. Though the sportsman's presence in the Kankakee is a matter now largely of a most glorious and romantic history, a few geographic landmarks remain: the abandoned Louisville Clubhouse near Baum's Bridge, where stands the historically famous relict houseboat of Lewis Wallace of Ben Hur fame; the Diana Club House near Thayer; the Alpine Clubhouse near English Lake; and the Cumberland Lodge in southern Lake County. The first three represent river sites characteristic of the times (Fig. 20). The last has a marginal marsh-island, oak-grove situation.

Several considerations appear to have influenced the clubhouse sites. In the first place, the river itself was a most potent factor, if one may judge from the distribution pattern. It had its own peculiar charm in its beautiful winding and wooded course. By it many a hunter, fisherman, and river resorter entered the region. The general situation gave ready accessibility to both the hunting and the fishing grounds. Clubhouses, however, were not scattered at random along the river, but usually were located at points of vantage representing either favorable dry and elevated sites or transportation advantages of a road or a railroad crossing the river. The combined influence of communication and favorable drainage conditions is illustrated by the agglomeration of clubhouses and tent camps which were at Shelby and at Water Valley. At the latter site, still a popular summer resort, were the Chicago Sportsman Club, the Capitol Club of Indianapolis, the Indianapolis, the Rensselaer, and the Dally clubs, with the Diana Club just south of the river. The Baum's Bridge clubhouse site illustrates by way of general situation the potent influence of the tongue of high and ever-dry sandy upland "Plainfield" soils, extending southward to the river. This, together with a similar elevated belt on the south side of the river, forms a sort of ridge that bridges the marsh (Fig. 21).

A most important trail of the aborigine, this crossroads of the river, swamp, and marsh was instrumental in making Baum's resort famous. Here located the clubs of Louisville, Pittsburgh, Rockville, Terre Haute, and Indianapolis. ...

The Swamp and Marsh "Natural" Industries

Lumbering

The axe encroaching on the swamp, the sickle advancing into the marsh, the barbed-wire fence enclosing the range, the plow breaking up the prairie sod where the stream dredge had dug wide and deep drainage ditches river-bound -- these are additional expressions of the human occupance of this period which we shall now consider.

Lumbering, already started in the last epoch, attained its greatest yet rather restricted development during this period. Among the most enterprising sawmillers at this time was A. H. Ahlgrim, who built sawmills successively near Thayer, Roselawn, and Water Valley. He still resides at Water Valley where he now operates a summer cottage resort.

As early as 1875 logs were rafted down the Kankakee River to Momence, and, since the timber swamp adjoins the river, this would seem to have been an ideal situation. But river rafting did not prove any too practicable, owing to the tortuous and snag - infested channel. The numerous spikes which had to be used to secure the rafts often proved a menace to the sawmiller. In the course of time stationary and then portable mills came to be located at the source of timber, the latter being particularly useful in the small and scattered oak-grove "islands".

The swamp elm, ash, maple, pin oak, and burr oak constituted the chief species marketed from the swamp. On the sand knobs and ridges white oak was extensively exploited. Fence posts and firewood have taken their share of the timber toll. The "setting out of fires" has reclaimed some of the swamp land for agriculture, but extensive tracts of fired timber are unutilized and present a pitiable spectacle of despoliation.

Marsh Haying

Marsh-hay exploitation at this time was a commercial venture on a large scale. With the subsidence of the high spring floods about the first of May the wild sedges and grasses were ready to be cut in July and August. What was not summer-pastured, or fed locally as winter forage, was baled by large steam presses and exported. The varieties of short and long, tender and tough sedges and grasses adapted the hay to various uses. From the upper shallower marsh sites and along the "islands" was cut the shorter, tender, more succulent, and nutritious feeding hay; the lower deeper marshes yielded rank and tough growths, which were shipped, to Chicago, for example, as bedding or packing hay.

Stock Grazing

The marsh-hay pastures and the "island" oak groves invited a cattle economy which was developed first and foremost by Nels Morris, the Chicago packer. Practically all the true Kankakee marsh and swamp lands of Jasper County and northeast Newton County, totaling 23,000 acres, were taken over by him. Thousands of head of cattle, many from Texas, were shipped in and grazed on tracts fenced into units the size of a section or so, imparting the aspect of a western ranch with its picturesque professional cowpuncher.

Other ranches included the well-known Brown estate in southern Lake County, partly protected from flood by a privately constructed dike or "levee"; and another ranch of about 5,000 acres near Thayer, Newton County.

The Reclamationist's and the Resorter's Kankakee
(1910--)

The Kankakee is a quandary. If one were to ask today "What does the Kankakee represent?" the answer would probably be one of two opposing types: (1) It represents a land that "God forgot to finish," a man-reclaimed area of extraordinary fertility; (2) It represents a manhandled marsh, a failure as a reclamation project, a substitution of unproductive lands for the most ideally adjusted wild-life forms of plant and animal, so essential to the nation's conservation program. A survey of the physical and cultural setup should help in clarifying the situation. The regional quality of the Kankakee may be assayed (1) by comparing it with its neighboring morainal uplands and (2) by taking a qualitative-quantitative inventory of the resources of its component divisions. ...

The area as delineated represents the river territory of some 620 square miles embraced within the so-called "Kankakee Grain and Pasture" agricultural division of northwest Indiana. This division practically coincides with the sandy "Maumee-Plainfield-Newton-Muck" soil province, to which the Kankakee proper adds the Swamp. Once an ancient lake bottom, the far-flung Kankakee terrain, interrupted only locally by sand knobs and ridges, conduced to readiness of cultivation in large field units. Quarter or half sections of corn divided by few fence lines are not uncommon. Large level field units favor tractor farming, and make for large farms, many of them a half section or more, as compared with the quarter-section farm on the rolling rimming moraine. But large farms involve large investments, particularly in the case of virgin bottom land held at initial high figures and subject to drainage assessments. The result is that the larger Kankakee farms show an extraordinarily high percentage of tenant operators, as high as 85-90 per cent in some localities, whereas on the neighboring uplands one half or more of the farms are operator-owned. Combined frequently with uncertain or short-term leases, such a system conduces to a more or less exploitative type of grain farming, without proper regard for the place of the animal industries in helping to maintain soil productivity. Once famous for its large ranches of beef cattle, the Kankakee today is noted for its cereal culture. Livestock consists chiefly of small dairy herds normally ranging from six to a dozen head and of swine about twice that number. The swing in latter years to dairying in the form of whole-milk production reflects the proximate position of the Kankakee with respect to Chicago. Its more distant position and poorer quality of pasture, however, put it at a certain disadvantage as against the closer competing areas. ...

The Physical Setting

Drainage System

As pointed out above, the chorographic development of the Kankakee is a function of the drainage ditch, without which the expansion of agriculture would have been impossible.

Dug by hand in pioneer days, then by oxen and horses, and finally by steam dredge, introduced at the beginning of the last epoch (1884), drainage ditches were extended farther and farther from the marsh margin into the river swamp. The Kankakee River itself finally was straightened in Indiana, first in its headwaters and then all the way to the state line (1906-17). In addition to the drainage ditch, the reclamation system locally includes tile drainage and levee protection (for example, Brown Levee in southern Lake County).

The most remarkable fact about the present drainage set-up is its marked artificial character. This is strikingly expressed by the rectilinear pattern of the numerous ditches with straight angular courses and profiles, frequently accentuated by high-banked spoil ridges flanking the ditches.

The reclamation program utilized in part the original natural channels of stream drainage, which were straightened and enlarged. Much more ditch mileage, however, is represented in the newly dug trenchlike drainage lines which in large areas conform to the regularity of a road pattern. Together these form an elaborate dissection of the Kankakee plain, in which practically each section lies within only a mile, or a mile and a half, of a drainage ditch, whereas the majority of sections regularly have one and occasionally two ditches transecting or flanking them. ...

Agricultural Forms

Crops

"Corn is King" in the Kankakee, apparently occupying more

acreage than all other cultivable crops together. Oats ranks next,
followed by wheat. Both plow pasture and forage crops are close
rivals of wheat for third place. This order likewise expresses the
normal sequence of crop rotation (c-o-w-p) though the cycle may
stop with three or two crops. Thus plow pastures are renewed normally about every fourth year. ...

Pasture and Waste Lands

The Kankakee is identified with the so-called Grain and Pasture region of Indiana. In the Kankakee reclaimed area proper
about one eighth of the cultivable area is in plow or rotation pasture, and with grain shares the better lands, the Maumee and the
Muck. Much of the Kankakee pasturage, however, is relegated to
the marginal, light, rolling and partly wooded Plainfield and closely associated Newton. As much as 25 to 40 per cent of the Plainfield groves is pastured. This type of native pasture is of rather
inferior quality, with a carrying capacity of one grazing unit to
5-10 acres.

A much smaller percentage of the Swamp is used for pasture,
on account of the inadequate drainage and the extensive cover of
timber, brush, and rank weeds.

Contrasting with the regular rectangular grain fields and
plow pasture, the outline of the native pastures is notoriously
irregular, bounding a Plainfield ridge or knoll or enclosing an
irregular brush or stump clearing in the swamp.

While most of the Swamp and much of the Plainfield timbered areas represent practically waste land, the "broken" marsh
and swamp areas have an insignificantly small acreage lying idle.
The small widely scattered units amount to hardly three sections
of all those mapped, or barely two per cent of the whole cultivable
area of the inner Kankakee basin. Even some of this represents
only temporarily fallow fields.

One of the most singular expressions of agricultural adjustments arising from the ditch-digging program in the Kankakee
is the appropriation of ditch water for livestock. A large number
of ditches are sufficiently below the ground water table to offer a
more or less permanent supply of good water, though stagnation
and heavy iron flocculations sometimes result when the water table
gets too low, or when partial clogging of the ditch occurs, as mentioned
above. But ditches were not designed to be "natural watering
troughs" for stock to trample around in; in fact, there appears to
be a regulation against the use of the drainage ditch for this purpose. At any rate, in nearly every case the ditch is outside the
regular pasture bounds, and its water is made available to stock
by extending the fence at certain points part way into the ditch. ...

Regional Subdivision

The Kankakee region may be regarded as made up physio-
graphically of only two consolidated divisions: a narrow but

practically continuous timber swamp in the river bottoms and the extensive marsh prairie of the flat-floored valley. A very general distinction may also be recognized topographically (geographically) between the eastern and western halves in that the former lies higher, has a greater average width but a narrower and finally disappearing swamp; features larger muck areas, with mint culture (altogether absent in the west); and produces proportionately more wheat and truck. On the other hand, practically all the river resorts and amusement centers were and still are in the western half.

Basis for Areal Differentiation

Except for the general divisions given above, the Kankakee does not appear to lend itself to a simple dissection into unified homogeneous units. Subregional treatment rather involves a recognition of a unit form as consisting of small patches of the landscape related in structure and origin, however discontinuous and dispersed they may be. The basis for such areal differentiation is found in the diverse land-soil formations of the valley. Comprising a dozen or more soil types, the soils for purposes of a regional classification may be reduced to five structural classes reflective of land surface as well as soil characteristics -- Plainfield, Newton, Maumee, Swamp, and Muck. ...

Recreation and Conservation

The Swamp represents the last line of retreat for the recreationist. And by the final straightening out of the old meandering Kankakee in Indiana the resorter has lost all but a few remnants of the natural landscape which lends charm to such a river retreat. The name Kankakee itself seems doomed to extinction, since some people now refer to the Miller, Place, Marble, and Williams' ditches instead (Fig. 20).

The deeply trenched and highly banked river ditch, a chain, or two wide, with its rather rapidly moving current and load of sand, has little to offer in the way of river scenery or sport. Once nationally famous for its natural charm, for fishing and boating, the dredged Kankakee of today seems popular locally only for bathing where the current is not too swift. The effect of river straightening on resort developments is strikingly manifested by contrasted conditions on the two sides of the Illinois-Indiana state line. The Illinois Kankakee above Momence, with its essentially unmodified meandering course, can boast of nearly a score of resort establishments. These include some 275 cottages within the short distance of less than a dozen miles of river front; whereas, on the Indiana side, for a distance of over 85 miles, there are hardly a half-dozen resort groups, which number only some 125 cottages, including the unusually large Bohemian resort of about 80 residences. ...

SUMMARY AND CONCLUSIONS

The Kankakee region of northern Indiana represents an intermorainal marsh reclaimed sector of the Corn Belt, with a unique historicogeographic setting.

A study of the conditions of the fundament reveals threefold classification of primary land-surface forms: the herb marsh, the timber swamp, and the uplands consisting in part of sandy "barrens" and dunal oak groves. The uplands made possible the early habitation of the otherwise inhospitable marsh-swamp, a site influence in modified form still conspicuously noticeable in the present reclaimed Kankakee.

After a treaty by the native Pottawatomie with the Federal Government in 1832, providing for the relinquishment of the territory held by the Indian, the marsh wilderness entered upon a century of progress, paralleling the period of urban development of the neighboring metropolis, Chicago, less than fifty miles from its western extremity.

The drama staged in the Kankakee presents a succession of distinct areal scenes and groups of actors. The general theme, as disclosed by the several regional forms of occupance, features a continuous struggle between two forces -- those intent on preserving the wild-life forms of plant and animal for their economic, recreational, and conservational utility, as against the group organized to further the program of reclamation. A network of drainage ditches tributary to the straightened, deepened, and widened Kankakee River attests to the complete dispossession of the former group, except locally along the river ditch.

A regional land-surface and soil survey of the reclaimed Kankakee suggests a fivefold physiographic division based on homogeneity of structural and genetic features. Except for the Swamp, these constitute an otherwise disordered pattern. They include the Plainfield, or farmsteaded "island" and woodlot-pasture formation; the Newton, the Plainfield-Maumee transition; the Maumee, the "cornscape"; Muck, the mint soil; and Swamp, the river-timber formation and resorter's retreat. These constitute approximately 13, 5, 60, 15, and 7 per cent of the area, respectively.

Rural settlement within the area is found to be most remarkably related to the diverse surface and soil influences. Farmsteads average a little less than three per square mile; the proportions of farmhouse distribution for these physiographic divisions approximate 22:1; 9:1; 5:1; 1.5:1; 1:1, respectively. Some four hundred resort cottages are found along the river ditch, mostly along the "natural" Kankakee on the Illinois side.

A sectional grid road system, 55 per cent hard-surfaced, makes for ready internal circulation and external contact with the rim of a score of towns which outline the boundary of the early marsh.

Agitation to restore parts of the once nationally famous "hunter's and fisherman's paradise" raises the questions, "Has the reclamation program justified itself?" and "Is partial marsh restoration practicable?"

Inventory of soils, crops, and occupance conditions seems to prove the general fitness of the Kankakee for agricultural use. The lands of marginal utility or waste areas are included chiefly in the narrow imperfectly drained Swamp, and the local spots of the droughty sandy Plainfield. Yet it is doubtful whether such a grand haven of wild life would ever again be permitted to be despoiled by man.

Salvaging areas for wild life presents both economic and engineering difficulties. Most promising is the swamp tract of some twelve sections of fire-scarred timber, chiefly in northern Jasper County.

In addition to the possible limited expansion of the swamp conservation and resorting program, we may expect other changes in the future: smaller farms, a larger animal industry, particularly dairying, and increased trucking. On the basis of the predicted unprecedented growth of the metropolitan district to the northwest, the Kankakee trucking areas may yet become "The Garden of Chicago."

CHAPTER 13

Derivatives of
Type 5 (Analytical Economic)

Geographic analysis of localized industries and other forms of human activity has gone on vigorously and has involved an increasing number of geographers. It is found in "The Kankakee Marsh" in the previous chapter.

This approach has been applied no less to other industries than to farming. "South Range, Keweenaw Copper Country: a Mining Pattern of Land Occupancy" by R. S. Platt, 1932, is taken as an example of such application to mining. The field method involves reconnaissance observation and systematic inquiry among key personnel. The work was done in view of earlier stages except that of type 8 (Culture Origin) which is not included.

Application of the same approach to manufacturing is represented by "A Classification of Manufactures, Exemplified by Porto Rican Industries", by R. S. Platt, 1927. This is a field study only in the broad sense of having a background of reconnaissance observation in Puerto Rico without mapping or systematic inquiry. The work was done in view of type 5 (Analytical Economic) and without benefit of type 6 (Areal Uniformity), 7 (Areal Organization) or 8 (Culture Origin).

The purpose of the study was to apply the method of analysis of localized human activity to the kind of industry which seemed least directly tied to the natural environment and therefore had troubled geographers looking for simple relationships between man and nature. Studies of the localization of manufacturing are now commonplace, in geography bordering on economics and in economics bordering on geography.

Geographic analysis of human activity extends into the field of planning. "Summary Memorandum on the Bad River Indian Reservation" by R. S. Platt, 1940, is a simple example of geographic field work done for planning purposes. The work was undertaken at the suggestion of the U.S. Office of Indian Affairs and the report was written for that agency. The intention of the study was to make what seems to be an appropriate contribution of geography to planning; namely, to understand natural and human phenomena in an area as they are at the present time before planning to change them into what they should become in the future - starting not with a blank page on which to write but with an existing pattern of life.

The field method is that of observation and inquiry among key personnel in accordance with types 5 (Economic Analysis) and 6 (Areal Uniformity), mapping in accordance with types 6 (Areal Uniformity) and 7 (Areal Organization) and systematic inquiry among inhabitants of the area in accordance with types 7 (Areal Organization) and 8 (Culture Origin). This study is the first example in this series made in view of all the types, including both areal functional process (type 7) and culture process (type 8), a fact which is not made evident in the memorandum itself.[1]

Geographic analysis of localized activity is applicable in political as well as economic geography. A pioneer field study in political geography following a similar approach is: "Geographic and Political Boundaries in Upper Silesia" by R. Hartshorne, 1933. This not only follows ideas of type 5 (Economic Analysis) but also makes use of ideas of areal uniformity and diversity (type 6) in recognizing and recording the localization of relevant phenomena, thus advancing toward solution of a special problem in political geography as a subject in which the phenomena are hardly observable in the visible landscape. Moreover this study deals with phenomena of areal organization and culture clearly and competently, even though this was done without reference to ideas expressed in types 7 and 8.

---

1. An earlier study written to take account more explicitly of all eight types is: "Reconnaissance in British Guiana" in Annals AAG, vol. 29 (1939), pp. 105-126.

SOUTH RANGE, KEWEENAW COPPER COUNTRY:

A MINING PATTERN OF LAND OCCUPANCY[1]

by R. S. Platt

Copper mining in the Keweenaw Peninsula has been discussed in voluminous works from the viewpoints of geology and mining engineering. This article from a geographical viewpoint deals with the mining pattern of a normally developed part of the peninsula, a district that has been responsible for about 13 per cent of the copper output of the region.

FEATURES OF THE PATTERN

The heart of the South Range is a string of mines on the east flank of a range of hills, and in relation of these mines other features of the cultural landscape fit into their respective places (Fig. 22)--stamp mills ten miles to the northwest on the Lake Superior shore, smelter and docks five miles to the northeast on the Portage Lake shore, a railway connecting these focal establishments, villages clustered near them and power plants to serve them--all distributed in the background of hills and valleys and enclosed in a forest frame. . . .

FEATURES RELATED TO DISCOVERY

The most clearly fundamental features of the pattern, the mines themselves, represent the present stage in a solution of the problems of discovering and extracting ore. The mines are few and unevenly distributed; mining operations occupy but small and irregular spaces in the district. These facts reflect circumstances of ore distribution and discovery. Ore bodies are relatively few in number, small and irregular in extent, and unevenly distributed. The process of discovery has had no easy rules for success; discovering ore has been by finding it. Each of the four mines represents a separate, fortunate discovery.

Irregularity, then, is one aspect of mine distribution. But this is within a larger regularity in which definite and orderly arrangement is evident. All the South Range mines are inland from the Lake Superior shore on high land and have a northeast-southwest alignment (Fig. 22). All the ore discoveries have been within a well-defined belt three miles in width extending northeast and southwest--part of a longer belt reaching the full length of the Keweenaw Peninsula, in which many ore bodies have been discovered and many mines established.

1. *Econ. Geog., vol. 8 (1932), pp. 386-399.*

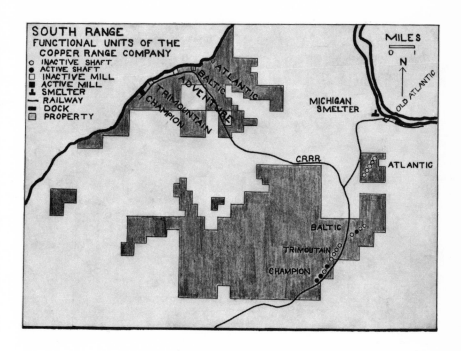

Fig. 22. "Functional units of mining in the South Range area" Lake Superior
shore northwest, Portage Lake waterway northeast.

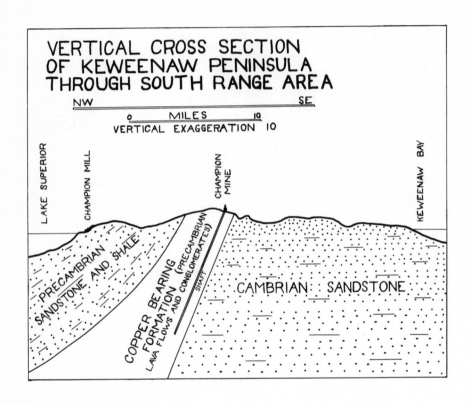

Fig. 23. "Cross section of Keweenaw Peninsula showing surface configuration and underlying formations". Example of a geological device adopted in geography.

Fig. 24. "The four shafts of the Baltic Mine, looking northeast toward Portage Lake. Waste rock piles below shaft houses, southeast part of village at extreme right". The line of shafts follows the strike of the copper-bearing formation and the slope of each shaft house follows the dip. The shaft house is a focal establishment in the functional pattern of organization.

Fig. 24 is included as an example of photographs showing individual features of nature and culture on the scale of human sight and occupance in their site associations. It does not show the generalized uniform areas of a landscape map.

This picture might serve to illustrate a study made according to any of the eight types. Actually the work was done in the light of the first seven types, and the picture viewed in connection with traverse, areal survey, land forms, environmental adjustment, economic analysis, areal uniformity and areal organization. The study was not made in the light of type 8 (Culture Origin) and so the shaft house was not properly appreciated as among cultural immobilia of the Occidental industrial realm introduced here from a North Atlantic culture hearth, modified in detail by local invention in the Copper Country.

Fig. 25. "Aerial view of the three more southerly mines and villages, the commercial village of South Range, and the central railway junction. (Courtesy of Abrams Aerial Survey, Lansing, Michigan)".

Fig. 25 is included as an example of incidental use of a photographic mosaic from aerial survey, in connection with field study. This shows on a small scale some features of the pattern of occupance as in a map of areal organization, and some distinctions of areal uniformity and diversity as in a landscape mosaic map, through accidental symbolism in shades of gray, black and white. At this scale the same row of shaft houses as in Fig. 24 appears as a row of dots within the larger pattern.

Since then (1932) photographs from aerial surveys have been used systematically as a tool in connection with geographic field study done on the ground, particularly in the survey of landscape uniformity and diversity (type 6), as in the Tennessee Valley Authority.

This belt is the backbone of the peninsula, formed by the outcrop of resistant rocks dipping steeply northwest (Fig. 23). In most places the rock does not outcrop literally at the surface but is covered with a mantle of glacial drift varying in depth from place to place. The copper bearing series is for the most part of rocks containing a mere trace of copper, basic igneous rocks formed by Pre-Cambrian lava flows on a horizontal surface and later tilted to their present position. These layers of basalt are massive and relatively impervious, with the exception of a few in which the upper part originally became porous as a result of gas bubbles and cracks made during rapid cooling of the lava flow surface, and with the exception also of a few interbedded strata of conglomerate and some subsequent fissures through the rocks.

The spaces in these thin pervious layers are now filled with mineral matter, apparently deposited by water rising from below after the rocks had been tilted to their present position. Most of the mineral deposit is worthless--but a small fraction of it is copper, almost pure copper, in fragments ranging in size from invisible specks to enormous masses, associated with various other minerals some deposited before copper and others after in a series of replacements, concentrated where the lode has been particularly pervious to great depths and practically absent elsewhere.

Thus it appears that the copper lies within a rock series limited by a persistent fault on the southeast and by overlying sedimentary rocks on the northwest; that within these rocks copper is practically confined to about 1 per cent of the thickness of the series in a few well-recognized lodes and associated fissures; that along these lodes copper has been found concentrated in a limited space within a much greater extent of unproductive lode rock, and that the significant concentrations form ore bodies averaging about 1 per cent copper.

These facts of orderly arrangement in the distribution of ore bodies condition not only the distribution and form of mines but also the development of systematic patterns of prospecting. Unfortunately the detailed irregularity of ore bodies has prevented a complete victory of system over chance.

PROGRESS OF DISCOVERY

Time is a factor in the present pattern of mining. In the South Range there are no ancient mines. The four mines of the district all are relatively modern--large and systematically laid out. The northernmost of the group is the least modern; for many years it has been inactive. The other three are more modern and are still active--two of them in the last stages of activity and the southermost at the height of its career.

These facts reflect the progress of mining in the peninsula, which in turn reflects distributive circumstances of copper occurrence and discovery. Of the various districts in the Copper Country, the South Range was developed most recently and penetration took place from the north--a history associated with an absence of fissure deposits containing conspicuous masses of copper, with the presence of an uncommonly thick mantle of glacial drift increasing in depth toward the south, and with the proximity of the Portage Lake waterway cutting across the peninsula just north of the district.

Fissures containing conspicuous masses of copper have been found mainly in districts far northeast and far southwest of the South Range at opposite ends of the peninsula, near the tip and near the base. In these other districts copper was mined in prehistoric times and the first historic mines were opened in the middle of the nineteenth century. Lode deposits in the rock beds, larger than the fissure but containing inconspicuously small fragments of copper, were discovered later at the place where Portage Lake cuts across the outcrop of copper-bearing rocks in the middle of the peninsula. From the Portage Lake shore discovery spread northeastward over a smooth upland with a shallow mantle of glacial drift to include the great deposits of the Calumet and Hecla Mines in a district practically coalescing with that at the tip of the peninsula. Then finally discovery spread from Portage Lake southwestward through the South Range, into the area of rougher land and deeper drift. There it has stopped, separated by many miles of deep drift from the old district at the base of the peninsula. Attempts have been made to push the frontier of the South Range farther southwest. Diamond drilling indications led to the sinking of a shaft in glacial drift beyond the southern margin of the district, reputed to be the deepest sand shaft in the world, abandoned after failure to find more than a small pocket of ore. Perhaps there are more ore bodies, but quite likely there never will be more mines than those of the past and present.

As already implied, there was a considerable time interval between the opening of the first mine in the South Range, the Atlantic, and the opening of the second, the Baltic Mine. But thereafter, the third and fourth, the Trimountain and Champion, were opened in quick succession. The distribution of the four mines indicates circumstances conditioning this development: the later mines close together in a line at a considerable distance from the first (Fig. 22). The Atlantic Lode is high in the copper-bearing series, outcropping in the northwestern part of the copper belt. The Baltic Lode is the lowest productive member of the copper series, near the great fault at the southeastern margin of the belt. And from the Baltic Mine discoveries were made along the strike of the same lode in adjacent properties, where the Trimountain and Champion Mines were established.

FEATURES RELATED TO EXTRACTION

So much for the discovery of ore and establishment of mines as reflected in the South Range pattern. A second problem represented in the pattern is that of extracting ore from the ground. This involves a great array of specialized mechanical equipment

systematically distributed below and above ground at each mine
(Fig. 24), men to operate the equipment, and power to drive it,
timber to maintain underground openings, water for boilers,
coolers, and human supply, buildings distributed above ground to
shelter equipment and people and establishments to serve the
people, supply houses and the supplies themselves for constant
replenishment of machines and persons, an intricate pattern of
transportation lines to move various of these items to the area
or within it--railways, roads, pipelines, and wires (Fig. 25).

The mines have been developed in an area previously almost uninhabited. All these things have had to be provided, most
of them from outside the area. In spite of previous lack of development, the location of the district has made this relatively
easy, for it touches the Great Lakes waterway at the port of
Houghton on Portage Lake and the railway network of the United
States at the same point (Fig. 22).

SOURCES OF SUPPLIES

A few things have been obtained locally: timber, water,
some food, and some power. Timber occupied all the land originally and the supply has been more than enough to timber the
mines and build the houses of the South Range. The present stand
of virgin timber represents the existing surplus after years of
cutting in more accessible tracts on property not reserved by
mining companies for future supply.

The forests on most of the land are of mixed hardwoods
containing a large proportion of hemlock, not yielding high-
grade structural timber, but no less available for the short-
lived requirements of mine props and miners' houses. . . .

Another question of mine supply is raised by the water
situation. The mines are on high land near the headwaters of
streams, and for many years a deficiency of water existed.
Water for domestic supply was obtained from wells and that for
mining purposes pumped from small streams dammed at lower
places in their courses. Recently underground workers at the
southwestern end of the Champion Mine broke into a drift-filled
valley and tapped such a flow of ground water that it threatened
to fill the mine until large pumps were installed. For this ad-
versity partial compensation has been found in the incidental
supply of water more than ample for both mining and domestic
purposes, piped to the three active mines and the four villages
near them.

POWER AND TRANSPORTATION LAYOUT

The South Range source of water supply is not a source of
power but a consumer, and there is no potential waterpower site
in the immediate vicinity. The need for power was easily supplied
at the outset by means of coal obtained cheaply from Lake Erie
ports as a return cargo in iron ore vessels. In view of the large

amounts of power needed, a still cheaper source has been sought recently in the development of a hydroelectric plant outside of the mine area. The narrow part of the peninsula affords no large watershed but at the base of the peninsula is the Ontonagon River, with a sharp fall in its west branch and a considerable flow partly regulated by Lake Gogebic. Here a plant has been constructed, generating power for the South Range and incidentally a surplus for nearby towns.

The high tension power line cuts through the forest and ramifies in the South Range as one element in the transportation pattern of the district. Other elements have been mentioned incidentally. The railway pattern is most fundamental. Not only have the mines depended on the railway, and the railway on the mines, but it is the railway that has given unity to the South Range as a district. The line built originally to serve the Atlantic Mine has been superseded. Its successor, the Copper Range Railroad, started as a line to connect the Portage Lake towns and the far southwestern district of the Copper Country. When the Baltic Mine was established a short branch line was built to it and a connection with the Lake Superior shore. Then the Baltic branch was continued to the Trimountain and Champion Mines and beyond to become the main line, superseding the original route which did not happen to be near the newly discovered ore bodies. The railway has maintained its line southwest of the district and added a line northeastward beyond Portage Lake, but these extremities are relatively unimportant appendages as compared with the section serving the mines within the South Range area, the essential part of the system.

Here the railway pattern is a fairly direct connection between three essential points--the mines, the Lake Superior Shore, and the Portage Lake shore--by way of a central junction, skirting the slope of the central range of hills and descending by moderate grades to the two shores (Fig. 22).

The function of the railway is to carry the product from the mines and supplies to the mines and associated establishments. Passenger trains have been almost discontinued in view of motor traffic over the short distances involved.

The road system is of minor importance in the mining enterprise, the highway pattern supplementing that of the railway for carrying people and some of their supplies, and the byway pattern giving access to dispersed rural areas.

The unity of the South Range district has been attributed to the railway system. This is not only a matter of traffic movement but of united control and organization. The Copper Range Company originating in connection with the Copper Range Railroad has acquired control of the four separately established mines, and all associated establishments and mine property, thus uniting the district under a single administration for copper production.

All the aforementioned features of the pattern--buildings, clearings and transportation lines--and the movements within the pattern, of power, timber, and other supplies, have a part to play in solving the problem of extracting ore from the ground. But obviously they function in connection with other problems also. One of these is the elimination of waste matter mixed with the copper.

FEATURES RELATED TO WASTE ELIMINATION

The pattern of establishments includes not only the mines with piles of waste rock (Fig. 24), but also stamp mills on the Lake Superior shore and a smelter on the Portage Lake shore (Fig. 22). The presence of these and their distribution represent a solution of the waste rock problem.

The material mined underground is about 1 per cent copper and 99 per cent waste matter. Some of the waste can be eliminated immediately by the miners themselves. Care in discarding low-grade material underground has increased until more than half of the mined rock is discarded, and now ore hoisted to the surface contains over 2 per cent copper.

Except for crushing this ore to convenient size and picking out by hand a few large pieces of mass copper, nothing more can be done to separate the 98 per cent waste from the copper without pulverizing and washing it down with water. Obviously it is worth-while to discard the waste as near as is convenient, but in the milling process each ton of ore has needed about thirty tons of water. The former scarcity of water at the mines has been mentioned. Moreover, the disposal of twenty-five tons of pulverized rock suspended in water for every ton of copper concentrate obtained is a problem in itself.

MILL LOCATION

Some of the older mines in other districts had small mills on the banks of streams in the interior, but others have resorted to lake shore sites. The Atlantic Mine first had its mill at the nearest point on Portage Lake, but the accumulation of discarded stamp sand began to encroach on the narrow steamship channel and a change was ordered by the government. For a new mill the best alternative was the nearest point on the northwest shore of the peninsula.

The example of the Atlantic was followed in succession by the other mines. One mine outside of the Range, the Adventure, in the district far to the southwest, also established its mill here, presumably attracted by the through connection already created by the Copper Range Railroad. The railway reaches the shore through a valley gap and thence extends southwestward to the newest and farthest mill (Fig. 22).

The mills have no harbor facilities and require none, in view of the ease of receiving their coal and other supplies and of shipping their product of copper concentrate by rail connection with the Portage Lake shore--traffic of small bulk in comparison with the trainloads of ore shipped from the mines to the mills. Fortunately, the mill site allows a downward haul for this heavy ore traffic.

The mills, like the mines, need not only rail connections and supplies, machinery and power, but also men and houses and living facilities. All these fit into the pattern.

SMELTER LOCATION

The mill performs its function efficiently, disposing of all but 2 per cent of the 98 per cent waste matter in the ore and thus producing a concentrate which is more than half copper. The process of waste elimination has gone far enough to allow transportation of the residual product to any convenient point for the final purification. The final processes are distinct from milling and require ten times as much coal per ton of raw material. Formerly the South Range concentrates were shipped toward the coal fields and markets of the east for smelting. But in view of the cheapness of coal shipped westward on the lakes, the remaining 2 per cent of the refuse from the ore, composing 40 per cent of the concentrate from the mill, is now eliminated in the district by the Copper Range organization.

The smelter is on Portage Lake at the nearest point west of the docks where there is space for the plant between the railway and the shore, and space for depositing the waste material without interfering with navigation. Slag from the smelter is much less in amount than the stamp sand from the mill and is not washed out in the water to spread and settle widely.

The smelter has its own group of buildings and machines and its own requirements for power, labor, and supplies, provided in the same way as for the mines and mills. In addition to coal, limestone also is brought from outside the district. Green timbers are obtained from nearby tracts of second growth forest, and charcoal is provided by wood from the same source, burned in ovens within the wooded area above the smelter. These needs are small, as is also the need for water, adequately supplied by a brook, descending from the upland back of the plant. No separate village is needed at the smelter because of its proximity to Houghton.

The establishment is a refinery as well as a smelter. The smelting process eliminates all but a tiny fraction of the waste matter and there is no need of further purification in order to avoid transportation of refuse. But the refining process is advantageously carried on under the same roof as smelting in order to handle the molten metal without interruption. It is a simple addition and provides the Copper Range Company with the completed marketable product of the mining enterprise.

FEATURES RELATED TO SHIPMENT

Shipping the copper to market is the only remaining problem represented in the South Range pattern. The Copper Range dock is the main feature involved in the solution.

The dock is on the south side of Portage Lake near the west end of Houghton. This is the place at which the Copper Range

Railroad coming in from the southwest reaches the waterfront at the
principal port and commercial center of the Keweenaw Peninsula.
The port is located where the sheltered navigable Portage Lake
waterway crosses the copper-bearing lodes, and is the nearest
shipping point for the South Range.

In addition to the copper and coal docks, the railway shops
are also here, located not with reference to copper shipment but
primarily with reference to the main urban center and source of
labor and supplies, the original focus of the railway system. . . .

DETAILS OF PATTERN FEATURES

In general, the mines are narrow slits cut into the earth a-
long ore bodies extending downward toward the northwest (Fig. 23).
In detail the cutting of these slits has such distributive complexity
that every corner represents the solution of a local problem and
has its own place and form in the pattern. Each shaft assumes the
dip of the adjacent part of the lode. Each level drift follows the
ore body. Each stope takes form by selective excavation.

The texture of the pattern is made by advance and shrinkage
stopes above, by retreat and filled stopes at greater depths under
excessive timber strains and rock bursts.

The spacing of shafts reflects the efficiency of underground
movement (Fig. 24). Each shaft is a focus for the distribution of
features below ground and above.

Each building has its form and place: the shaft house itself
with sloping northwest side and bulging southeast side (Fig. 24);
the nearby hoist and power house, coal dump and rock pile on lower
land; the dry house and timber pile on higher land; the more distant
village on a selected site with clusters of community establishments: the school, the church, the homes of officials; the separate
commercial village of South Range with its stores (Fig. 25).

Even bare enumeration of details indicates their significance
in the general pattern, as parts fitting together in their respective
places to form the focal establishments of the district.

Apart from the mines, the stamp mill on its sloping shore,
separating copper by a process minutely adjusted to local circumstances and character of ore; the other mills abandoned under
unified organization, but all their villages persisting, the largest
at the north, the smallest at the south; the smelter also on a slope
applying different processes under different circumstances; the
power plant on its river, with dam and reservoir, mile-long pen-
stock, surge tank, and power house; the docks at Houghton, shipping
copper.

Much more might be added concerning the pattern, not only
in detail, but also in general: on economic aspects, production
costs and quantities; on form and distribution of land holdings
(Fig. 22) and subsurface rights; on form and distribution of political units: Houghton County of the central Copper Country,
Adams Township of the South Range mines and Stanton Township
of the mills; on social aspects of unified organization by non-

resident control; on kind and number of people; on the impending termination of the function and accompanying disintegration of the pattern--topics all postponed indefinitely and probably forever.

A CLASSIFICATION OF MANUFACTURES, EXEMPLIFIED BY PORTO RICAN INDUSTRIES[1]

by R. S. Platt

Porto Rico is not classed as a manufacturing country. Yet 75 per cent by value of the exports of Porto Rico are classified as "manufactured," and there are many other commodities manufactured and not exported. This apparently anomalous situation results from the fact that the term "manufacture" is used with both broad and narrow meanings and therefore at the outset calls for definition.

In a broad sense the term applies to any part of the series of processes by which raw materials are changed and combined from their original production to the final consumption of the finished product, whether or not the necessary labor is carried on in factory buildings or is aided by mechanical means. The series of processes may be very short and simple, or very long and complicated, the finished product of one manufacturer becoming the raw material of another.

In a narrow but at the same time a less definite sense, manufacturing is thought of only in connection with complicated processes carried on by machinery and organized groups of laborers, especially in industries for which power, labor, and transportation are important localizing factors. In this sense, simple processes of preparing commodities for consumption are not considered as typical manufacturing; nor is every stage of a complicated series of processes so considered. Preliminary processes at the beginning, closely connected with the original production of material, may be considered a part of agriculture or mining; and final processes at the end, close to consumption, as a part of household utilization. Intermediate processes, carried on mechanically at factories located at transportation centers, or at labor or power centers, are the distinctly manufacturing industries, and give rise to typical manufacturing districts.

In the light of these distinctions it is easy to classify the industries of Porto Rico. Presumably the principles involved may be applied elsewhere, even though the form of classification may need modification.

1. *Annals AAG,* vol. 17 (1927), pp. 79-91.

THE GROUPS DEFINED.--In the accompanying table industrial establishments of Porto Rico are grouped according to factors that affect their presence in the island. For Group I the principal raw materials are produced in Porto Rico and the markets are elsewhere. For Group II the market is in Porto Rico and the principal raw materials are imported. For Group III both the market and the sources of materials are in Porto Rico. For Group IV neither the market nor the sources of materials are in the island, and Porto Rican labor is an important factor.

The table is evidence of the fact that Porto Rican industries are varied in their relations, and that geographic significance is not to be measured by value of products nor by alphabetical order in an undivided list. Details of geographic adjustment are brought out by further analysis of individual industries in each group.

GROUP I

Sugar Milling.--The leading industries of Group I have to do with products of agriculture. These industries supply most of the exports of Porto Rico, the one commodity sugar making up 60 per cent by value of the export total. The island is conspicuously agricultural and sugar cane is the leading crop, occupying most of the fertile level land and engaging as farm laborers more people than any other occupation.

It is taken as a matter of course that not only is sugar cane grown in Porto Rico, but also that the raw material is made into sugar there. There are 55 sugar mills in the territory representing an average investment of more than $1,000,000 each, and sending out annually a product valued at almost $1,000,000 each.

That this industry should be carried on in Porto Rico instead of having the raw material exported is natural for compelling reasons. Sugar cane deteriorates rapidly after being cut, losing two per cent or more of its recoverable sucrose every day after the first 48 hours. Therefore it is not economical to delay it on the way to the mill. Moreover, about 89 per cent of the cane is waste matter, and it is not economical to transport ten tons of cane farther than necessary to obtain little more than one ton of sugar. This in itself is a sufficient reason for the distribution of the sugar mills around the island, each in the heart of its own cane fields, rather than concentrated at shipping points or labor markets. A mill site on a harbor for shipment of products and receipt of minor materials is only a secondary consideration, accepted as an advantage if found within the cane area, but not chosen at a distance in preference to the cane area. Concentration of the industry has proceeded only to secure the efficiency of large scale operation, in central mills, each in the midst of an area formerly served by five or more small mills, grinding much faster and extracting 40 per cent more sugar. These mills are classed as factories and their products as manufactured goods. Yet in their location, their organization, and their operation they are inseparably connected with Porto Rican agriculture; they represent a manufacturing development in the broad but not in the narrow sense.

TABLE I. MANUFACTURES IN PORTO RICO

Group I Porto-Rican Materials, Foreign Markets	Group II Foreign Materials, Porto Rican Markets	Group III Porto Rican Materials, Porto Rican Markets	Group IV Foreign Materials, Foreign Markets
Sugar mills Tobacco factories Coffee establishments Fruit canneries Copra kilns Bay oil distilleries Cotton gins	Bakeries Printing & publishing shops Foundries & machine shops Boot and shoe factories Clothing factories Flour and grist mills Car shops Planing mills Marble works Millinery factories Trunk factories Mattress factories Wagon shops Furniture factories	A. Close to markets Ice factories Soda water bottling plants Potteries B. Close to materials Lime kilns Brick and tile yards Salt ponds	Embroidery & drawn work agencies Straw hat & basket agencies

In their utilization of a perishable material, sugar mills are like cheese factories, which are located in the heart of dairy country, and like vegetable canneries, located in the heart of truck-farming country. In their elimination of waste material they are like lumber mills located close to forests, and like ore-concentrating plants located close to mines.

The sugar is not refined in Porto Rico. This fact is hardly less natural than that the cane is crushed in Porto Rico. In the series of processes between cane production and sugar consumption, there is some economy of transportation in making sugar close to the cane fields and in refining it close to the market. Raw sugar requires less care in handling than does the refined product, and is shipped from many centrals to a few large refineries in the United States for storing, refining, and distributing according to market requirements through the year.

The tendency to refine the product away from Porto Rico is strengthened by other factors, particularly the advantages elsewhere of power and capital. Obviously the localization of this and other industries is not fixed simply in relation to raw material and market. If there is only a slight margin of advantage in transporting before or after fabrication, other factors--power, labor, capital--are likely to be critical.

The advantages in favor of refining sugar elsewhere may be overbalanced by the cost of bagging raw sugar for shipment, and to eliminate this item, as well as to supply the local market, there may be an increasing development of refining in Porto Rico.

Sugar milling gives rise to certain by-products, and the first processes connected with these fall naturally into the same group of industries. Some final molasses is exported for the production of alcohol. Crushed cane refuse, bagasse, is used as fuel in the sugar mills, being a valuable substitute for imported fuel. In general sugar milling processes appear as manufacturing in a broad sense, closely connected with the agriculture of the island.

Coffee Cleaning.--The coffee industry illustrates the same tendency toward preliminary manufacturing processes carried on in Porto Rico to improve carrying quality. Coffee is the leading crop of the rugged interior of the island. It occupies more land and engages more farm laborers than any other commercial crop except sugar cane. Coffee is the chief export of Porto Rico to countries other than the United States.

Treatment is necessary before exportation. The coffee beans, contained in "cherries," covered with useless pulp and subject to deterioration, must be pulped, fermented, washed, dried, hulled, sorted, sized, and polished to eliminate waste matter, fix the elusive flavor, and standardize the product. Methods of performing these operations differ greatly, the small producer doing by hand work that in large establishments is accomplished mechanically.

In many cases the first four processes are performed on the plantations and the last four in the larger establishments in port cities. The first four processes are those which eliminate most of the waste matter and prevent deterioration, and these are carried on near the coffee groves, just as cane is crushed near the cane fields. Following these processes the coffee is readily transportable any distance with at least as great facility as later after the removal of the protective coat of parchment and the cleaning of the product. In this respect it is like raw sugar, and the last four processes may be compared with the refining of sugar.

That these latter processes are carried on in Porto Rico rather than nearer the market may be explained by the character of the coffee industry in contrast with the sugar industry: (1) the coffee, unlike sugar, is a distinctive Porto Rican product prepared in a distinctive Porto Rican way; (2) it is distributed directly to various foreign markets which demand this product; (3) it is more valuable for its bulk than sugar, and can bear a greater cost for careful handling; and (4) the processes of hulling, sorting, sizing, and polishing are easily accomplished by wholesale dealers in connection with their handling of the product without much equipment or labor.

These latter coffee processes may be considered as belonging to a class of industry different from the earlier plantation processes and from the sugar milling industry in that they do not prevent deterioration nor eliminate waste but add finishing touches for market. They are not in the producing area but in ports on the Porto Rican coast, conveniently located to collect from the producing area and to distribute to various countries, in contrast with the sugar refineries on the American coast collecting from various countries and distributing within one country. However, these coffee processes are so simple that certainly they constitute manufacturing only in a broad sense.

A wrong impression of the magnitude of these processes is given by the total value of their product, more than $11,000,000 annually, second only to sugar milling. More than 95 per cent of the value of the coffee is due to the production of the crop and to the plantation processes, and less than 5 per cent is value added by manufacture in the cleaning and polishing establishments. This fact serves to indicate how unsatisfactory is the total value of the product as an index to the importance of a manufacturing industry.

Tobacco Manufacturing.--Tobacco, third in the triumvirate of great Porto Rican crops, gives rise to industrial activity which exceeds coffee preparation in value added by manufacture and is second only to sugar.

The preparation of leaf tobacco is comparable to that of coffee. The first process on the plantations is relatively simple, consisting in hanging the plants in specially constructed sheds to dry for three or four weeks. This is followed by fermentation in storehouses; then soaking, drying, baling, stripping, classifying, bundling, barrelling, seasoning.

As in the case of coffee, the latter processes are carried on for the most part in the establishments of dealers in port cities, and have to do with bringing out the distinctive quality of a distinctive Porto Rican product. The processes are somewhat more elaborate than in the case of coffee so that the business tends to become more of a separate industry apart from distributing. Moreover, most of the leaf is exported to the United States rather than being distributed to various countries. But there is still reason enough for carrying on this activity in Porto Rico, as in coffee cleaning, rather than in the United States, as is sugar refining, because these processes are important in fixing the quality and compacting and protecting the product for shipment, and therefore belong close to the agricultural industry.

There is a further stage in tobacco preparation which has quite a different significance from either the preliminary or the later processes of leaf treatment. Most of the Porto Rican tobacco is exported in leaf form, but there is some local manufacture of cigars and cigarettes. This industry takes the prepared material and from it makes a product which is less compact and more difficult to ship. The fact that the product is more valuable than the raw material does not account for its manufacture in Porto Rico. Other reasons than the production of material prevail, and, in this respect, the industry does not belong in Group I. Most of the cigarettes are for the local market, thus attaching part of the industry to Group III. Most of the cigars are for export under circumstances which point to Group IV, to be discussed later.

Fruit Canning.--Fruits, which are fourth in importance among the commercial crops of Porto Rico and are the chief product of American settlers in the island, differ from sugar cane, coffee, and tobacco in requiring no transforming processes. The packing and shipping houses are conspicuous establishments, but their work is that of transporting and not of manufacturing, their object being to arrange and forward the fruit to market in an unchanged condition.

However, a secondary industry, the canning of fruit, has grown up as an adjunct of the fresh fruit industry, another example of a manufacturing process in preparation for transportation to a distant market. In the canneries, the perishable material is made into a nonperishable product more readily transportable. Surplus fruit, especially that which does not quite meet fresh fruit standards in grade and size, is material for canning. Lower transportation costs and a market widened and lengthened by the imperishability of the product thus make possible the export of a commodity not otherwise marketable. That the process belongs in the fruit growing territory is obvious.

The principal canned fruits are pineapples and grapefruits. Oranges, which are most plentiful throughout the island but least exportable on account of competition in the United States and the inaccessibility of much of the crop, have not been canned thus far for lack of a suitable process.

Copra Drying.--Coconuts rank next to fruits among commercial crops, and like fruits, they are transported preferably unchanged to market. Likewise, there is special treatment of a surplus not otherwise marketable. The making of copra is a simple process of drying the coconut meat, thus greatly condensing the product to be exported for oil production.

The relative proximity of Porto Rico to the United States is an advantage in reaching the market for fresh coconuts, less valuable by weight but more valuable by number. Consequently most of the Porto Rican crop is marketed fresh and copra making is a minor activity, far less important than on distant East Indian coasts.

Bay Oil Distilling.--Several minor crops induce small industries. Bay trees are grown in one district. From a hundred pounds of bay leaves a little more than one pound of essential oil is produced by distillation and decantation. This proportion of almost 99 per cent of waste matter to one per cent of product, together with the perishability of the crop, explains the location of distilleries in the two towns of the crop district.

A further process is the mixing of bay rum, containing a small portion of bay oil and a large portion of alcohol, a byproduct of sugar. This is not attracted to the bay crop district but to a convenient meeting place of the ingredients on the way to market. Much of the oil is exported to the United States for treatment, but some bay rum is made in Porto Rican ports.

Cotton Ginning.--A small amount of sea island cotton is grown in the island. Cotton gins are not commonly considered as factories, but they belong in the same class as the other establishments under consideration, separating the byproduct seed and making compact bales for shipment. Later cotton processes, which do not increase the mobility of the material, are not attracted to the producing area but are localized by other factors, not in Porto Rico.

Conclusion for Group I.--All of the manufactures of Group I take the raw materials produced locally by fundamental industries and prepare them as far as economically desirable to avoid uneconomical transportation. Most of them belong in the very districts within Porto Rico where the fundamental production takes place. Those processes which are carried on in port cities away from the producing districts are not typical of the group but verge on other groups, as illustrated by the final treatment of coffee and tobacco. This is to be expected in view of the fact that transportation from the producing district to the port is likely to be a costly part of the journey to market, in some cases the most costly part.

Distribution of the processes within producing districts depends to a considerable extent on the scale of the industry. If the manufacturing is organized on a much larger scale than the fundamental production, there is necessarily concentration within the district, manufacturing at a few points for production on many farms. This is illustrated by the sugar industry, in which the increased cost of transporting cane to a few centrals is much more than balanced by the decreased costs of large scale production. If the manufacturing is organized on as small a scale as the fundamental production, then the process is widely distributed; every farm has its factory. This is the case in the first treatment of tobacco and other commodities, merging into the fundamental production, and at its inception lacking separate identity as manufacturing even in a broad sense.

GROUP II

There is a much longer list of industries which do not produce export commodities and which largely import their raw materials. None of these are very large or very conspicuous. They
are important in quite a different way from the group previously
discussed, but are as easily accounted for. They are distributed
not with reference to fundamental production but in relation to
population centers.

A conspicuous illustration of these are bakeries, first in
number of establishments, in number of workers, in value of products, and in value added by manufacture. Obviously this is an
industry in which the finished product and not the raw material is
perishable and difficult to transport. Manufacture must take place
close to markets, which in this case are population centers in
Porto Rico.

To a less extent the same thing is true of the manufacture of
flour and meal, the raw material being somewhat more easily transported than the finished product. The advantage for flour mills is
so much less impelling than for bakeries that only a small proportion of the flour used in Porto Rico is milled locally, most of the
supply being imported ready for the bakers from large American
mills.

The small scale of the baking industry is indicated by the
large number of bakeries, widely distributed in town and village
markets, not centralized by any imperative advantages in large
scale operation.

In the same class is printing and publishing, newspapers and
periodicals, and jobbing. This is just as clear a case of perishable
product for which the factory cannot be far from the market. In job
printing there is also the element of direct individual service tying
it to the market.

Foundries and machine shops are classed as factories, and
if they are to be considered such, they belong in this group. Their
raw materials are imported and their markets are the local industries, for which they provide mechanical repairs and items of
equipment. They are tied to the market not by the perishability nor
by the greater bulk of the finished products as compared with the
raw materials, but, like job printing, by the retail character of
their service: instead of manufacturing to sell in an open market
they are filling individual orders which need attention on the spot.
Similar relations are evident in sheet metal shops, railroad car
shops, planing mills, and marble works.

Makers of shoes, clothing, millinery, trunks, mattresses,
wagons, and furniture have either or both of these reasons for
their presence near the market, making their imported materials
into more bulky products and in some cases performing direct
individual service.

Most of these industries meet more or less competition from
factories elsewhere, in proportion as the margin of advantage for
local production is small or large: small for clothing factories,

large for bakeries. The more typical of these industries are manufacturing in a broad sense. Extreme examples merge into individual neighborhood services.

GROUP III

The third group of industries has something in common with
each of the groups preceding: it has both raw materials and markets
close at hand.

Some of the industries of Group I have a minor phase belonging to Group III. A small proportion of the sugar crop is refined
specifically for local distribution. Some coffee and some tobacco
likewise are produced and used in Porto Rico. Ninety-eight per
cent of the cigarettes made in Porto Rico are for the local market.

The distinct industries of Group III differ conspicuously from
Group I in the character of their materials. Instead of being peculiar to Porto Rico and demanded by other countries, these materials are so widely distributed and commonly available in the
world as to be unsought and unused except for nearby markets.

Ice manufacturing is the first of the group, in number of
persons engaged, in capital invested, in value of products,--in fact
in every important particular except cost of materials. The general
availability and cheap abundance of the only material used in large
bulk is evident. The prime consideration is the tropical Porto Rican
market for a product so perishable and bulky that there is little
competition from outside sources.

Soda water bottling ranks second in the same group of industries. The product does not deteriorate, but, as in the case of
ice, the bulk of the material is water, and transportation to market
from a distance is uneconomical. Imported flavoring extract is of
small bulk, and imported bottles can be reused, becoming a sort of
circulating capital instead of part of the product. Until recently a
brewery and a distillery were operated with the same advantage,
their principal material by weight being water and their lesser
materials, such as malt, being readily imported.

These industries are more closely tied to market than to
source of raw material, since their products are less easy to
transport than their materials. Pottery making is another example of the same sort.

Certain other industries in Group III are more closely tied
to source of material than to market. Lime, brick, and salt are
made for the local market from local materials. Unlike ice, these
products are transported more easily than their raw materials.

These relationships to markets and sources of material are
indicated by localization of the industries within the island: lime
kilns are close to quarries, brick kilns close to clay pits, and salt
ponds close to the sea. On the other hand, ice plants are in centers
of population, and not at the sources of water supply.

Most of the industries of Group III, like those of Group II,
meet some competition from imported manufactures. Production
elsewhere with special materials or with advantages in other

factors overcomes to a greater or less extent the advantage held by Porto Rican producers. Porto Rican pottery and salt are inconspicuous in the home market; while Porto Rican ice has practically a local monopoly.

GROUP IV

None of the first three groups of industries give Porto Rico standing as a "manufacturing" territory. The great sugar milling development is looked upon as a completion of the agricultural industry. Likewise coffee cleaning, tobacco stripping, fruit canning, are considered adjuncts of agriculture, preliminary preparation of raw materials to be exported. Similarly, the other groups are looked upon not as distinct manufacturing but as activities of subsistence in modern life. Bakers, printers, machinists, cobblers, tailors, farriers, lime burners, stone cutters, accompany civilized groups of people everywhere in the modern world, without having special significance as manufacturers.

The idea of a manufacturing district seems to carry with it another implication: not preliminary preparation of raw material for shipment nor immediate provisioning of the local market, but fabrication dependent on other advantages, particularly power or labor.

Porto Rico has no coal, oil, or gas. It has some available water power as a result of heavy rains on abrupt mountains; but the small size of the streams in a country of such small water sheds offers the prospect of little surplus power beyond the ordinary needs of urban communities and densely populated farming country.

With respect to labor the situation is different. Porto Rico is one of the densely populated territories of the world, having almost four hundred per square mile, intelligent and poor people, needing work and not able to find it. The island is a market of cheap and fairly capable labor.

Labor without power leads naturally to hand industries without much machinery, inconspicuous and on a small scale. Thus production which seems to have some characteristics of a distinct manufacturing development is, to a large extent, household industry.

Embroidery, lace and drawn work are made in Porto Rico and have become familiar in American cities. The materials are imported and the product is exported. Porto Rican women have become skillful under instruction and are willing to work for wages which are very low according to American standards. The industry does not figure in the statistics of industrial establishments, but there are reported to be several hundred agencies, 22,000 persons engaged and exports valued at more than $6,000,000 annually.

A similar industry is the weaving of straw hats and baskets from palm leaves. This was based originally on production from local materials for the local market, and there is still this phase belonging to Group III. But it has grown beyond this into Group IV, with the importation of material and the exportation of hats of the Panama type, depending on cheap and skilled household labor.

Cigar making has been mentioned as not belonging typically to Group I, although most of the material is produced locally and 70 per cent of the product is exported. Cigar manufacture at a distance from the market, under a disadvantage in transporting the product, depends for its success in large part on the labor factor. Cigars, more than cigarettes, are the product of cheap hand labor in shops large and small. The manufacturing of almost 200,000,000 cigars annually may therefore be classed with the making of embroidery and hats.

To say that these industries without factories, machinery or power, more truly than sugar milling, represent manufacturing in the narrow sense is perhaps taking too great liberties with an accepted meaning. Nevertheless these industries rest on foundations that tend toward distinct manufacturing, not adjuncts of agriculture or of urban life.

Porto Rico is relatively well developed so far as fundamental natural resources are concerned. Agricultural land is the chief of these and most of the fertile land is in use. Industries which depend closely on agriculture promise only small slow growth to accompany slight extension and intensification of agriculture. Industries which depend on the local market promise little more, since population cannot increase much further and since increase in per capita buying power is likely to be rather limited.

But there is surplus labor in quantity, and the utilization of this resource invites development of the types of manufacture in which cheap dextrous labor is the critical factor. Such development should tend to follow the lines already suggested by embroidery and cigars. Although it could not be great enough to overshadow the agricultural character of the country, nevertheless it should result in some prosperous enterprises and should help to some extent in solving the Porto Rican problems of unemployment and poverty.

SUMMARY MEMORANDUM ON THE BAD RIVER INDIAN RESERVATION, BASED ON REPORTS OF FIELD STUDY[1]

by R. S. Platt

The Bad River Indian Reservation makes a bad first impression and improves on acquaintance. Snap judgments on its problems, its people and its government officials are easy to make and likely to be wrong. Mature consideration leads to appreciation of

1. Dept. of Geog., Univ. of Chicago, 1940.

all these and constructive hopes for the future. For purposes of presentation this memorandum begins with the superficial bad aspects and ends with the fundamental good possibilities.

I

The Reservation "is recognized as an economic and social maladjustment by all closely concerned with it – the Indian Service, the state, counties and townships in which it lies, the farmers living within its boundaries,"[1] "as one of the sore spots of all Indian Reservations in the United States". Bad River has a reputation as an ugly, despised, troublesome place.

(1) Ugly according to visitors passing through the Reservation: dismal cutover land along the highway; "the desolate and unkempt village" of Odanah, ragged loafers, a highway speed trap, and no trace of picturesque Indian life. Even the fact that some houses have been repaired and painted white hardly improve the scene; in fact these repair jobs emphasize rather than relieve the depressing picture, like new patches on old clothes.

(2) Despised according to white neighbors in Ashland, where Indians are poor customers in stores, where Indian employees have failed to meet city standards as wage earners, and where Indians are seen conspicuously drunk. White farmers nearby have a similarly poor opinion of the Indians, knowing them as the worst of farmers. Even the Catholic Indian mission in the Reservation shares this opinion and refuses to employ Indians as farm laborers. Racial feeling and discrimination against Indians is almost universal in the vicinity.

(3) Troublesome according to government officials concerned with the Reservation, – troubled by difficulties of law enforcement, by failure of economic and social programs, and by burdens of Indian relief wrecking finances of local government. The Indians are "poverty stricken"; more than 60% of them depend on "public assistance"; only 10 or 15% are entirely self supporting and most of these make a bare subsistence living, on the land or by minor bits of local employment. In a total population of 275 Indian families, government expenditures for relief amounted to $128,000 in 1939, apart from other thousands spent or loaned for Indian welfare apparently without avail.

II

Bad conditions are the more disconcerting because underlying elements are not bad.

1. *"Quotations are from student reports on file at the University of Chicago."*

(1) The site of the Reservation was selected by and for the
Indians as a choice and ample part of the ancestral homeland. Forest cutting was carried out according to a reasonable government program supposedly for the benefit of
the Indians. The ugliness of Odanah is that of "a once prosperous sawmill town in which now there is no industry".
Off the highway much of the Reservation is still beautiful
and suitable for Indian life with surviving tracts of virgin
forest, second growth woods serving as game cover, sandy
beaches on Lake Superior and Chequamenon Bay, a river
system teeming with fish, a waterfall, a network of picturesque sloughs abounding in wild life and bordered by valuable plantations of wild rice, – a concentration of primitive
land and water resources hardly exceeded elsewhere in the
region and about as good now as it ever was for the original
Indian way of life.

(2) The Indians themselves are of good racial stock and are not
personally despicable. Their Chippewa blood has been di-
luted with white blood, but there is no convincing evidence
that this mixture with pioneer stock has made them inferior.
Most of the people of the present generation are cooperative,
and desire to play a worthy part in a good social order. A
knowledge of Chippewa culture has survived.

(3) Government representatives entrusted with the welfare of
the Reservation are capable and conscientious. The local
members of the Indian Service are well qualified specialists bent on doing creditable work in their respective fields
and exerting themselves to achieve success in their assignments. "The Indian Service is honestly trying to care for
the Bad River Indians". Other representatives of federal,
state, county, and township government are equally earnest
and honest in their relations with the Reservation and are
qualified to fill the positions which they hold. Such are
the County Agent and the Chairman of the County Board.

III

What then are the causes of trouble?

(1) "The Reservation," due to an intricate history, is such a
complex tract of land, and "the Indians" such a complicated group of people, legally, politically, and otherwise,
that they cannot properly be treated as simple units, and
no solution of their problems is to be found in simple for-
mulae. The Reservation is not "reserved" in any real
sense but contains the following categories of land ownership and jurisdiction, intricately dividing the tract in at
least eleven ways:

> Land allotted to individual Indians, tax free;
> heirship land

Land owned by individual Indians, taxable

Land owned by white residents

Land owned by non-resident corporations

Tribal land held in common

Tribal land assigned to individuals

Federal land: Resettlement Administration –
                        Soil Conservation Service

Federal land: Indian Reorganization Act

Ashland County land

Iron County land

State–claimed land

"The ownership status of the land is confused, and in some cases, conflicting; likewise, the terms used to designate the various types of land are in themselves ambiguous". Law enforcement and land use are conditioned by a confusion of jurisdictions.

The people of the Reservation are no more homogeneous than the land and are divided into almost as many categories on various bases:

Indians: resident members of the Tribe

                non–member residents of the Reservation

                non–resident members of the Tribe

                   wards of the federal government

                   non-wards

                       25% or more Indian blood

                       less than 25% Indian

Whites: non–Indians on alienated land

               members of the Tribe

"Any solution of the problem becomes more complicated because we are dealing with an Indian Reservation on which both Indians and whites are living". The various classes on a legal basis are cut across by other categories on social, political and economic bases. Stratification into social groups is as well developed as in other communities, not only into Indians and whites, but also into Catholic society, and "a young wild tavern crowd," not numerous but so conspicuous that their drunkenness fixes a bad reputation on the whole community, - at least in the eyes of people who classify Indians together as birds-of-a-feather in superficial generalization. After all, "every Indian is an individual and must be treated as such."

Equally complex and "in part growing out of the complications of land and population status" is the political organization. The Reservation area is divided among the following units of local government:

Sanborn Township,	Ashland County	- all within the Reservation
Gingles Township,	" "	- partly within the Reservation
White River Township,	" "	"
Ashland Township,	" "	"
La Pointe Township,	" "	"
Saxon Township,	Iron County	- "

The Indians are voting citizens of their townships, but a majority are at the same time wards of the federal government free from taxation and from jurisdiction of local courts. "A perfect dilemma exists between the Bad River Reservation and the Township of Sanborn."

In addition to township organization there is the tribal organization authorized by law, and a survival of the older and separate tribal system not authorized by law.

Other agencies of government operating in the Reservation overlap in their functions. Roads in the Reservation are in the hands of eight or more separate agencies. Relief is handled by five or more agencies. Two or more agencies are concerned with each of several other governmental functions: farm development, education, law enforcement, etc. "Spheres of authority and jurisdiction either overlap

or are vague as to delineation." "Thus the ordinary superstructure of government current in modern life has been
multiplied for this Indian Reservation," subdividing it er-
ratically, and "tying it to local, state, regional and national
offices through both direct and indirect channels."

(2) Problems of the Bad River Reservation are inseparably
woven together and not to be solved without coordinated
planning for all the resources, Indian abilities, and established interests as a whole. Government action through
separate specialized departments does not provide for
balanced integration of forestry, agriculture, hunting, road
building, social life, Indian culture, etc. "To complete this
circle, W.P.A. projects are provided which lure the Indians
off their farms after the government has spent large sums
in rehabilitating them."

This difficulty is not the fault of government representatives in the area, who cooperate with each other as well as
possible. But these representatives are not directed under
a comprehensive plan covering the Reservation, and are
separately responsible to their respective departments
each reacting according to customary modes of procedure.

(3) Problems of the Reservation are peculiar to the locality and
the Northern Lakes Region, and are not to be lumped together with those of Indians in other regions, as if reservations and Indians were fairly similar throughout the
United States and could be covered by uniform regulations
and arrangements. The Bad River Reservation has more
in common with adjacent lands and problems in Northern
Wisconsin than with reservations and Indians in the semi-
arid Southwest. "The Chippewas, traditionally hunters and
fishermen, people of the woods and streams do not find
farming to their liking."

"The Indians have been expected to adjust their lives to
white man's habits. However, because of the paternalism
of the United States government, the majority of the Bad
River Indians have lacked incentive to find activities to
supplant lumbering; nor has the government supplied any
industries for them."

An Indian program on a national scale, patterned after the
economic and social system of white people to provide
Indians with new habits of rural life, might succeed under
favorable circumstances. But at Bad River the circumstances are unfavorable. Not only do the Indians lack
aptitude for farming, but the environment is poor: the
growing season too short and cool, the land difficult to
clear, markets adverse; the soil in the Reservation heavy,

difficult to work and quickly depleted, worse than the average of farmland in the region.

Even white settlers accustomed to farming have been relatively unsuccessful in the Northern Lakes Region. Whatever economic success has been achieved in the area rests primarily on extraction of ore and lumber, and the continued vitality of Ashland as a lake port is based on resources no longer shared by the Reservation. Problems of permanent rural settlement in the region have not been solved, and experts on land use are advising retrenchment in farming and emphasis on wild land economy. The Indians of Bad River, "less successful in farming operations than white families on similar land," need such advice more than their white neighbors and are better equipped to profit by it. Yet they are more closely held by a conventional system in which farming offers the main possibility for productive industry. Thus while white settlers are being directed away from farming to activities more like those of Indians, the attention of Indians is being directed still toward farming by experts in agriculture. This is not the fault of the Indians, caught in a system beyond their control; nor is it the fault of the agricultural experts, who recognize the regional limitations of their technical skill and work on their assignments without hope of doing more than give slight relief from adverse conditions.

Regional problems are touched still less by the Catholic mission, which emphasizes mystical and other-wordly aspects of religion rather than immediate questions on the Reservation. Public education has been entrusted to the Catholic Church and this provides a grade school curriculum of "strictly the conventional textbook type, no vocational training of any kind being offered to the boys and girls of the community."

The Indian Reorganization Act of 1934, designed to restore Indian life and culture, might seem to support the regional advice mentioned above. But this national legislation is not adjusted to meet regional needs of the Bad River Reservation. Old channels of action remain and application of the act has tended to complicate existing arrangements rather than to restore Indian life. "The present philosophy seems to embrace the paradoxical notion of keeping the Indians as Indians and at the same time expecting them to conform to the white economy of the area," - and that economy a poor one at best.

What can be done?

Three alternative policies are possible:

(1) The first is preservation of the status quo indefinitely, –
    continuing services and activities as at present, to keep
    the Reservation as it is and the Indians as they are. This
    is not a reasonable alternative and is not approved by le-
    gitimate interests. Elimination of confused jurisdiction, of
    scattered effort and of regional maladjustment obviously is
    desirable; therefore some other alternative is in order.

(2) The second alternative is liquidation of the Reservation
    and of the Indians as such. This is a reasonable alterna-
    tive. Many current problems would solve themselves, if
    this policy were adopted and consistently followed.

    Liquidation could be promoted in the best interests of the
    Indians and of the community by gradual withdrawal of
    privileges in excess of treaty obligations and by helping
    Indians as individual citizens rather than as members of
    a segregated low-caste group. "Break down the barrier
    between Indians and whites by placing the Indians on the
    same legal basis as their white neighbors....The Indians
    should be treated as residents of Wisconsin and the entire
    reservation put under the same legal set-up as non-reser-
    vation land....All the farms in the reservation, both Indian
    and white, should be put under one agricultural agent. . . .

    Approval of a liquidation policy has been expressed by lead-
    ing members of the tribe as well as by others concerned
    with the Reservation. To facilitate the policy, local di-
    rection is needed with intimate and accurate knowledge of
    existing complexities in the Reservation and with the con-
    fidence of Indians and whites, and such direction is avail-
    able in the person of the Field Aid already in charge at the
    Reservation (August 1940). Executive authority is needed
    close at hand with power to act, and for this purpose the
    requisite competence, initiative and integrity are already
    present in the person of the Indian Agent of the Great Lakes
    Jurisdiction.

    The policy is not to be carried through in a hurry and its
    goal would not be reached for many years. But it could
    begin at once, and the following specific points of attack
    are possibilities for immediate assistance:

    (a) Clarification of legal status and law enforcement,
         by partial withdrawal of federal jurisdiction and

other means. "The federal-state-county-town-tribal council tangle should be handed to experts for simplification."

(b) Coordination of work assistance services to advance undeveloped resources of both white and Indian economy. A simple picturesque restaurant and trading post "serving as an outlet for Indian handicraft" "could be constructed as a WPA project."

(c) Orientation of the school program toward specific problems of the community. "The goal of the vocational training would be to teach young people skills and trades for making a living either in that area or in other areas, while the goal of the rehabilitation program would be to make Odanah into a community with many interests and with beauty that any community has a right to possess.... Armed with skills with which to make a living and backed by a community in which pride can be taken" the next generation can move out to opportunities elsewhere or transform the Reservation into a self respecting American community. An example of conspicuous success under excellent white and Indian leadership is provided on the Reservation in a project of adult education conducted by the C.C.C.-I.D.

(3) The third alternative is to move in the opposite direction: away from liquidation, toward re-Indianizing the Indians, emphasizing their culture and traditions and conserving these as a distinct and vital element in the United States. This also is a reasonable alternative, - a potential contribution to the country attainable without greater expenditures than are now being made on the Reservation.

This alternative is more difficult than the second and would require even more whole-hearted acceptance and consciousness of the objective and redirection of money and effort. It would be in apparent accord with the intention of the Indian Reorganization Act on the one hand, and not inconsistent with advice of the Northern Lakes States Planning Committee on the other.

The feasibility of the policy rests upon a persistent foundation of Indian culture, which still survives. Chippewa art and technology survive in plentiful pieces of handicraft and in artistic skill of individuals. Chippewa economy survives in activities of woods and water for subsistence living. Chippewa political organization, religion and ceremonial tradition survive in chiefs and medicine men, and in dances, rhythmic music, and symbolic constumes. Most of the group understand the Chippewa language, and less tangible elements of culture are pervasive, – of philosophy, morality and views of life, "the stoic, reserved, patient and stable temperament; the short-sightedness in planning for tomorrow accompanied by a vision looking forward to future generations.". . .

The project should aim to bring satisfaction to the inhabitants and an object lesson to modern Americans. It should not be a mere exhibition for curiosity seekers, but under careful protection it could use tourist interest to aid in self support. Such an example of Chippewa life need not bar contacts with outsiders but could assume a status of intercourse and exchange such as existed in the period of the fur trade.

Chippewa culture could make a contribution worth having in American life and particularly valuable at a time when Americans need to regain contact with nature, to assume local responsibility for local problems and to develop simple arts and crafts, and when the American system is in danger of disaster not only in the Northern Lakes Region but everywhere.

Finally, a combination of the second and third alternatives is possible, – or at least adoption of the second policy of liquidation carried out in such a way as to conserve values of Indian culture in American life. In any case liquidation of the Indian community should not be hurried, and Indian assets might well serve as a means toward some of the ends involved. Indian culture and special abilities are the most neglected economic resources of the Reservation and could be used to advantage in helping residents of the Reservation to independence. Instead of being an isolating factor such a project "would constitute their peculiar donation to American life and give them an active instead of dormant group morale, and a basis (now lacking) for self respect. The process of gradual adaptation of the Indians to prevailing ways of life and belief could be accomplished without disregard of their own cultural donation.". . .

There should be no vacillation between alternatives. A vacillating policy is a possibility as bad as that of preserving the status quo. A history of vacillation in the past is partly responsible for evils of the present. A future policy of consistent procedure toward one reasonable objective is needed.

GEOGRAPHIC AND POLITICAL BOUNDARIES
IN UPPER SILESIA[1]
by R. Hartshorne

INTRODUCTION

Problems connected with political boundaries have frequently elicited the interest of geographers. In all countries with chronic or acute boundary problems the geographers are drawn into the general discussion, more or less as experts, and in some cases the professional geographer has actually been called upon to assist in the determination and demarcation of boundaries. The interest of the geographers in this subject appears to be strikingly practical rather than academic. While almost every geographer in Europe has concerned himself at some time in the past twenty years with some particular boundary problem, very few have attempted any systematic theoretical study of the problem as a whole. It could easily be shown that the practical contribution of geographers to the specific problems have suffered greatly from this lack of academic preparation. For the most part their work shows the earmarks of knowledge expert but unorganized; lack of technique, no recognized terminology, and no means of measurement. Hence, the pursuit of such vague concepts as "natural boundaries," a term seldom defined and usually meaning something different to each writer, and which Sieger, Maull, and Sölch have all admirably demonstrated should be banned from scientific literature.

The purpose of this paper is to suggest a method and some terminology that might be applicable for any border study. Upper Silesia will serve as the specific case study to be treated from the laboratory point of view.

This area is a part of the great border belt between Germans and Slavs, more specifically a border corner where Germans, Poles, Czechs, and Slovaks meet and mix. Divided politically before the war among three empires: Germany, Austria-Hungary, and Russia, it is likewise divided now, but with different lines, between Germany, Poland, and Czecho-Slovakia. Although in many respects geographically united, the area has never had political unity within itself, but rather was always a peripheral zone subject to the political expansion of neighboring states. In the course of the latter Middle Ages the various feudal duchies into which Silesia was divided were controlled successively by the kings of Poland, Bohemia, and finally, Austria. The separation of Silesia from Poland dates, for practical purposes perhaps from 1163, formally certainly from

1. _Annals AAG,_ vol. 23 (1933), pp. 195-224.

the renunciation of Silesia by Casimir the Great in 1355. Prussia entered the area first in the early eighteenth century when Frederick the Great, by means of the Silesian Wars, forced Maria Theresa to cede him the rich lowland of Lower Silesia, together with the then unimportant lowland of Upper Silesia. The highland areas, together with the Moravian Gate between them, remained however with Austria. Silesia therefore has been separated from Poland on the east for six or seven centuries and united more or less closely, to different states, chiefly German, on the south and west. It had no part in the historic divisions of Poland of the eighteenth century, which gave Galicia to Austria, Posen to Prussia, and the area between to Russia.

NATURAL DEFENSE BOUNDARIES

Perhaps because European boundaries are most commonly determined after armed conflict, the first consideration in drawing them has usually been their defensive character. In the Upper Silesian border area, strong natural lines or zones of defense are not to be found. The low mountains of the Sudetes and the Beskides, broken by many valleys, offer but minor aids to defense--in comparison say, with the High Tatra farther east between Poland and Slovakia. Far more open is the plain on the north, continuous from Germany into Poland, for the most part sufficiently well-drained by the headwaters of the Oder and the Vistula, and offering no obstacles excepting the minor ones presented by those streams.

Likewise for the purposes of peace-time control of the boundaries--against smuggling, etc.--little assistance is offered by nature. Only the rivers, where large enough to be uncrossable except by bridge or boat, are of some aid to the border patrol, and smuggling flourishes as one of the ordinary occupations of the region.

BOUNDARIES MARKED IN NATURE

International boundaries, particularly in well-populated areas, must be clearly and accurately marked. In former times boundary commissions depended so far as possible on any natural lines that could be used. In some parts of the Sudetes and the Beskides the crest-line is sufficiently well-marked to furnish such a line, but more commonly neither crest-line nor watershed is readily visible. This is particularly true on the plain, so that though the division there between Germany and Poland is roughly that of the drainage basin of the upper Oder on the one hand, and the Vistula and the Warta on the other, the actual watershed, hardly visible in the landscape, has never functioned in boundary drawing. Only the streams offer this second type of natural boundaries, which can better be called naturally marked boundaries, or boundaries marked in nature. For this purpose small streams are as suitable as large ones, perhaps even more so because more accurate. The centuries-old boundary between Silesia and Poland utilized such smaller streams through most of its course, whereas the most recent boundaries largely ignored them. These were drawn in the age in which international boundaries are marked with lines of stones each visible from the next. Even then however, the careless pedestrian, or child, may unwittingly find himself in the wrong country and be arrested under suspicion of smuggling or espionage.

The discussion so far has treated boundaries from the point of view of the bounding states as space-organisms requiring a defensive epidermis, so to speak, against undesirable invaders, whether armies, smugglers, or immigrants. But this point of view overlooks the original, primary function of boundaries, namely, to bound, i.e. to determine the limiting line on the earth's surface on one side of which all men and things are subject to the jurisdiction of one state, whereas the moment that line is crossed everything is subject to another state. Such a line has therefore enormous effect on the lives of the people whose citizenship it alone determines. Not merely under what government they must live, for what state be ready to fight and die, but even where they may sell their products, where to purchase their supplies, what language their schools must, for the most part, use, what history, literature and songs their children will be taught, under what national, cultural, and moral influence they will be brought up--all of these are determined for millions of people by the exact location of an international boundary line in such an area as this.

The remainder of this paper, therefore, is based on the assumption that where international boundaries run through settled areas, it is those areas rather than the bounding states that are most concerned, the inhabitants of the border regions rather than those in the internal areas of the states who are most to be considered in studying or locating boundaries.

The proper study of an international boundary is, then, primarily concerned with the associations, of all kinds, of the different parts of the border area with each of the bordering states. The geographer in particular is interested in those associations which be observes in the features of the landscape, but he may not leave out of consideration other very important associations. In both cases the associations are of two kinds: those similar in character and those, which, though perhaps dissimilar, have mutual interests. Each of these groups will be studied in detail.

BOUNDARIES BASED ON AREAS SIMILAR
IN LANDSCAPE FEATURES

Along margins of areas similar in landscape features, "natural boundaries" of a third sort can be drawn. Sölch calls these choren grenze or chorographic boundaries. The map shows six major types of landscape forms. Four are rural landscapes resulting from combinations of two principal contrasts: that between the low mountains and hill country on the south, and the level to gently rolling plain on the north, and that between cleared and cultivated land and extensive forests--the latter covering great stretches of sandy soil on the plain as well as the rougher parts of the highlands. Though these differ notably in appearance, they produce no major differences in interest such as would be served by, or of themselves justify, separation into different states. Quite different is the case of the mining and industrial landscapes developed on the continuous coal-field in one small part of the area. Here the population has in many respects more in common with that of Westphalia, the Black Country of England, or the Pittsburgh area than with its neighboring rural districts.

Something, therefore, might be said for a political separation of the entire mining and manufacturing region as a separate political unit were it not for the lack of any historical basis. But certainly the division of the industrial district into different states causes constant difficulties because of the multiplicity of associations that normally tend to develop between adjacent industrial towns. These will require more detailed treatment later.

Although the rural landscapes offer no major differences east and west of the border zone, they do show minor differences in the character and extent of development that are highly significant in reflecting differences in the social character of the populations. Some of these are suggested by the maps and pictures.

Fundamental is the marked decrease in accessibility to both railroads and road, east of the old Polish frontier. Even more marked is the difference in the quality of the raods. There are no paved roads, hard-surfaced roads are few, even the main routes between the largest cities are sometimes little more than field tracks. In consequence rural life is on a much more primitive subsistence basis.

While the fields show the same crops: rye, wheat, oats, hay, and the all-important potatoes--lesser care in cultivation and less use of fertilizers are reflected in notable decrease in crop yields, as shown on the maps of Polish geographers. Livestock are notably less in importance--the boundary shown on Finch & Baker's map of swine remains clearly marked today, though the political basis for it has been removed.

Farmyards and farm buildings reflect likewise the more primitive stage. In contrast to the predominating brick or stone houses west of this line are the frame and rough-hewn log huts, commonly with thatched roofs, that predominate east of this cultural divide.

Similar differences are seen in the towns. One is impressed, as was De Martonne, by the frequent lack of sidewalks, by dwellings which would not be tolerated west of the divide, the workers' barracks with bare dirt between them, and by the incompleteness of water and sewerage system, developed only since the war, even in larger centers. In general all parts of the industrial towns look like the worst parts of those west of the former German frontier.

The total impression of all these differences is such that anyone travelling ten miles across this cultural landscape boundary between Silesia and old Poland, feels that he has travelled farther than from Chicago to Silesia.

HUMAN BOUNDARIES

The boundaries of the different population groups of the region--Germans, Poles, Czechs, Slovaks--have little manifestation in the landscape; are, if you like, non-geographic (though some students include these also in "natural boundaries"). Even the language seen on the street signs, in the railroad stations, and in other public places, reflects in many cases not the language of the inhabitants but merely the official language of the state. Nevertheless in studying a boundary problem the geographer must not ignore these factors since they may, as in this case, constitute the very cause of the problem.

Race, in the strict anthropological sense, has in this district, as in general in Europe, no geographical, and perhaps no cultural significance. Teutonic and Slavic stocks are hopelessly intermixed with no more correlation with present language or nationality groups than blondes and brunettes in England. All the differences in the population that are of significance for the border study are of cultural, not of biological origin.

The important boundaries in this area are those of language, of folk (Volk, as the Germans say) as distinct from language, of religion, and of nationality, the last being in large part a product of the others. The religious boundary, elsewhere on the German-Polish border zone so important, is hardly found here, as almost the entire area, regardless of nationality, is strongly Roman Catholic.

In Upper Silesia, as generally in Eastern Europe, the language boundary is exceedingly difficult to draw. Except for the definitely German county of Leobschütz and the district of Moravian dialect in Hultchini, the entire plebiscite area of 1921 was a region of two languages, with predominately Polish or predominately German communities close together, and with many people using both languages. Before this division German predominated in the middle-class urban centers, Polish in the poorer workers' districts, in the coal-mining towns, and for the most part in the poorer farming areas. In total, the overwhelming majority are the descendants of Polish-speaking peasants native in the area, and retain a Polish dialect as their native tongue. The German population did not originate from political colonization but rather: first, in small part from centuries-old settlements of Middle German farmers who maintained their language and culture in the midst of the Poles; second, from the middle-class urban population who migrated from other parts of Germany into the growing cities during the past century and a half, and finally, not least, from the voluntary Germanization of thousands of Polish workers who, in moving from the country to the industrial cities, took on German language along with city ways. The latter tendency was so marked as to warrant the conclusion in 1915, that the industrial district itself would within one or two decades show a German majority.

The Czechish-German boundary lies for the most part well within Czecho-Slovakia so that the western part of the provice of

Silesia in that country is almost solidly German in language. Where the linguistic line crossed north of the pre-war boundary, in the Hultchini district, the political boundary was changed, in the Treaty of Versailles, to conform roughly to it--though without consulting the wishes of the inhabitants, later shown to be opposed to the change. But where the language line lies south of the political line, in the Sudetes, no such changes were considered.

In Teschen Silesia there is considerable mixture of Polish and Czechish speaking peoples. The new state boundary dividing the area between Czecho-Slovakia and Poland was drawn somewhat east of the language divide. Most extraordinary is the case of the city of Teschen, where all three language groups are present, the German predominating, and which has been split between Poland and Czecho-Slovakia.

The Polish spoken in Silesia differs greatly from standard Polish, as would be expected in an area separated from Poland for over seven centuries and ruled by peoples of different tongues. Some Moravian and many German words are used with Polish endings, and many old Polish words are found which are obsolete elsewhere (cf. Canadian French). But careful students, including Germans, agree that the difference between this so-called "Wasserpolnisch" and standard Polish is no greater than that between Bavarian and High German. The important point is that when the Silesian Pole speaks his dialect, Poles from the outside can, with some difficulty, understand and speak with him, Germans cannot. The essential community of language must therefore be recognized as one major factor connecting most of the population of the region with Poland.

On the other hand in such elements of social culture of the whole population (as distinct from individuals) as education, social character and standards, living conditions, etc., there is a marked cleavage between the Silesian Poles and those of Galicia and former Russian Poland. The pre-war frontier remains as the boundary between the area of nearly universal education and that of high illiteracy, between the countries in which cleanliness is considered essential and those where dirt and insects are easily accepted, between the areas where social welfare is an important function of the state and those where beggary is a regular profession. It is also the western boundary of the area in which the large Jewish population represents a separate folk or even nationality, speaking their own language, Yiddish, wearing distinctive costumes, and living apart from the rest of the population.

All these differences, some of which are manifested in the cultural landscape as previously noted, are well recognized by the inhabitants on both sides of the cultural divide. They constitute a main reason for the fight of Polish Upper Silesia (Slask), including the Poles, to maintain autonomy within Poland. Certainly in many such ways, including the background of literature and art within the area, it can with some reason be maintained that Upper Silesia, though Polish in language, is German in culture. German writers commonly assume that this is the result of the many centuries of partial connection with the ancient German empire, but comparison with other sections along the former Polish–German border of more recent date, and the descriptions of Upper Silesia when taken over by Prussia from Austria, indicate that the present differences are largely the result of the century and a half of Prussian rule.

Most difficult of the human boundaries to determine is that of nationality. No country of Central Europe has made a reliable count of its nationalities. Some indication is given by minority party votes at parliamentary elections, but several of the postwar plebiscites showed that such votes were not trustworthy. Personal observations must be ruled out, both as inadequate and as unreliable. In Upper Silesia there is the official record of the national views of the inhabitants recorded in the plebiscite of March 21, 1921. The reliability of that vote has been disputed from both sides because of the undeniable pressure brought to bear on the voters by landlords, employers, priests, officials, and terroristic bands. Nevertheless the fact that over 90% of those eligible to vote actually cast their votes in what was generally admitted to have been a peaceful and secret vote, honestly counted, appears to justify accepting the results as fairly representative of what the population felt at the time. Particularly significant is the fact that, in addition to practically the entire German-speaking population, a large proportion, perhaps 40%, of those speaking Polish likewise professed German nationality as many even in the now Polish part still do. Geographically the results of the plebiscite were so confused as to make it impossible to draw a definite nationality boundary. Simplifying the map on the basis of combining districts with important geographic connections brings out two boundaries. West of one of these, German nationality clearly predominates, east of the other, Polish. But between them is a large rural area with a small Polish majority, and the all-important industrial district practically surrounded by Polish areas, but with a definite German majority (54%).

The actual boundary finally determined, by recommendation of the Council of the League of Nations, compromised by splitting the industrial district, although it was not possible to do so without having a slight German majority in the portion of that district awarded to Poland. The central rural area of small Polsih majority was of necessity then left to Germany. Another rural district, around Lublinitz, with a slight German majority, was however, quite unnecessarily awarded to Poland. The new political boundary could not therefore be claimed to conform to a nationality boundary.

Since the partition there has been considerable change, both in sentiment and in shift of population. The study of the minority movement of each side indicates, I think, that no district including both town and country on either side of the line could now show a majority vote for the foreign nationality. In other words, the new political boundary has perhaps forced the nationality boundary to conform to it.

BOUNDARIES OF AREAS ASSOCIATED BY TRADE

In determining political boundaries it is obviously desirable, in addition to maintaining the unity of regions of similar character to associate together so far as practicable, regions having important economic interrelations. Thus more significant than the landscape boundary between the plain of Silesia and the Sudetes hill and mountain region would be, according to some students, an "organic" or "harmonic" boundary (also held to be a type of natural boundary) which would include a major portion of the highland area within the plain.

Likewise it is claimed the industrial district should be included with the country with which it was organically developed on the basis of sources of capital, technical equipment and management, and which provided, in comparison with the present Poland, the greater markets for the coal, iron and zinc.

A more significant conclusion, attested by the economic difficulties of this district both before and since the war, is that no boundary which excludes any of the surrounding territories from the market area of Upper Silesia--which any international boundary under present conditions would do--can be called an "organic boundary".

Upper Silesia suffers from the fact that it has politically a peripheral location with respect to each of the states concerned, but in consequence of its mineral deposits in the interior of the continent, it has an industrial development, a density of population, and an economic and strategic importance which can best be associated with a politically central location.

LOCAL ASSOCIATIONS WITHIN THE AREA

The more immediate local associations of different localities and districts within the border area was studied from several different angles. An attempt was made to find trade divides based largely on the road and railroad patterns. Natural barriers to trade, such as that found farther east in the High Tatra separating Slovakia from Galicia, are not to be found within this area, since roads and railroads find no impassable obstacles. Nevertheless natural communication divides of a lesser degree of effectiveness are to be noted. Thus the crest-lines of the Sudetes, the Beskides, and the Tatra, coinciding for the most part with the watershed between the streams of the northern plain and those of the Danube Basin, appear as well-marked, though not complete, trade divides. But where the low mountains break down in the Jesinky (Gesenke) and disappear entirely in the Moravian Gate no such divide is found. On the plain the original poverty of Upper Silesia east of the Oder, together with the mere factor of distance, led early to the development of all of eastern Upper Silesia as a dividing zone between the areas influenced from Breslau on the one hand or Krakow on the other. The modern development, particularly in the industrial area, has tended to break down the separating force of this zone, but a strong remnant remains following the pre-war frontier.

This former Polish frontier, one of the oldest boundaries in
Europe, is still one of the strongest divides on the map. Fewer
roads and railroads cross it than almost any other divide in this
part of Europe, outside of the high mountains. This is true not
merely in respect to the number of roads and railroads crossing
the line, even to-day, but also in the amount of traffic on them.
The force of long established connections, together with the influence of the marked social differences already noted on either side
of this line are stronger than the newer forces for national economic unity. Somewhat similar is the case of the former Russian-
Austrian frontier, so that two of the strongest divides on the map,
which may be called "antecedent boundaries," are no longer used
for international frontiers, but are included within the territory of
Poland.

Far less effective is the boundary which formerly divided
Silesia between Prussia and Austria, now the frontier of Germany
and Czecho-Slovakia. This is a "subsequent boundary" drawn less
than two hundred years ago as a compromise between the sword
of Frederick the Great and the diplomacy of Maria Theresa, passing through previously developed and united areas. Probably few
boundaries in Europe show as little relation to the road pattern.
Local trade areas of principal centers are artificially limited and
farmers forced to trade in more remote towns; highways in several
places are cut by salients of the other country; even villages are
cut in two. . . .

Although the road pattern appears largely unaffected by the
boundary, the traffic of course is greatly hindered by the tariff
walls, customs and pass stations. The change since the war at
the former Austrian stations from German-speaking officials to
Czechish has intensified the hindrances by introducing a narrow
language barrier where, for the most part, none existed before.

Along the new German-Polish frontier, there are, to be
sure, few such extreme instances, but the actual disruption is far
greater because of the importance of the industrial district through
which the line passes. In its curious double course through this
district the boundary crosses surely more lines of transportation
than any other equal stretch of international boundary in the world
(Fig. 26). Although a few of those shown on the map--one railroad
and six or seven roads--have been closed, the general pattern remains unchanged and the traffic, on the roads at least, although
certainly less than before, is vastly greater than that passing even
now across the abandoned, antecedent boundary.

In addition to the dense network of roads and railroads the
economic unity of the industrial triangle in the formerly German
area was strengthened by a narrow-gauge freight line connecting
the mines and factories, an interurban electric system, electric
power systems, and water supply systems covering, in each case,
almost the entire district. All of these were inevitably seriously
affected by the new boundary cutting across them, breaking the
streetcar lines at five points, each of the other systems at about a
dozen points. In each case the separate parts have been reorganized

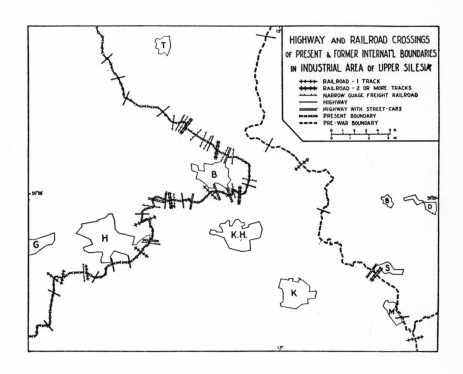

Fig. 26. Crossing places, German-Polish boundaries of before & after 1st World War.

on either side of the line and many of the connections permanently broken, but a large measure of connection and interrelation still remains, particularly across the peninsula of German territory at Beuthen. On the other hand, of all these systems only one has developed any connections across the old frontier, the interurban line to Sosnowiec and the Dombrow area (Fig. 26).

Unique is the relation of the new boundary to the mining operations. Property lines in this area are independent at three different levels: on the surface, in the overlying zinc-lead formations, and in the lower coal measures. In consequence it was impossible to avoid cutting many mining properties by the new boundary. Many workings have been definitely closed at the line, except for vital water and air connections; in nine coal mines and four zinc-lead mines mining has continued across the line underground, under special agreement, terminating in 1937; and two new mines, one coal and one zinc mine, though economically quite superfluous, have been constructed at a cost of several million dollars, in order that important coal and zinc deposits might be retained for Germany.

The mines and factories in the former German industrial district were closely tied together in major units, both vertically and horizontally, throughout the entire district, while there was almost no connection with those in the Dombrowa and Krakow districts across the old border. In the iron and steel industry adjustments to the new boundary have led to almost complete separation, in operations as well as ownership, of the plants on the now Polish side from those on the German side, but little or no connections have been made with individual plants across the former international, now merely provincial boundary. In the zinc industry, however, the fact that all the furnaces happen to be on the Polish side while some of the mines, washeries, and rolling mills, and nearly all of the markets, are located in Germany has caused this industry, even though divided corporately, to continue the movement of commodities back and forth across the new boundary.

For the individual inhabitants of this almost continuous urban district countless connections have been disrupted. Thousands of workers in mines and factories became foreigners with no rights of citizenship in the places of their work, and obliged to pass border inspection daily on their way to and from their homes. Thousands of related families living in neighboring towns, or in town and country, found themselves likewise separated from each other by the restrictions of the new boundary. The children of two such families are more or less forced to receive education in different languages, and taught to hate or despise each other's country.

The conclusion with reference to local associations is obvious. The former frontier, as an antecedent boundary, conformed to an extraordinarily strong and clearly marked divide, which has been but little altered after ten years; the new subsequent boundary was drawn across a great complex of intimate associations, many of which still remain. The old line separated locally, districts and peoples who were in many, though not all, important respects different from each other, whereas the new line through the industrial district conformed to no geographical or human boundaries. The force of this boundary, as built up by the tariff wall, by passport and other governmental restrictions, make it, in spite of the ameliorations of the Geneva Treaty, extraordinarily disruptive to local associations. With the termination of that agreement in 1937, the boundary will presumably be greatly strengthened as a barrier.

CONCLUSION

Upper Silesia, to summarize, is a border area in which the various geographic and human boundaries significant to states, instead of converging closely, diverge over a wide marginal zone which includes within it a major industrial district of dense population. The political boundaries, representing diplomatic compromises, add to the confusion, geographically, by neglecting for the most part any one geographic boundary, and thereby developing a new one, and, in particular, by cutting through the very type of cultural landscape least suitable for boundary location.

C H A P T E R   14

Derivatives of

Type 6   (Areal Uniformity)

The concept of areal uniformity and diversity
continues to be the most distinctive and well
recognized device in geography – though not the
only proper device, as for a while it seemed to
be considered. It is used in one form or another
in a majority of the field studies in this series.

After the systematic formulation by Jones and
Finch an immediate need was for extending the
field method to larger areas. Efforts in this
direction are exemplified in the railway and air
traverses included already in chapter 9 as
derivative examples of the traverse method
(type 1).

A part of "Augusta County, Virginia – A Study
of Patterns" by G. D. Hudson, 1935, is included here as an exhaustive effort to extend
the method by all available means – traversing,
sampling, interviewing and searching for compiled data, in view of the first six types in this
series, but especially type 6 (Areal Uniformity).
Aerial survey photographs would have been particularly useful in such work done under the
concept of areal uniformity and diversity, but
these did not become generally available until
shortly thereafter. Soon after the making of this

study Hudson undertook work along the same line for the Tennessee Valley Authority, and in that project aerial survey photographs were the principal base on which areal uniformity and diversity were recorded.

In recent emphasis on statistical studies in geography the idea of areal uniformity and diversity has commonly been taken for granted. Occasionally this has been overdone to the extent of taking for granted not only the general idea of uniformity but the specific areal units themselves from whatever source. Normally statistical studies in geography depend on data from other sources assembled in areal units by non-geographers and not collected in geographical field work. Accordingly the ready acceptance of untested areal units of assumed uniformity has made this a weak link in some otherwise sophisticated statistical work. But the need for testing can readily be filled when realized and even field study is not necessarily excluded from advanced work.

A pioneer example of statistical or mathematical geography is here included: "A Method of Mapping Densities of Population: with Cape Cod as an Example", by J. K. Wright, 1936. This does not take the areal units for granted; and it has a background of observation in the field, even though it uses no technical field method.

It is a successful application of statistical method to quantify more accurately some concepts of areal distribution and particularly to check and improve the areal units of distribution. It is concerned by choice with type 6 (Areal Uniformity) as providing a suitable approach.

This study serves also to represent population geography, in which geography overlaps demography and in which likewise data are generally from other sources and not from geographical field work. It employs the useful device of taking generalized population density as the criterion for distinguishing uniform areas. Thus people are not lost from the area, as they may be in a preoccupation with visible landscape, even though they are found only in the generalized static form of areal uniformity.

The concept of areal uniformity has been applied first and most in rural areas. But it is no less applicable in urban geography. "Field Mapping of Residential Areas in Metropolitan Chicago" by W. D. Jones, 1931, is a direct sequel to "Field Mapping in the Study of the Economic Geography of an Agricultural Area" by Jones and Finch, 1925.[1] This is a pioneer effort to carry the method from the country to the city.

The primary interest in areal uniformity extends over areas of landscape and is not directed to urban functions. So this interest is here expressed in primary concern with residential land use (covering larger areas), rather than

1. pp. 99-105 above.

with central business land use, even though the latter may have otherwise greater urban significance. The word "functions" is used in the study but only in a static sense, as in type 6 (Areal Uniformity).

The original publication of this study contains no maps, although the text is based on maps made in the field. The map included here is based on a fragmentary field map by Wellington Jones and recent field work done under the specifications in the text by J. D. Clarkson, 1958.

A later application in urban geography of the same concept, of areal uniformity, is represented by "A Unit Area Method of Mapping Gross Land-Use Associations in Urban Regions" by A. K. Philbrick, 1952. This shows a recent phase of the method in which Wellington Jones pioneered. This is urban morphology presented now in connection with interpretation of a city as a functional phenomenon and not merely as a mosaic of landscape uniformities. The work uses the ideas of type 6 (Areal Uniformity) but is made in view of type 7 (Areal Organization) also and of all previous stages.

In this study the concept of areal uniformity and diversity is not taken as a statement of inherent characteristics in the landscape to be found there by observation, but is treated as a flexible device to be applied in strict consistency with complex abstract criteria to reveal otherwise unknown aspects of the urban pattern.

The idea of areal uniformity and diversity expressed in a mosaic of generalized spaces is practically indispensible in modern geography as a device applied in connection with any dominant concept. But hopes of giving more elaborate idealized formulation to landscape regionality as the dominant unifying concept by itself have been disappointed – hopes expressed theoretically in "The Morphology of Landscape" by C. O. Sauer, 1925,[1] from which the author turned quickly and successfully to the unifying concept of culture process; and hopes expressed again differently in the "Compage" of D. S. Whittlesey, 1952,[2] lacking a unifying process in its nodal form if divorced from functional organization in dynamic form. Nevertheless it is not to be forgotten that even such abortive efforts have been stimulating and revealing steps along the way in the development of geographic thought and method.

---

1. *Univ. of Calif. Publ. in Geog.*, vol. 2, 1925, pp. 19-53.
2. "The Regional Concept and the Regional Method" in *American Geography: Inventory and Prospect*", pp. 35-51.

AUGUSTA COUNTY, VIRGINIA - A STUDY OF PATTERNS [1]

by G. D. Hudson

Section 1. Area, Purpose, And Plan

The Location of the County. - Augusta County lies in the
northwestern part of Virginia, occupying approximately the upper
third of the Shenandoah Valley. The eastern and western boundaries of the county follow the summits of mountain ranges, the Blue
Ridge on the east and the Shenandoah on the west. The southern
boundary extends across the valley from ridge to ridge, following
in a general way the divide between the head streams of the James
and Shenandoah rivers. The northern boundary cuts across the
valley at right angles to its axis. The county thus forms an approximate square. It measures roughly thirty-three miles from east
to west and thirty-one miles from north to south, enclosing 1,006
square miles within its borders. . . .

The Purpose and Plan of the Study. - This dissertation is
concerned with outstanding patterns of Augusta County. It is based
on detailed quantitative data, the accumulation of which followed a
preliminary but thorough reconnaissance survey of the county.
These data were accumulated from two sources, namely, systematic
traverses and census schedules covering individual farms. In the
development of the methods adopted and the subsequent use of the
data obtained, the technical problem arose of how to apply fractional and other recently developed techniques to an area the size
of Augusta County. In addition to presenting a pattern treatment of
Augusta County, therefore, this dissertation represents an experiment in scale of geographic research in point of area, time,
and detail.

The methods used. - The methods devised are based upon the
theory of sampling. The first step involved the use of an arbitrary
grid that divided the county into 115 equal area rectangles, measuring two and one-half miles by four miles. Each of these rectangles was studied in the field and on the basis of census data.

1. Measurements made in the field. - Field measurements
were made by running a series of road traverses across the county. Ninety-six of the total 115 rectangles were included. The remaining seventeen were not included because they are without
roads. Without exception, however, these seventeen rectangles
covered areas that could be seen to be virtually entirely wooded,
and they were so recorded. In making the traverses a record was
made for each side of the road of the frontages of each type of land
utilization. These frontages were measured with a double crop-
frontage meter.

1. Dept. of Geog., Univ. of Chicago, 1935.

The isopleth method was employed in determining and presenting the distribution of the many items studied. The frontages obtained in each rectangle were expressed in terms of their percentages of the total length of roads traversed in that rectangle. For example, if the total frontage of corn land on the roads of a given rectangle was found to be one mile, and the total length of roads traversed in that rectangle came to ten miles, the frontage of corn land was expressed as 10 per cent of the total. On the assumption that the ratio of the frontage of corn land to the total length of the roads traversed is the same as the ratio of corn acreage to the total area of the rectangle, the amount of corn land was taken to be 10 per cent of the total. To determine the distribution pattern of corn land, these percentages were plotted on a map of the county, each figure being placed in the center of the rectangle it represented. The precentages were grouped into convenient class intervals and isopleths were drawn, representing the upper and lower limits of the intervals. The areas thus marked off by the isopleths, because more than one rectangle was enclosed, are described throughout the study in terms of the upper and lower limits of the class intervals. . . .

The techniques employed. - In determining the final distribution patterns in connection with both the field and census data, isopleths were drawn according to their numerical position in relation to the centrally placed figures in each rectangle unless known factors drawn from maps, the literature, or from observation in the field warranted their deviation. The methods employed in connection with field and census data involved, then, the application of such established techniques of research in geography as observation, photographic and written records, compilation, reconnaissance, the traverse, and the isopleth. In addition, for the first time, an equal area, small mesh grid is used giving the traverse areal as well as lineal application and census data are distributed over a sizable area in units less than townships. In connection with the urban parts of the county, the conventional classification and methods of mapping were employed. Essential details that could not be observed in the landscape were obtained through interviews with appropriate persons. . . .

Section 4.   The Patterns of Rural Land Utilization

The rural uses made of land constitute the principle components of the county's patterns and reveal the county's dominantly agricultural personality. The total area of Augusta County is 1,006 square miles, or approximately 641,920 acres. About 635,920 acres can be classified as rural land, the remaining six thousand being taken up by the two towns, Staunton and Waynesboro. Nearly 55 per cent of the rural land, 346,047 acres, is in farms. The rest is, for the most part, forested. Not all of the farm land produces agriculturally. There are 38,648 acres of unpastured woodland, 1,275 acres on which crops failed, 5,254 acres of idle or fallow land, and 12,934 acres in farmsteads, and other agri-

culturally non-productive uses. This makes a total of 58,111 acres
of farm land which do not produce agriculturally, leaving a total of
287,936 acres of productive agriculture land, or 42 per cent of the
area of the county. There are, then, three major types of land in
the county: (1) productive agricultural land, (2) non-productive
agricultural land, and (3) non-agricultural land. The uses to which
these three major classes of land are put and the physical settings
to which they are related are brought out in the sections that follow.

The Five Major Divisions of the County. - The patterns of
rural land utilization in Augusta County are based on the uses made
of the land and the uses made of the products of the land. On these
bases five major divisions become evident, namely: (1) the non-
agricultural forested mountain division, (2) the woodlands-pasture
foothill division, (3) the pasture-crop-woodlands valley plain division, (4) the pasture-crop rolling plain division, and (5) the crop-
pasture undulating plain division (Fig. 27).

The non-agricultural forested mountain division. - The non-
agricultural forested mountain division, as revealed by the isopleths
of 100 per cent unpastured woodland and forests, falls into three
sections: (1) along the eastern boundary of the county the forested
mountain slopes form a strip about one mile wide from the northern
county boundary to a point east of Sherando. At that point it bulges
westward, covering approximately forty square miles in the southeast corner of the county. (2) The forested area of North and Crawford mountains constitute an irregular, elongated north-south
section, pointed at both ends. It measures about three miles at its
widest point and is about sixteen miles long. (3) The Shenandoah
forested area is about eight miles wide along the northern county
boundary. It maintains this width to Jennings Gap. From there it
tapers off rapidly, curving westward around the head of Calf
Pasture Valley in a strip from one to three miles wide.

Most sections are above the two thousand foot contour line.
Excellent views are thus provided of the foothills and valley plains
that lie below. Attractive ruggedness is provided by steep slopes,
innumerable narrow valleys, and sharp, rocky ridges and cliffs.
Scattered here and there throughout the mountains are small park-
like areas, some natural and some representing old clearings.
These give pleasant variety to the mountain scenery. All of the
slopes are wooded, some quite heavily. The entire division is cut
by mountain streams, many of them broken at frequent intervals
by water falls and rapids. During the months of rain they are
rushing torrents, but during the dry months many of the streams
disappear, leaving deep, rock-strewn gorges. The soils are, for
the most part, the coarser types of the residual shale and sandstone group. Alluvial soils occur in the valleys and residual
granites occur on the higher levels of the Blue Ridge. All the soils
are shallow and low in fertility, and many of them are broken by
outcrops and strewn with rocks and boulders. Although these
mountain sections are sought for recreational purposes because
of their natural beauty, this function is decidedly secondary to the
major function. As forest preserves they play an important part

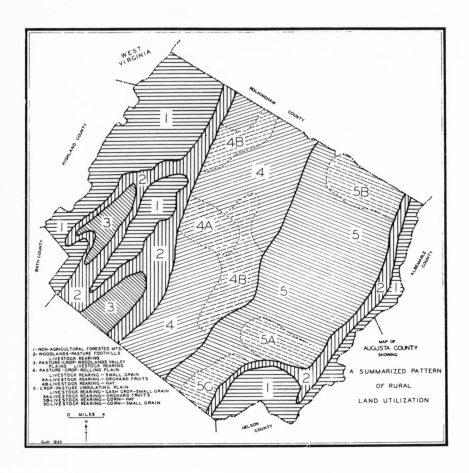

Within the map:

WEST VIRGINIA

ROCKINGHAM COUNTY

HIGHLAND COUNTY

BATH COUNTY

ALBEMARLE COUNTY

NELSON COUNTY

1 — NON-AGRICULTURAL FORESTED MTS.
2 — WOODLANDS-PASTURE FOOTHILLS
        LIVESTOCK REARING
3 — PASTURE-CROP-WOODLANDS VALLEY
        PLAINS   LIVESTOCK REARING
4 — PASTURE-CROP-ROLLING PLAIN
        LIVESTOCK REARING — SMALL GRAIN
    4A — LIVESTOCK REARING — ORCHARD FRUITS
    4B — LIVESTOCK REARING — HAY
5 — CROP-PASTURE UNDULATING PLAIN
        LIVESTOCK REARING — CASH CROP — SMALL GRAIN
    5A — LIVESTOCK REARING — ORCHARD FRUITS
    5B — LIVESTOCK REARING — CORN — HAY
    5C — LIVESTOCK REARING — CORN — SMALL GRAIN

0   MILES   4

N

MAP OF
AUGUSTA COUNTY
SHOWING

A SUMMARIZED PATTERN

OF RURAL

LAND UTILIZATION

GuH 1933

Fig. 27. Map of qualitative distinctions in areal uniformity. "A summarized pattern of rural land utilization. To present a complete geographic summary of the land utilization of an area at least three things should be included, namely, the major uses of the land, the major natural factors to which the uses are related, and the major uses of the products of the land. This pattern represents an attempt to present Augusta County in this manner. It is a composite of those foregoing patterns that are based on field data and the uses that are made of the products of the land as determined by the census data. The titles of the five divisions thus obtained reveal the major uses of the land and the topographic features to which they are intimately related. The secondary titles indicate the major uses of the products of the land, livestock rearing, and the primary non-livestock crops that are grown. Each of the first three divisions are relatively uniform in the three items represented. The last two show some variation. These variations are characterized in tertiary titles, names for the major sub-divisions".

-272-

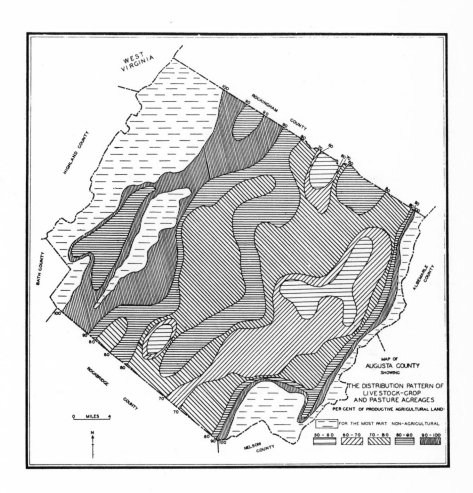

Fig. 28. Map of uniformity and diversity on a quantitative scale. "The distribution pattern of livestock-crop and pasture acreages (per cent of productive agricultural land)".

in the control of floods, the retardation of erosion, and the development of power and transportation in the Great Valley of which they are a part. With proper care and development they also can play an important part in the supplying of timber for future generations.

The woodland-pasture foothill division. - The woodland-pasture foothill division consists of two belts. The first forms a strip averaging about one and a half miles wide along the base of the Blue Ridge from the northern to the southern county boundary. The other belt lies in the western part of the county. It is about two miles wide from the northern boundary in the Stokesville area to Jennings Gap, forming a strip along the bases of Narrow Back and Lookout mountains. At Jennings Gap it divides into two bands. One band continues southward along the bases of Crawford and North mountains, widens out to include Little North Mountain, and then divides to form a short, narrow strip on each side of Little Calf Pasture Valley. The other band continues southward from Jennings Gap, dividing into two narrow strips, one on each side of Calf Pasture Valley.

A relatively small amount of the land in these areas produces agriculturally, the remaining sections being, for the most part, unpastured woodlands. The distribution of these two types of land, is, as was previously noted, definitely related to the topographic features of the land. Nearly all of the productive agricultural land is in pasture, some cleared, and some wooded. The distribution of these pastures is related to topographic features and to the prevalence of coarse, residual shale and sandstone soils, relatively low in fertility. Obviously the pastures in these ares can be used only for the rearing of livestock. The result is, that from 90 to 100 per cent of the productive agricultural land can be classified as livestock land (Fig. 28). What remains is used, primarily for producing food for the families of farm operators.

The pasture-crop-woodlands valley plain division. - The pasture-crop-woodlands valley plain division consists of the plain areas in the two Calf Pasture valleys. The Calf Pasture area forms a rough triangle with its base extending east and west across Hamilton Draft and Calf Pasture valleys. It is about four miles wide at the base and about ten miles long from base to apex. The Little Calf Pasture area forms a loop with its base at the southern county boundary. It is about four miles wide and eight miles long.

Most of the land in these two areas is used for pasture, some is cultivated, hay being the dominant crop, and some is in unpastured woodland. These uses are associated with the topographic and soil features of the land. Narrow bands of relatively level land and alluvial soils border the streams. These areas are used primarily for pastures and crops. The rest of the land is rolling to steep, and is provided, for the most part, with coarse residual shale and sandstone soils. Pastures and unpastured woodland dominate these sections. Not so much of the productive agricultural land is used for livestock rearing as in the foothill areas. The percentage thus used ranges from 80 to 90 (Fig. 28). The small remaining proportion is about equally divided between cash crops and foodstuffs for family consumption.

The pasture-crop rolling plain division. - The pasture-crop rolling plain division is bounded on the west by the western belt of foothills. The eastern boundary divides the major valley plain into halves, following rather closely the Valley Pike and roughly approximating the isopleth of 45 per cent harvest land. Thus included in this division are the more rolling sections of the major valley plain, the eastern halves of the two western quadrants noted in connection with the landscape view of the county. The soils are almost exclusively of limestone origin, with fine sandy, silt, and clay loams predominating, and gravelly and stony clay loams holding prominent, though secondary ranks.

Pastures occupy most of the productive agricultural land, a use that is associated with the rolling topography and prevalence of excellent limestone soils. Small grain is the leading crop in most sections of the division. Three exceptions occur. Hay is the leading crop in a diagonal belt of land that lies between Mt. Solon, and Parnassus and Centerville (Fig. 27). It is also the leading crop in the central portion of the division around, and north and south of Staunton. Commercial orchards between Swoope, Churchville and Staunton give orchards a prominent place among the crops in that section, sharing first ranks with hay.

This division is distinctly a livestock rearing area except in the commercial orchard section (Fig. 28). In five of the twelve rectangles in the northern part of the division between 90 and 100 per cent of the productive agricultural land is used for livestock rearing purposes; in three, from 80 to 90 per cent of the land is so used; and in four, the percentage of the productive agricultural land used for livestock is between 70 and 80. In five of the thirteen rectangles that occupy the southern part of the division from 80 to 90 per cent of the productive agricultural land is used for rearing livestock; in seven rectangles the percentage is between 70 and 80; and in the last, a small grain area, between 50 and 60 per cent of the productive agricultural land is so used. In one of the four middle rectangles from 80 to 90 per cent of the productive agricultural land is used for livestock. In twenty-five of the twenty-six rectangles thus far noted, then, less than 25 per cent of the productive agricultural land is in cash crops. In the small grain section noted in the southern part of the division 40 per cent of the land is in cash crops, small grain being the leading crop. The remaining three of the four middle rectangles include the commercial orchards previously noted. In these rectangles between 25 and 30 per cent of the productive agricultural land is in cash crops, that is, orchards, whereas pastures and livestock crops occupy from 70 to 75 per cent of the productive agricultural land. Taking the division as a whole, a smaller percentage of the productive agricultural land is used for supplying products directly to the families of farm operators than in the divisions already treated. In general, the percentage so used ranges from 1 to 5, with the majority of rectangles around 2 per cent.

The crop-pasture undulating plain division. - The crop-pasture undulating plain division occupies the eastern half of the major valley plain. It thus includes the broad undulating plain of the lower Middle River Valley and of South River Valley. The soils are of three main types, forming three longitudinal belts of approximately equal size. From west to east they are: (1) a V-shaped area of "blue slate" land, residual shales, (2) limestone soils, mostly fine sandy and silt loams, and (3) residual soils from old alluvial deposits. A fourth type, deep, rich, alluvial soils is scattered in narrow bands along the many streams of the division. In all rectangles included in the division more productive agricultural land is used for livestock rearing purposes than for any other purpose, but in twenty-five of the thirty-one rectangles the percentage of land so used is below 75 (Fig. 28). In other words, this division should be characterized as a livestock rearing-cash crop area. Two sections are exceptions to this general rule. One section includes the four eastern of the northern row of five rectangles. In these rectangles from 75 to 90 per cent of the productive agricultural land is used for livestock. In them, pastures, corn, and hay are prominent features. The other section includes the two southernmost rectangles that border the foothills. In them from 75 to 80 per cent of the productive agricultural land is used for livestock. This section is, essentially, a pasture-corn-small grain area. In other words, then, these two sections are like the preceding division just as the commercial orchard area of the preceding division is like this one.

The remaining twenty-five rectangles show some individual variations, but they are alike in that from 25 to 47 per cent of the productive agricultural land is in cash crops. Most of this acreage is in wheat, but in some sections, particularly those between Stuarts Draft and Sherando, and to a less degree, those around Staunton and Waynesboro, orchards occupy enough land to stand out in the cash crop acreage. Roughly speaking, the western margin of the division is occupied by seven transitional rectangles with the cash-crop acreage amounting to between 25 and 30 per cent of the productive agricultural land. In the central and north-central rectangles, numbering fourteen, the amount of cash-crop land is from 30 to 47 per cent of the productive agricultural acreage with the higher percentages in the areas of larger wheat acreages. Of the remaining three rectangles, those lying around and between Stuarts Draft and Sherando, the two westernmost, have a cash-crop acreage of around 35 per cent of the productive agricultural land. The last has a percentage of only seventeen. In these three rectangles the cash-crop is primarily orchard fruits. As a whole, this division is much the same as the preceding one as to the amount of land that is used for producing farm foodstuffs. In general, the percentage of productive agricultural land thus used averages about two.

<u>Livestock Rearing in August County</u>. . . <u>Summary</u>. - Through the treatment of the distributions of the major types of livestock, it is evident that the main factors involved are: (1) the amount of land producing agriculturally, and (2) the amount of agricultural land used for livestock crops and pasture. In other words, higher densities occur where a relatively large amount of land produces agriculturally, where the pasture acreages are relatively large, where the livestock crop acreages are relatively large, and where the two combined constitute a relatively large amount of land. It also is evident that livestock rearing is of major importance in the county at least in terms of land used for that purpose.

The interest in this type of agriculture, is, in large measure, a reflection of the qualities of the land that make possible the production of excellent bluegrass pastures and abundant hay. The importance of cattle and sheep, as compared to other types of livestock, is in keeping with these pasture and crop conditions. The relative proximity of densely peopled industrial areas in the Eastern Seaboard, not to mention the market possibilities of Staunton and Waynesboro, goes far toward providing an explanation for the attention paid commercial dairy farming in the cattle rearing phases of Augusta County agriculture. The sparse, though relatively even distribution of swine and poultry, indicates the subsistence nature of these types of livestock rearing and the relatively sparse distribution of horses reveals, in large measure, their primary function as farm work animals. . . .

<u>Productivity and the Five Major Divisions of the County</u>. - The patterns of rural land utilization and those displaying the distribution of livestock furnished abundant evidence of the relative agricultural importance of the five major divisions of the county described in Section Four. The pattern showing the relative productivity of productive agricultural land adds sufficient evidence to leave no doubt as to the relative agricultural importance of these divisions. The first division, the non-agricultural forested mountains, can be disregarded in this connection. The woodland-pasture foothills division is distinctly low in productivity as compared to the remaining three divisions. Even the pasture-crop-woodlands division is below average, a fact that is indicated by the presence of woodlands in the combination of major land uses. The last two divisions stand out, as would be expected, as the more productive of the five. There is, however, an observable difference between the two. The pasture-crop rolling plain division is quite evidently less productive than the crop-pasture undulating plain division. It is about equally divided between land slightly below average, average, and slightly above average in productivity. Most of the land in the crop-pasture undulating plain division, on the other hand, is average or better, and of these two classes, the latter covers slightly more area. The situation these patterns depict finds its expression in the relative prosperity of the various parts of the county. . . .

Section 8.   Findings and Conclusions

The findings and conclusions of this investigation divide into two groups. Group one deals with the patterns studied, and group two deals with the methods and techniques employed.

Group I.   Findings and Conclusions Dealing With Patterns

The findings and conclusions dealing with patterns are centered around the thirteen patterns presented in the foregoing pages, but it should be understood that they are based on the eighty-nine patterns included in the complete manuscript. As presented here the findings and conclusions are classified under the four major aspects of land utilization in the county.

Uses Made of Rural Areas. - The outstanding importance of agriculture in Augusta County is demonstrated by two patterns dealing with the uses made of rural areas.

1. A summarized pattern of rural land utilization. - The summarized pattern of rural land utilization (Fig. 27) brings out two major characteristics of the county, namely, the striking simplicity of the agricultural pattern and its close adherence to the longitudinal grain of the county. The former is indicated by the five well-defined divisions. The latter indicates the primary importance of topography and the secondary importance of soils in the broader uses of the land. When compared with the patterns of population and transportation the summarized pattern of rural land utilization displays the close correlation that holds between the intensity with which rural land is used, the density of population, and the spacing of highways.

With specific reference to pasture land Fig. 27 shows:

(1) that, taking the county as a whole, pasture land is more important than harvest land;

(2) that pasture land is of outstanding importance in the plains of the minor valleys and in the marginal and western portions of the major valley plain, whereas, it is of minor importance in the eastern portion of the major valley plain;

(3) that pasture land is closely associated with woodland areas, with rolling to hilly land, and with soil types that are coarse, comparatively low in fertility, or not well adapted to cultivation;

(4) that pasture land, in its distribution, indicates the areal extent of land used for rearing livestock and partially explains the distribution of population, the irregularities in the transportation pattern, the relative intensity with which the land is used, the variations in the size of land holdings, and the relative prosperity of various parts of the county; and

(5) that, taking the county as a whole, pasture land represents a wise adjustment to the natural resources of the area.

With reference to crop land Fig. 27 points to:

(1) the close relationship between the use of land for crops and the occurrence of relatively level to gently rolling land and fine-textured, relatively fertile soils;

(2) the primary importance of topography and the secondary importance of soils in the distribution of crop land;

(3) the relative unimportance of livestock rearing in the eastern portion of the valley plain in terms of area given to that purpose;

(4) the close association of crop land with population densities, with closely spaced highways, with the intensive use of land, with comparatively small land holdings, and with relative agricultural prosperity; and

(5) the effective use that is being made to the resources of the area.

With reference to non-agricultural land Fig. 27 shows conclusively that Augusta County is of major importance as a watershed and timber area in the Shenandoah River system and that the segregation of these areas from the predominantly agricultural portions of the county should make for the effective use and efficient administration of both types of land. . . .

Group 2. Findings and Conclusions
Dealing with Methods of Research

An Evaluation of the Methods Used. - The size and nature of the area selected, and the resources that were available precluded the strict application of the fractional and certain other detailed methods. The problems relative to research methods thus became: (1) how could these methods be modified to meet the requirements of the study, (2) what new methods could be devised that would permit a maximum amount of detail investigation, and (3) on how large a scale could the study be carried forward without endangering the accuracy or reliability of the work and without sacrificing any essential details. In evaluating the methods, then, two major questions arise, namely: (1) do the methods permit a maximum amount of detailed investigation in relation to the size of the area and available resources, and (2) was the area selected too large, endangering the accuracy or reliability of the work and sacrificing essential details.

1. The amount of detailed investigation. It is relatively impossible to determine whether or not the maximum amount of detailed investigation was attained. There is conclusive evidence, however, that the amount obtained is more than adequate in terms of the scale of operations adopted. Major items that should be noted are:

(1) each of the rectangles into which the county was divided covered ten square miles, an area small enough, in terms of the agricultural pattern of the county, to provide data sufficiently detailed to bring out not only the uses of the land but the efficacy of the uses to which it is put;

(2)   the entire county was included in the study; (a) nearly 90
      per cent of the county was covered by sample field
      measurements, (b) approximately 75 per cent was cov-
      ered by sample census data, and (c) the areas not cov-
      ered by either (a) or (b) were covered by field obser-
      vations;
(3)   the field measurements were in the form of traverses,
      a form of geographic research that has already proven
      its worth, and the sample census data, in most cases,
      covered not less than 10 per cent of the rectangle it
      represented, a sample sufficiently large to promise
      reliability;
(4)   the data obtained concerned all major forms of rural
      land utilization, livestock densities, agricultural and
      financial income, and farm wealth;
(5)   urban areas were studied in sufficient detail to reveal
      the major features of their patterns, the major com-
      mercial, industrial, social, and political functions they
      performed, the efficacy with which the land was used
      and the services rendered, and their major maladjust-
      ments; and
(6)   in all cases the data were sufficiently detailed to dem-
      onstrate the relationships that existed between the uses
      made of the land and their physical settings.

2. Accuracy and reliability. A true test of the accuracy and
reliability of the methods used would involve a large amount of
statistical work, or the detailed mapping of a large portion of the
county, or both, -- a task larger in proportions than this study.
Without this definite proof there still remains sufficient evidence
in the study itself to warrant the assertion that for the scale of
operations adopted the results are strikingly reliable. Three
points, mentioned previously, should be noted again:
(1)   the high degree of coincidence in the areal distribution
      of closely associated items;
(2)   the high degree of coincidence in the areal distribution
      of identical items, one distribution based on field
      measurements, and one on census data; and
(3)   the failure to find significant discrepancies when the re-
      sults of field measurements and census data were
      checked against field observations.

The Place This Type of Research Has in the Field of Geography. - One of the major good qualities of the methods employed
in this study is that they are not entirely new, but represent, to a
considerable degree, modifications and new applications, of a
series of well established tools of geographic research including
the reconnaissance, the traverse, and the isopleth. The modifications and new applications removed much of the qualitative
aspects of these methods, whereas their quantitative aspects were
strengthened and applied on a scale heretofore impossible.

The need for these modifications and new applications has
been appreciated primarily only since the more detailed methods

were developed and thoroughly tested. In this sense, then, the experiment carried forward here is both appropriate and timely.
Refinements should and undoubtedly will be made. In their present
form, the techniques offered here constitute only the beginning of
the bridge that should span the valley from the qualitative reconnaissance of large areas to the very detailed study of relatively
small areas.

This experiment is appropriate and timely in another sense.
With the national point of view pointing toward a more united effort relative to the effective use of resources, there is a growing
need for methods of geographic research that have the accuracy
and reliability of the quantitative approach, but at the same time
strike for findings and conclusions of major significance and covering large areas. The methods herein employed should be
valuable in such undertakings. They should not supplant the more
detailed methods in all situations. Their major utility lies in their
ability to throw into relief accurately and in a relatively short time
the larger aspects of a given area upon the basis of which plans of
action can legitimately be inaugurated. In doing so they will bring
forward the phases or features of the area that should be studied
in more detail. The expense saved in time and money would be
great, but yet smaller than the savings in terms of the attainment
of the objective desired.

A METHOD OF MAPPING DENSITIES OF POPULATION:
WITH CAPE COD AS AN EXAMPLE[1]

by J. K. Wright

The first of the maps presented in Fig. 29 is a conventional
population map of Cape Cod in which a symbol for the density
covers the whole area of each township. The map is not particularly realistic. Anyone who has visited the region knows that
large parts of it are uninhabited. Terminal-moraine ridges run
parallel to the north and east shores of the Cape's "upper arm" --
to use a term implying comparison of the Cape to an arm shaking
its fist at the Atlantic. These moraines are wildernesses of
burnt-over land covered with scrub oak and stunted pine. Fringing
Nantucket Sound is a string of villages, but elsewhere the sandy
outwash plains that intervene between the moraines and the sound
are thinly peopled, and one often drives for several miles without
seeing a house. At the tip end of the Cape the map shows a

1. <u>Geog. Rev.</u>, vol. 26 (1936), pp. 103-110.

density of 200 to 500 to the square mile in the "fist". As a matter of fact, nearly all the people here live in the compact village of Provincetown along the harbor, and the greater part of the "fist" consists of sand dunes, where the density actually approaches zero. Most of this tract of dunes is maintained by the state as a reservation known as the Province Lands, where the vegetation is carefully fostered in order to prevent the sands from overwhelming the village. Fig. 29-1 gives no idea whatever of these local differences.

On Fig. 29-2 "uninhabited" areas have been marked off and densities calculated and plotted for the remaining parts of each township in which such areas occur. Just what is an uninhabited area? Conceivably on a map of extremely large scale one might classify one's back yard in this category. On the other hand, if all areas that people enter or cross from time to time are held to be inhabited, no part of the Cape could properly be regarded as uninhabited, for even the wildest parts are visited each year by hunters, berrypickers, forest wardens, or fire fighters.

The areas shown as "uninhabited" on Fig. 29-2 are, in general, either wastelands not in farms or areas occupied only part of the year by summer residents. They were determined in a rough-and-ready manner from an examination of the topographic sheets of the U. S. Geological Survey supplemented by personal recollections. Obviously their outlines are not precise, but, even so, everyone will concede that Fig. 29-2 is a more realistic density map than 29-1.

Similar rough-and-ready methods of mapping have been carried a stage further on Fig. 29-3. Here an attempt has been made to divide the inhabited areas within each township into tracts of different densities. In view of the fact that no population statistics exist for tracts smaller than townships on the Cape, Fig. 29-3 is based largely on guesswork. As will be explained, however, it is what might be called "controlled guesswork," and the picture is certainly more realistic--more truly geographical--than that furnished by either 29-1 or 29-2. Perhaps it is about the best that could be accomplished without intensive field work. Fig. 29-3 is based on "the premise that the distribution of population is not a phenomenon of uninterrupted, continuous gradation and hence is not properly portrayed by a system involving isopleths, as are portrayed such gradational phenomena as slope in topography or gradient in climatology." It is a map of the type to which the Russians have applied the term "dasymetric" (density measuring).

Another method by which the distribution of population within the townships could have been shown is the well known dot method. In this method the total population of each township determines the number of dots to be placed within its limits. On the basis of available evidence -- topographic maps, field observations, etc. -- the dots may be distributed so as to conform to what is believed to be the actual distribution of the people. This method, however, is hardly more precise than the method used of Fig. 29-3. On a dot map thus constructed, although the total number of dots to a town-

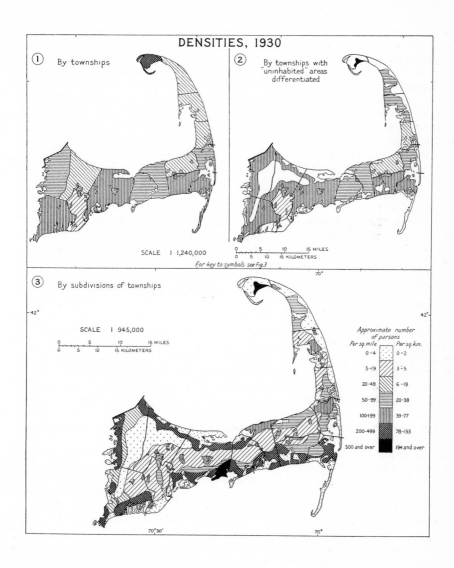

Fig. 29. *"Population Maps of Cape Cod"*, on a quantitative scale of density.

ship may be statistically correct, individual dots do not necessarily represent the exact population of the areas where they are placed. Similarly, on 29-3 the several densities assigned to the different parts of each township are consistent with the known density of the township as a whole (i.e. the density as shown on 29-1), though the individual density assigned to any given area may be inexact.

Such a map has one advantage over a dot map. It provides definite figures to which one may refer. For example, with reference to 29-3, one may write: "The map shows that the northeastern part of the township of Falmouth has a density of 5 to 19 to the square mile, whereas densities in excess of 200 to the square mile prevail over the southern part of the township." With a dot map one can merely state in vague terms that the dots are much more thickly clustered in the southern part of the township than in the northeastern part.

THE DISTRIBUTION OF POPULATION ON CAPE COD

Fig. 29-3 shows the distribution of the permanent population of the Cape as indicated by the census of 1930. Were it possible to map the densities in summer, certain localities along the Buzzards Bay and south shores appearing as very sparsely settled or uninhabited on 29-3 would probably contain some of the highest densities anywhere on the map. It has been suggested that house dots on the topographic sheets give a clue to the arrangement of the population. Unfortunately the topographic sheets for the Cape are not particularly useful in this respect because they show fewer houses than actually exist today or existed when the surveys were made in the late eighties. The Soil Survey map shows more house dots than the topographic sheets, but many of these dots stand for summer cottages, and the map offers no way of distinguishing between these cottages and houses occupied by the permanent residents. The same difficulty, moreover, exists in the case of aerial photographs. Indeed, the topographic sheets, incomplete as they may be, are perhaps a better guide than the Soil Survey map, because most of the house dots on them represent the older centers --the centers where the "natives" now reside.

The sparse densities indicated in the interior of the Cape's "upper arm" represent to a large extent a population of Portuguese immigrants from the Azores and the Cape Verde Islands. "These hard-working peasant folk successfully cultivate cranberry bogs and raise strawberries and vegetables on sandy soils that had long been avoided by Yankee farmers." Their presence probably accounts in part for the increases in population that have occurred in certain townships. It does not, however, furnish the entire explanation of these increases; for these same townships all contain villages that have become popular shopping centers for summer residents and tourists--Hyannis, Falmouth, Monument Beach, Buzzards Bay, Chatham. This fact has doubtless served to hold the local population as well as to attract outsiders. The barren outer Cape has fewer Portuguese, and, although many summer people go there, no one of the villages has developed as an important shopping center serving a large area, and the outer Cape, like many other parts of rural New England, has been losing population.

THE METHOD

It was pointed out above that the several densities assigned to the different parts of each township on Fig. 29-3 are consistent with the known average density for the township as a whole. Assume, for example, a townhip with a known average density of 100 persons to the square mile. Assume, further, that examination of topographic maps and consideration of other evidence have shown that this township may be divided into two parts, m, comprising 0.8 of the entire area of the township and having a relatively sparse population, and n, comprising the remaining 0.2 of the township and having a relatively dense population. If, then, we estimate that the density of population in m is 10 persons to the square mile, a density of 460 to the square mile must be assigned to n in order that the estimated densities m and n may be consistent with 100, the average density for the township as a whole.

The figure 460 for the density of n was obtained by solving the following fundamental equation:

$$\frac{D - D_m a_m}{1 - a_m} = D_n \text{ or } \frac{100 - 10(0.8)}{0.2} = 460,$$

where D is the average density of population of the township as a whole, D the estimated density in m, a_m the fraction of the total area of the township comprised in m, 1 - a_m the fraction comprised in n, and D_n the density that must accordingly be assigned to n.

D_m and a_m are estimated approximately. It is not necessary to measure a_m accurately, since the margin of error in a rough estimate is likely to be less than the margin or error in the best possible estimate of D_m. Study of neighboring townships sometimes gives a clue to a value that may reasonably be assigned to D_m. For example, the topographic map may show what would appear to be similar types of population distribution prevailing over T_m, or part of one township, and over the whole of S, an adjacent township. It would be reasonable, therefore, to assign to T_m a density comparable with the average density in S.

Having assigned estimated but consistent densities to two parts of a township, one may then divide each (or one) of these parts into two subdivisions and work out densities for the latter in the same manner; and the process may be repeated within each subdivision. Fig. 29-3 was prepared in this manner.

The method is merely an aid to consistency in apportioning estimated densities, either of population or of other phenomena, within the limits of townships or other territorial units for whose subdivisions no statistical data are available. Obviously it should not be applied in mapping densities of population within counties in the United States, since census figures are published for the townships and other minor civil divisions within the counties. On the other hand, it might well be applied in mapping various phenomena for which statistics are available by counties but not by minor civil divisions.

Table I enables one to solve the fundamental equation without either multiplication or division. This equation may be written

$$D_n = \frac{D}{I - a_m} - \frac{D_m a_m}{I - a_m} \quad .$$

Values of $\dfrac{D}{I - a_m}$ and $\dfrac{D_m a_m}{I - a_m}$ may be extracted from the table as follows. The table is entered at the top with a_m and entered at the side with D or D_m as arguments. When D is the argument, the left-hand column under the particular value of a_m gives values of $\dfrac{D}{I - a_m}$. When D_m is the argument, the right-hand column under the particular value of a_m gives values of $\dfrac{D_m a_m}{I - a_m}$.

In order to obtain D_n, subtract the value obtained from entering the table with D_m as argument from the value obtained from entering the table with D as argument. (If this value is a minus quantity, then the value of D_m is too large to be consistent with the value of D and of a_m.)

For example: D = 100, D_m = 10, a_m = 0.8.

From row 100 and left-hand column under 0.8 extract value 500; from row 10 and right-hand column under 0.8 extract value 40; 500 - 40 = 460 = D_n.

D or D_m	a_m										
	0.1		0.2		0.3		0.4		⟩⟨	0.9	
	D	$D_m a_m$	D	$D_m a_m$	D	$D_m a_m$	D	$D_m a_m$		D	$D_m a_m$
	$I-a_m$	$I-a_m$	$I-a_m$	$I-a_m$	$I-a_m$	$I-a_m$	$I-a_m$	$I-a_m$		$I-a_m$	$I-a_m$
I	I	0.1	I	0.3	I	0.4	2	0.7		10	9
2	2	0.2	3	0.5	3	0.9	3	1.3		20	18
3	3	0.3	4	0.8	4	1.3	5	2.0		30	27
4	4	0.4	5	1.0	6	1.8	7	2.7		40	36
5	6	0.6	6	1.3	7	2.2	8	3.3		50	45
6	7	0.7	8	1.5	9	2.7	10	4.0		60	54
7	8	0.8	9	1.8	10	3.1	12	4.7		70	63
8	9	0.9	10	2.0	12	3.6	13	5.3		80	72
9	10	1.0	11	2.3	13	4.0	15	6.0		90	81
10	11	1.1	13	2.5	14	4.4	17	6.7		100	90
11	12	1.2	14	2.8	16	4.9	18	7.3		110	99
12	13	1.3	15	3.0	17	5.3	20	8.0		120	108
13	14	1.4	16	3.3	19	5.8	22	8.7		130	117
14	16	1.6	18	3.5	20	6.2	23	9.3		140	126
15	17	1.7	19	3.8	22	6.7	25	10.0		150	135
16	18	1.8	20	4.0	23	7.1	27	10.7		160	144
17	19	1.9	21	4.3	24	7.5	28	11.3		170	153
18	20	2.0	23	4.5	26	8.0	30	12.0		180	162
19	21	2.1	24	4.8	27	8.4	32	12.7		190	171
20	22	2.2	25	5.0	29	8.9	33	13.3		200	180
21	23	2.3	26	5.3	30	9.3	35	14.0		210	189
⟩⟨		9.0		22.3	128	39.5	148	59.3		890	801
90	100	10.0	113	22.5	130	40.0	149	59.9		900	810
91	101	10.1	114	22.8	131	40.4	151	60.6		910	819
92	102	10.2	115	23.0	132	40.8	153	61.3		920	828
93	103	10.3	116	23.3	134	41.3	154	61.9		930	837
94	104	10.4	118	23.5	135	41.7	156	62.6		940	846
95	105	10.5	119	23.8	137	42.2	158	63.3		950	855
96	107	10.7	120	24.0	138	42.6	159	63.9		960	864
97	108	10.8	121	24.3	140	43.1	161	64.6		970	873
98	109	10.9	123	24.5	141	43.5	163	65.3		980	882
99	110	11.0	124	24.8	143	44.0	164	65.9		990	891
100	111	11.1	125	25.0	144	44.4	166	66.6		1000	900

Part of Table I—Tabular Aid to Consistency
in Estimating Densities of Population

FIELD MAPPING OF RESIDENTIAL AREAS
IN METROPOLITAN CHICAGO[1]

by W. D. Jones

THE STATUS OF URBAN RESIDENTIAL STUDIES

A high proportion of the occupied area in every large American city is utilized for residential purposes. This type of land occupance occurs for the most part in definite districts that differ markedly in character one from another.

The distribution of many of the features which give residential districts their individuality can be shown more effectively by means of maps than by any other device. Not a few of these features are commonly recorded on several types of maps now in use. Standard large-scale topographic maps of cities, for example, show not only the street plan which divides residential districts into "blocks," but they also reveal something of the ground size and spacing of buildings. The latter facts are of necessity more or less concealed by generalization on all except very large scale maps, and in some cases the topographic map alone does not make it possible to determine whether or not a given section of a city is residential, in part or in entirety. Maps prepared by city planning commissions show facts as to size and type of buildings in residential areas. Large-scale maps, published and revised at frequent intervals by the Sanborn Map Company, give rather full details as to materials out of which buildings are constructed, as well as other information of special utility to real estate dealers and insurance companies. Maps exhibiting urban land values have been prepared by economists, and there exist for most municipalities maps which show land ownership. City maps made by sociologists reveal the distribution of various population elements, as well as the spread of selected social traits. Numerous maps of cities also have been made by geographers, showing among other things the location and extent of areas occupied for residential purposes, the spacing of structures within such areas, whether "close" or "open", the type of structures, whether single houses or apartment buildings, and the quality of the dwelling quarters afforded, whether "high," "medium" or "low."

In spite of the importance of residential land occupance as an element in the distinctive character of cities, this type of urban land utilization has hardly received the attention it deserves, especially in its cartographic aspects. An inspection of urban studies published in recent years by geographers reveals an in-

1. *Annals AAG*, vol. 21 (1931), pp. 207-214.

creasing attention to cities, but in most of such studies the accompanying maps give relatively few details for residential areas. The writer of this paper, therefore, within the last two years, has directed the attention of several groups of advanced students in the Department of Geography of the University of Chicago to the problem of field investigation of residentials areas, particularly field mapping, in Metropolitan Chicago. The aim has been to test out procedures already employed by geographers, as well as to develop new procedures. The experiment still is in progress, but this report on results thus far obtained is made with a view to obtaining constructive suggestions from others interested in the study of cities.

OBJECTIVES OF THIS STUDY

At the beginning of our work we formulated as a general objective, the discovery, analysis, depiction, explanation, and appraisal of land occupance and use within the metropolitan area. We agreed that discovery, analysis, and depiction of the facts of land utilization should precede explanation and appraisal of these facts, and that probably the most direct and effective way of acquiring many, if not most, of the basic facts was to make, in the field, a map of land utilization. The present paper deals only with the problem of mapping residential areas.

A preliminary reconnaissance into several contrasted residential districts in Chicago raised the question as to whether we should map "forms" or "functions," two terms which many American geographer in recent years have either brazenly courted in the open or shyly loved in secret. Each procedure had its adherents, but we finally agreed that as geographers we were interested both in such facts as the kinds of structures, that is "forms," and in such facts as the density of population to which these structures afford housing, that is, "functions." As we observed one residential district after another, it became clear that the character of each district, whether from the viewpoint of forms or of functions, might be analyzed into a number of individual elements or traits, which in combination or association gave the district its character or makeup. In mapping, however, even on a large-scale base and in detail, it did not appear feasible to record all of the elements which we were able to distinguish. The question, therefore, was which of these elements should be recorded on the map? As an aid in deciding this question we prepared two lists, one of what we called "form elements," the other of "function elements." The following residential form elements were recognized: areal extent of the individual establishment (building plus grounds), ratio of areal extent of building to that of associated grounds, number of floors or stories in building, type of structure, i.e., single house or apartment building, size of building, materials of construction, quality of construction, age of building, upkeep of building, and upkeep of associated grounds. The general function of all residential structures is to afford dwelling quarters. We analyzed this general function into such elements as the following: affording quarters for unit groups of different sizes (families with several servants, families without servants, single persons), affording quarters for different numbers of persons per unit of ground area, affording quarters for groups differing in luxury demands, and affording quarters for groups differing in the occupation of the breadwinners.

As we observed and listed these so-called "form elements" and "function elements" of residential districts we came to three conclusions: (a) the two sets of characteristics are intimately related, (b) the form elements can be much more quickly and accurately determined by field observation than can the function elements (several of the latter can be ascertained only by going inside the building, and some necessitate interviews), and (c) to a high degree, certain of the details of function can be inferred accurately from what can easily be seen on the details of form. On the basis of the last two conclusions we decided to map forms rather than functions.

THE MAPPING SCHEME

A series of experiments in mapping led us to select three form elements for record on the field map: (a) front spacing of buildings, (b) type of structure, and (c) upkeep of buildings and grounds. These three particular form elements were selected because (1) they appeared to constitute the irreducible minimum of readily observable facts necessary to give a clear picture of the manner in which each residential district was occupied, (2) they seemed to be those form elements from which could be inferred with a high degree of probable accuracy such significant functions as size of unit groups housed, density of population housed per unit of ground area, and standard of living or luxury demands of the population housed, and (3) they appeared to be associated features of residential land occupance closely related in distribution to kinds of sites occupied.

For each of these three form elements we determined through field observation several classes, the number of which we reduced as our study progressed, retaining finally only those classes which seemed to be of primary importance, as follows:

(a) Front spacing of buildings--three classes
    (1) Urban spacing--buildings 0 to 50 feet apart
    (2) Suburban spacing--buildings more than 50 feet apart.
    (3) Subdivisions--buildings on less than one-tenth of the lots

(b) Type of structure--four classes
    (1) Small to medium size houses--not more than ten rooms
    (2) Large houses-more than ten rooms
    (3) Apartment buildings with not more than six stories
    (4) Apartment buildings with more than six stories

      (c)   Upkeep of buildings and grounds--three classes
           (1)   Excellent
           (2)   Medium to fair
           (3)   Poor

In order that this classification of upkeep be less subjective than commonly is the case, we defined the three classes in terms of readily observable form characteristics, as follows:

      (1)   Excellent upkeep--outside parts of buildings calling for regular repair or replacement or attention, such as painted surfaces, roofs, gutters, down spouts, flashings, and brick pointing, in first class condition; grounds also kept in first class condition, with shrubs and flowers which require a good deal of attention.

      (2)   Poor upkeep--building in need of outside repairs, replacements, or attention; paint lacking or shabby; ground untidy and without a lawn.

      (3)   Medium to fair upkeep--intermediate between excellent and poor.

In actual field performance, the method of recording observations on the map is a matter of very practical importance. During the earlier stages of our work in Chicago we employed a numerical code to record the form elements of each residential establishment, each of the several digits in a number entered on the map indicating the classification of the particular form element to which it applied. Thus, in the number 221, the left hand digit referred to front spacing of buildings, "2" meaning "suburban spacing," the second digit from the left referred to type of structure, "2" meaning "large house," and the right hand digit referred to upkeep of buildings and grounds, "1" meaning "excellent upkeep" (see list of classes in the penultimate paragraph).

As our work progressed, we abbreviated the map record in two ways. In the first place, as a result of finding that particular kinds of residential establishments in most cases occupied several adjacent blocks, we ceased making a record of each individual establishment, and even to follow every street. Traverses run at least a quarter of a mile apart, with a few offsets, enabled us to determine satisfactorily the character and extent of most residential districts. In the second place, the repeated occurrence of particular kinds of residential areas made possible the recognition of a comparatively small number of types, eleven in all. In recording these types on the map, therefore, we employed a one or two digit number, rather than a three digit number, as follows (Fig. 30)[1]:

      (1)   Large houses with suburban spacing and excellent upkeep

      (2)   Medium to small size houses with suburban spacing and medium to fair upkeep

      (3)   Large houses with urban spacing and excellent upkeep

---

1. Map begun by W. D. Jones, about 1929; finished by J. D. Clarkson, 1958.

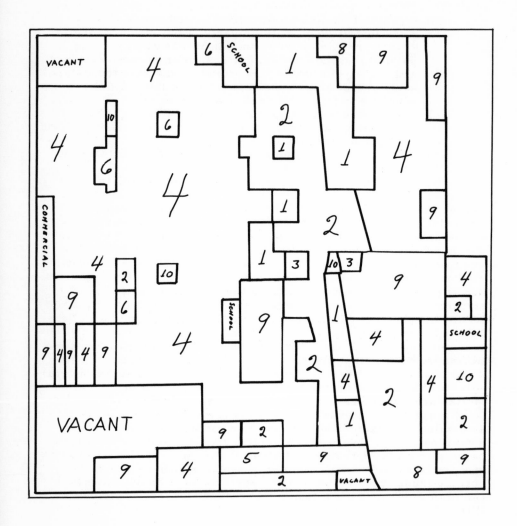

Fig. 30. Field map of a residential area in Evanston, Illinois, in the vicinity of Dempster St. and Ridge Rd. Scale: 1 inch to .2 mile.

(4) Medium to small size houses with urban spacing and medium to fair upkeep

(5) Apartment buildings with not more than six stories and excellent upkeep

(6) Apartment buildings with not more than six stories and medium to fair upkeep

(7) Apartment buildings with seven or more stories and excellent upkeep

(8) Mixtures of (3) and (5)

(9) Mixtures of (4) and (6)

(10) Houses or apartment buildings, or mixtures thereof, with poor upkeep

(11) Subdivisions with buildings on less than one-tenth of the lots. . . .

So far as our study enabled us to determine, the eleven types of residential forms which we mapped differed consistently in certain significant functions. As a matter of fact, these types were set up on the basis of form differences which preliminary study seemed to show were closely related to fundamental function differences, rather than on the basis of form differences merely striking to the eye. It is the opinion of the author of this paper that while the geographer is tremendously interested in landscape, urban as well as rural, he is or should be selective in the landscape details with which he concerns himself, and in so far as occupance forms are involved, he is much concerned with form elements that tie up with functions. In mapping residential occupance in Chicago we selected form elements which appeared to grow out of, or to be the cause of, or at least parallel to, such functional differences as, affording housing to unit groups of different sizes, affording housing to populations of different densities per unit ground area involved, and affording housing to groups with different luxury demands.

The production of city maps which show, in some such manner as that suggested above, differentiation in residential occupance, is in the opinion of the writer well worth the labor involved. Such maps are needed of all the larger cities of the earth, to show the layout, not only of residential occupance, but also of the several other major types of occupance, manufactural, commercial, transportational, and recreational. Such maps of cities are needed not only for the present, but back through time, so that we may see what these urban areas were like at different periods in their evolution. Maps of this type afford a sound objective and quantitative factual basis for the understanding of urban land utilization. Geographers cannot depend on workers in the other disciplines, or on public or private organizations, to prepare such maps. These other workers, in so far as they make maps of cities, quite properly direct their efforts to the gathering of data pertinent to their particular problems, and these problems, though they touch those of the geographer at many points, are not the same.

CONDITIONS EXPLAINING LOCALIZATIONS

A well-rounded geographic study of a city calls not only for systematic and effective analytical depiction of the facts of land occupance and use in written notes and in photographs, as well as on maps, but also for the explanation of this occupance and use. In the case of our study of Metropolitan Chicago, therefore, we constantly were asking ourselves and the persons we interviewed why the various sections of the city were occupied and used as we found them to be, why there was marked localization of particular types of land occupance, and whether there were disadvantages inherent in any of the existing localizations. So far as residential areas were concerned, we found that at least four sets of conditions commonly were significant:

(a) Physical site features, particularly surface configuration, surface drainage, and natural vegetation; subsurface materials, ground water, and soils were in most cases of little significance; we did not try to elaborate the numerical notation system to record such facts on the map sheets as that on which we noted occupance forms, but such a scheme appears to be feasible.

(b) The character of land occupance in adjacent areas, particularly as affecting the attractiveness of the area under consideration; thus, a noisy or dirty factory district adjacent to a residential area decreases the attractiveness of the latter, whereas a park adjacent increases the attractiveness.

(c) Distance to other sections of the city, and the character of the available transportation connections therewith.

(d) The character of earlier land occupance in the area.

For each residential district we endeavored to formulate an explanation, in terms of the four groups of factors just enumerated, as to why the area was occupied and used in the particular manner we found it to be. The presentation, however, of this phase of our work is beyond the scope of this paper.

The scheme we employed in mapping residential areas in Chicago may have to be modified as to details, but in general it seems to be an effective method of selecting and recording significant data. Not the least of its virtues is the way in which it compels, at the same time that it facilitates, systematic observation.

A UNIT AREA METHOD OF MAPPING GROSS LAND-USE ASSOCIATIONS IN URBAN REGIONS[1]

by A. K. Philbrick

THE PROBLEM

Maps recording land uses are a major instrument in geographic interpretation of human occupance. Consider, for example, the need for land-use maps in urban study on a regional basis. The majority of 20th century cities are expanding, and their surrounding areas are zones of accelerated land-use change. The institutions and facilities of urbanism are themselves articles of export to the country. Hence the areas between cities, particularly along interconnecting lines of transportation, are likewise experiencing urbanization. Of the continents, North America has proportionally the largest urban population. Urban expansion is a major trend of American occupance comparable in significance for the 20th century to westward settlement for the 19th century. Yet the jurisdiction and therefore the mapping of most public agencies engaged in urban study stops at the political city limits. To the geographer it is unthinkable to study cities as if they stopped at their political limits or without viewing them in their regional setting.

Such a situation calls for a reexamination of geographic methods of land-use mapping. Perhaps the most perplexing and time consuming problem of land-use mapping is the drawing of boundaries. The difficulty arises from the assumption that land-use maps should record limits of relative homogeneity. Such an assumption, in turn, leads to mapping at a large scale and in considerable detail.

The findings in this paper indicate an alternative possibility. First recognize those arbitrary units of area most easily distinguishable in the field, such as the city block in the case of an urban area. Then classify each such unit in terms of the actual combination of land uses which occurs within it. This approach eliminates time-consuming application of criteria and subjective judgment as to the location of limits of relative homogeneity.

PREREQUISITES

Prerequisites to this approach are considerations of scale, classification, and selection of a suitable type of unit area.

1. *Proceedings, 17th International Geographical Congress* (Washington: International Geographical Union, 1952), pp. 758-764.

Scale

For the study of "geographic" cities in their regional settings, maps of relatively large areas at a uniform scale are needed as well as supplementary maps of detailed observation in key areas and focal centers. In many cases the supplemental material already exists. What is lacking are regional land-use maps of medium scale recording the land-use associations of urban regions.

Classification

When dealing with arbitrary unit areas, each of which is characterized by a particular mixture of land uses, a detailed classification would result in a very great number of possible combinations. It is apparent that mapping by combinations of land uses in unit areas is theoretically best adapted to generalized observation. Actually, however, a wide range of choice as to degree of generalization is possible. Uniformly detailed observation and recording is not required throughout an area. The method provides a consistent framework, however, within which more detailed observation of homogeneous land-use areas or of their focal establishments may be recorded as desired during or after the original mapping.

Classification, it was found, was most usefully divided into three levels. First-order classification divides land uses into two kinds on the basis of the type unit area to be used. Where access is by streets in a pattern of blocks, land uses are classified as of the "block" type. At the edges of block-type settlement and between such areas, distances between establishments are greater, or their relation to a road is that of a row of beads to a string rather than that of a "box" containing a cluster. Such more extensive land uses are termed "open" or of non block type. The second order distinguishes two basic associations in block-type settlement and three in settlement of open pattern. They are residence and livelihood in the former, and nonagricultural residence and two types of livelihood--agricultural and nonagricultural--in the latter. Public, institutional, vacant, and other land uses are held in a neutral status in both kinds of unit areas. An additional category, vacant land, is used when the whole of a unit area is unoccupied.

For block-type settlement, classification into two categories presents three possible combinations: homogeneity of either category or a mixture of livelihood and residential uses in a given block. The degree of mixture may extend all the way from nearly wholly residential to nearly completely livelihood (business-industry-transportation), or it may be defined further by degree and type of mixture.

Within unit areas of open or nonblock settlement, classification into three categories presents seven possibilities: homogeneity of three associations, and their four combinations. These are (1) business-industrial-transportation, hereafter referred to

as "business"; (2) residential, i.e., non-agricultural residence;
(3) agricultural (including agricultural residence); (4) business-
agricultural combinations; (5) business-residential combinations;
(6) residential-agricultural combinations; and (7) business-resi-
dential-agricultural combinations. Again, subclassifications by
degree and type of mixtures are possible.

Classification of the third order consists of specific land
uses within any given association. Since the primary purpose of
this paper is to indicate land-use mapping possibilities over large
areas at medium scale, the third order of classification will not
be treated.

Unit Areas

The pattern and functional organization of human occupance
is that of localized human activity, focused in human enterprise,
and interconnected by human organization. Lines of transportation are visible interconnections dividing the surface of the occupied earth into small areas. Such areas, varying through a wide
range of both shape and size, are appropriate arbitrary areal units
for land-use mapping. Lines of access lead to human establishments. In so doing they focus attention upon localized activities
which characterize land uses. They also provide a platform from
which to observe combinations of land uses within the unit areas
they surround.

No other kind of boundary is at once so consistently visible
and characteristic of human occupance as that supplied by transportation. Useful supplementary boundary types are (1) certain
marked contrasts in nature, such as topographic features, vegetation, etc; (2) property boundaries; (3) survey lines; (4) political
boundaries; and (5) arbitrary boundaries drawn to fit the need of
the field-mapping problem. Property lines are invisible and difficult to verify directly from field observation, although they correspond closely with units of occupance. In some areas such as
the rectilinear survey areas of America, survey units are readily
identifiable because of the close correspondence of roads to section lines. Such units have the additional advantage of relatively
uniform size, analogous for the countryside to the relative uniformity of the city block.

APPLICATION

Two land-use mapping experiments with this method will be
discussed: (1) a small city and surrounding countryside mapped
as one continuous operation, and (2) the transformation, for a
great city, of data mapped primarily on the basis of the property
lot as a unit area, and in much greater detail, into more generalized land-use associations and their combinations within block
units.

The Porter-Chesterton Area

Fig. 31 shows the Porter-Chesterton area--Westchester, Liberty, and Portage Townships--of Porter County, Indiana. Combinations of land uses are recorded in arbitrary unit areas of both "block" and "open" type. In the case of the latter, they are quarter sections of the land survey, supplementally bounded by roads, railroads, and streams. A number of observations can be made concerning the land-use pattern which the map reveals.

1. Open patterned residences and commercial establishments scattered throughout the three townships are clearly not primarily related functionally to small focal centers. Quarter sections containing commercial enterprises, with few exceptions, are bounded or traversed by one or another of three east-west national and two state highways. . . Such establishments include motels, restaurants, service stations, and tourist shops catering to truck and automobile traffic, origin and destination of which are not primarily within Porter County.

Some establishments do serve residents of Porter County from sites along or near these highways; for example, a lumber yard and country abbatoir, with wide retail as well as wholesale outlets. Accessibility by automobile makes independent location in the open country feasible both for such establishments and for many of their retail customers. Non-agricultural residences also are distributed not with special reference to local centers but in accordance with a pattern of the open road.

2. Lack of relationship between "open" urban settlement and local centers raises the question of livelihood foci accessible by suburban transportation outside the area altogether. Examination of the position of Porter County with reference to Metropolitan Chicago and the great industrial enterprises of the Calumet District indicates the answer which more detailed investigation substantiates. These are non-agricultural residences of a wide range of Chicago area breadwinners, from industrial workers commuting to jobs in the Calumet District to professional men with offices in the "Loop". Each represents a flight from unattractive circumstances surrounding places of urban livelihood. It is apparent from the map that the area of greatest concentration of nonagricultural residences is traversed by a bundle of suburban transportation lines affording connections with Metropolitan Chicago to the west. These are the interurban Chicago South Shore and South Bend Railroad, the New York Central which operates commuter services as far as Chesterton, and U. S. Highways 12 and 20.

3. Land-use patterns of focal centers in part reflect their functions. The hamlets of Crisman, Crocker, and McCool are railroad junction points. In the case of Porter-Chesterton, the distribution of land uses with reference to the four railroads which intersect there, suggests a similar role. . . Investigation reveals that livelihood here, at one time, was centered in small manufacturing plants located along the railroads. On the other hand, in the case

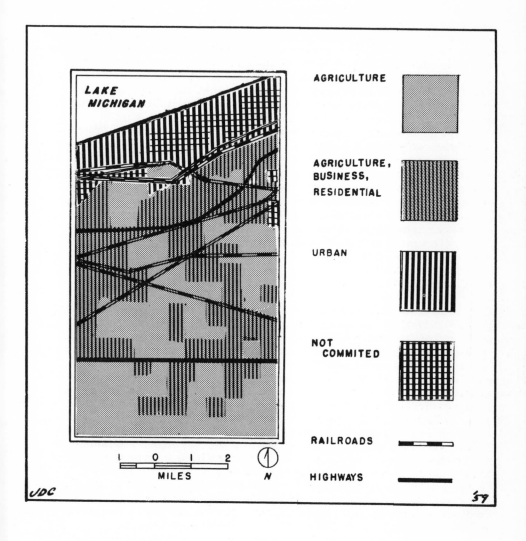

Fig. 31. Part of a map of "Gross Land Use Associations of Northern Porter County, Indiana," revealing extension of the urban fringe of metropolitan Chicago into a rural area.

of Ogden Dunes and Dune Acres, lakeshore location and absence of commercial enterprise reflects "dormitory" residential character. These communities achieve virtually complete separation of residence from place of work.

4. Urban land uses in open country are in some ways related functionally to local centers. It is by no means certain from the map alone that nonagricultural residents on the periphery of Chesterton or even those within that city are bound to it by occupational ties. Many are steel workers in the Gary mills or commute daily to other centers. For other purposes, however, such families' lives focus in Porter-Chesterton. Also, a certain proportion of the local population is tied to local service, industry, and the functioning of those railways to whose operation Chesterton owed its origin.

The land-use map is instrumental in making clear the existence of two distinct patterns of urban phenomena, one related to the railroads and the other to the automobile road. Establishments of the first tend to focus locally; those of the second are peripheral to a number of more distant foci in Metropolitan Chicago. The two are also interrelated. While they cannot be separated completely in terms of block- or open-type urban settlement, they can be characterized under those headings.

The map of Fig. 31 was produced in field form in approximately forty hours.

The City of Chicago

Examination of [a generalized block] map reveals in Chicago (1) an overwhelming preponderance of blocks containing a mixture of residence and place of work, (2) the linear nature of homogeneous livelihood areas, with the possible exception of the "knot" of such uses in and around the city's core, and (3) enclosure of the business-industrial association by areas of mixed livelihood and residence in turn grading into relatively few blocks in homogeneous residential use.

The city of Chicago is a great workshop!

It is difficult to get away from the physical and social circumstances of urban livelihood within the city limits. Thousands have chosen to separate as widely as facilities of transport and other circumstances would allow, their places of residence from places of work. Politically they have left the city. Economically they are still its citizens. By and large this has been an individually-planned migration in a competitive society, each member of which for his establishment or family unit is seeking the most favorable circumstances for his activities. The multiple factors with reference to which the individual and--in the mass--the collective decisions to accomplish this development have been made constitute one of the most challenging problems to all the disciplines of Social Science.

The [generalized block] map reveals the organizational center and major portions of the core of a great metropolitan region.

-300-

The core is not only the "Loop", but also the areas adjacent to the extensive linear pattern of connecting rail belt lines, industrial sidings which the belts serve, and the twenty major linehaul railroads they connect within the city. This network is both an arterial system and a skeleton. It gives shape and form to the areal arrangement of industry and commerce, which constitute the economic base of the metropolis. Translation of detailed data of the Chicago Land Use Survey into more general form was substantially faster than would have been the case applying the technique directly in the field.

CONCLUSION

Maps in Fig. 31 and [of Chicago generalized] depict land-use association in two sections of a single urban area. Mapping was in terms of associations and their mixtures observed within each of a large number of arbitrary units of land into which each section is subdivided by transportation or other readily identifiable boundaries. Land uses were recorded in terms of classification at two levels. The first distinguishes between types of settlement corresponding to block and open patterned unit areas. The second distinguishes between two basic land-use associations--residence and livelihood--in block-type settlement; and nonagricultural residence and two types of livelihood--agricultural and nonagricultural --in open-patterned settlement. It was noted that a third level of specific land uses is recordable within the framework of the first two orders of classification.

It was observed that this technique speeds up land-use mapping because it is not necessary to find and delineate boundaries of land-use homogeneity. Also, the maps could be made on a smaller scale than would have been feasible if mapping boundaries of land-use homogeneity. Yet location and differentiation of specific uses of land was sufficiently precise to enable formulation of tentative hypotheses and interpretation of human occupance suggested by the content of the maps.

In the case of the Porter-Chesterton section, the technique was applied on a continuous basis, to both block and open type land-use patterns. It was found possible to shift without difficulty from one to the other within the application of a single technique and a common system of classification.

In the case of the city of Chicago, it was found possible quickly to transform land-use data recorded on the basis of limits of land-use homogeneity into terms comparable to the system used for the Porter-Chesterton area.

It is possible that this technique may bring the recording of land uses for so extensive an area as the region within a 100-mile radius of the Chicago Loop within the range of feasibility. Wide use of this technique could materially increase the number, extent, frequency, and comparability of land-use maps of large areas, thus vastly facilitating the geographical interpretation of urbanization and of urban regions.

CHAPTER 15

Derivatives of
Type 7 (Areal Organization)

The approach to human occupance of the Earth through functional organization expressed in areal pattern has developed consistently though slowly. At first the term "microgeography" was applied indiscriminately by many geographers to field studies either in areal uniformity or in areal organization, as dealing in both cases with very small details. Moreover the whole subject was thought insignificant under a misimpression that the small details were an end in themselves and not a means of approach to larger geographic reality. So the basic purposes and differences in approach did not become clearly evident for a decade or more after the Montfort and Ellison Bay studies[1] were made.

Meanwhile the idea of areal organization has been applied under various circumstances for the solution of successive problems. An inescapable problem, as in the case of areal uniformity and diversity, is that of extending the field method from direct observation in small areas to generalization over large regions. One way of solving this problem is represented by "A Field Approach to Regions" by R. S. Platt, 1935. In this study, basic units of occupance are selected in reconnaissance as samples for recognition of large regions characterized

1. pp. 105-114, 117-139 above.

by uniformity of occupance. The field method involves general observation of uniformity and diversity, and detailed study by observation and inquiry at selected establishments, along a line of traverse, in view of the first seven types in this series, especially 7 (Areal Organization) and 6 (Areal Uniformity).

A statement in the study recognizes both large regions of uniformity (in which similar basic units of organization occur) and large regions of organization (in which small basic units of organization are grouped in the territories of larger focal establishments).[1]

But the former of these two ways of viewing regions is the one emphasized in the article – generalizing from basic units of occupance to uniform regions of similar occupance – and in regional geography this use of the idea of areal organization is the one that has usually been followed[2] until recent studies of heirarchies of organization.

Another application of the idea of areal organization is in urban geography, going from the country to the city more spontaneously and easily than in the extension of areal uniformity from country to city. "An Urban Field Study; Marquette, Michigan", by R. S. Platt, 1931, is taken as an example.

1. pp. 315, 316 below.
2. For example, "Habitats," R. S. Platt: "Latin America" (N.Y.: McGraw-Hill Book Co., 1942), pp. 485-517.

For this study Marquette was selected as a city large enough to have urban character but small enough to have the simplicity needed in a first attempt at urban geography from this viewpoint. The choice of Marquette was significant as a flight away from Chicago, where Wellington Jones had already experienced the difficulty of comprehensive urban study from the viewpoint of areal uniformity and diversity.

The field method involves specific inquiry, observation and mapping in the city and reconnaissance in the area for which the city is a focus, in view of the first seven types in this series, especially type 7 (Areal Organization). The phrase "regional and local establishments" in this study[1] is equivalent to "basic and non-basic establishments" as used later in urban economics and in geography.[2]

The concept of areal organization necessarily involves movement, and patterns of transportation are essential features of the overall pattern of occupance. Application of the idea of areal organization in the geography of transportation is consistent and easy. A part of "Problems of Our Time", by R. S. Platt, 1946, is taken as an example.

One purpose of this study is to make use of the concept of areal organization in combination with

1. *Fig. 38 below.*
2. *For example, A. M. Weimer & H. Hoyt: Principles of Urban Real Estate (N.Y.: Ronald Press Co., 1939); J. W. Alexander: "The Basic Non-Basic Concept of Urban Economic Functions" in Econ. Geog., vol. 30 (1954), pp. 246-261.*

other ideas, in view of all eight of the types in this series. Another purpose is to relate detailed study of a small area to general interpretation of large regions of organization and regions of uniformity based on one criterion, air transportation. The field method involves detailed field study of areal organization and items of culture by inquiry, observation and mapping in a small area, specific inquiry in major focal establishments, and reconnaissance in the territories of those establishments.

Finally the idea of areal organization is applied in another solution of the problem of extending field study from small areas to large regions, an alternative vaguely suggested but not followed out in early studies of areal organization. [1] An excerpt from "Principles of Areal Functional Organization in Regional Human Geography" by A. K. Philbrick, 1957, is taken as an example.

In this study the procedure is from small basic units of organization not merely to large regions of uniformity in occupance but to superior focal establishments and their larger territories in a nested hierarchy of organization. Meanwhile areal uniformity and diversity are not forgotten: at each level in the hierarchy uniformity of occupance is recognized in parallel establishments of the same order and their territories extending over a region of uniformity which may or may not coincide with an area of organization.

1. p. 128 above.

The field method involves reconnaissance of central places, tallying their establishments, and detailed study of selected centers of each order in the hierarchy by inquiry, observation and mapping of establishments and their territories, in view primarily of types 7 (Areal Organization) and 6 (Areal Uniformity).

The numbering of centers in the hierarchy is from the smallest unit of organization as first order to the largest as sixth or seventh order. In some studies by other geographers the numbering is reversed, beginning with the largest as first order and proceeding to the smallest as a fifth or higher order.[1] This seems to be a minor and obvious difference to be recognized and later adjusted.

FIELD APPROACH TO REGIONS [2]

by R. S. Platt

This is not The Field Approach to Regions but A Field Approach, starting with a particular approach to a particular region. ... Last August when my field party in upper Michigan finished work ahead of scheduled time, ... we planned a field approach to the regions between James Bay and Lake Ontario. ...
Making a dash by automobile to the road's end, thence catching a night train to rail's end, and thence canoeing downstream to Ship Sands on James Bay. ...
Inland from our landing place extended an almost featureless plain, carpeted with grasses and flowering herbs of familiar types, the soil clay and the ground poorly drained. The view was uninterrupted as far as the distant horizon where a jagged fringe

1. For example, F. H. W. Green: "Community of Interest Areas: Notes on the Hierarchy of Central Places and their Hinterlands", in Econ. Geog., vol. 34 (1958), pp. 210-226.
2. Annals AAG, vol. 25 (1935), pp. 153-172.

against the sky announced the edge of forest.

There were no signs of human occupance nor animals of respectable size. The air was bright and warm, and the scene pleasant except for one item which spoiled an otherwise agreeable environment: swarms of insects from which we had no means of escape, a few mosquitoes and innumerable vicious flies.

Our canoemen called this plain "the barren," and evidently associated it with the treeless lands extending to the north. Some atlas maps show this place at the southwestern corner of James Bay as tundra or barren land at the southern edge of a great region extending to the Arctic. Others show it as within the northern forest region, with the tundra boundary two hundred miles away.

This would seem to be an important regional boundary definitely determinable. Yet apparently either decision in regard to this James Bay shore may be correct, depending upon the basis of regional delimitation. Here is a plant association that is not forest and is like the tundra in aspect and practically continuous with it. Its animals are nomads of the barren lands. Human occupance is not that of the forest.

Yet from another viewpoint this plant association is not regionally distinct from the forest. The formation is edaphic, the absence of trees being due to lack of time for their growth between periods of flooding or of overriding of bay ice, coupled with relatively unfavorable drainage conditions. It is not bounded by a climatic tree line where old and stunted forms appear, but by a zone of young willows, which in turn abuts on full-grown forest on land that has long been available for tree growth. When the basis for regional delimitation is established a decision between the two alternatives in this case is easy.

At Ship Sands our regional traverse southward was started. From this point a record was kept of the land along the route for 720 miles. The record included character of the land and what was on it for each fraction of a mile--within practical limits of observation and classification. A system of fractional complexes was used with digits to represent slope, soil and drainage, and features of occupance.

In addition to the traverse record, eighteen reconnaissance studies were made of functional units selected as typical examples of occupance along the traverse. For these studies sketch maps were made and notes taken covering distributive characteristics and regional relations.

Along the first 10 miles of the traverse from Ship Sands up the Moose River, the treeless plain occupies the shores of the river mouth (Fig. 32). For the next 93 miles the traverse crosses a poorly drained, spruce wooded plain in which general uniformity is pronounced in spite of an undercurrent of minor variations.

The major theme is the forest of black spruce, a dense stand of small trees on flat wet land. The minor variations include transitions to open muskeg through areas of stunted spruce and tamarack; brulés; windfalls; and stream banks better drained than the

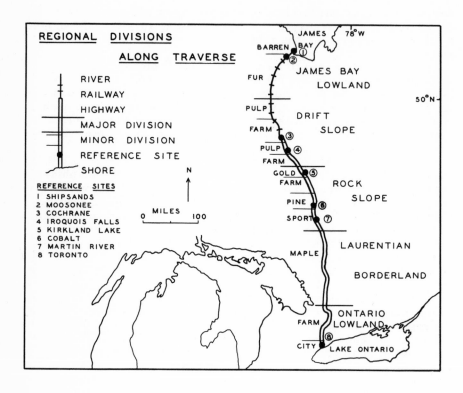

Fig. 32. Map indicating regional subdivisions of uniformity in basic organization of occupance.

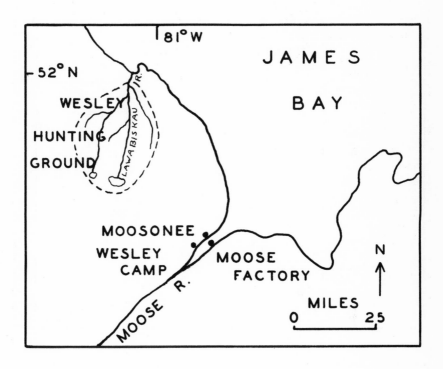

Fig. 33. Sample of a basic unit of organization (camp and hunting ground) in the fur region near Moosonee.

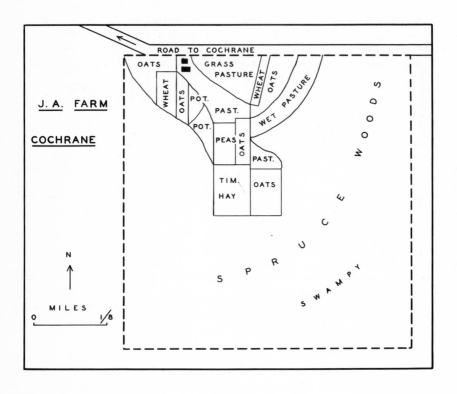

Fig. 34. "A farm in the northern Clay Belt, east of Cochrane", a sample unit of organization in the northernmost farm region of the Drift Slope.

land back of them, occupied by poplar and white birch.

This is the James Bay lowland or the Great Muskeg, a coastal plain of marine clay deposits underlain by Paleozoic rocks. Regional vegetation maps show it to be within the more extensive northern forest, and some show a boundary between dense and sparse northern forest cutting across the area, a distinction which appears not to apply along the traverse line.

Of human occupance no trace is revealed by the traverse record along the railway, except at a coal mine spur, and even this only an abandoned experiement in extracting lignite. But the evidence of no occupance is an indication of weakness in the traverse itself. Here is human occupance too thin to be caught in so coarse a filter. In this case one of the small unit studies fills the gap.

On the west bank of the lower Moose River is a camp of Cree Indians. This is the summer home of the Wesley family, of about twenty people, two brothers with their sons and grandchildren. There has been no clearing except for the shacks and tents themselves, no improvement of the canoe landing or of the path to it, and there is no garden and no store room. This is the most sedentary home of the family, occupied through the relatively inactive summer season, to be near a trading post and still carry on some fishing and hunting.

They prefer the winter when the weather is bracing, and there are no insects, and hunting is good. During the hunting season they move into the family hunting ground, the basin of Lawabiskau River. A map of the Lawabiskau River (Fig. 33) was drawn with sticks on the ground by one of the family. Perhaps it is the best map that has been made of the river. Published government maps show only a single dotted line.

The family right to this area has been respected, and they have used its resources as conservatively as if engaged in livestock farming, a practice made possible and necessary by the sedentary habits of most of the animals. In fact, the sedentary fur bearers are the basis for the whole system of land occupance throughout the forest lands around James Bay. The territory of the Swamp Cree Indians has been divided from time immemorial into family hunting grounds of which the basin of Lawabiskau River is typical. The traverse southward passes through two or three such hunting grounds without means of detecting them.

The density of population seems to be about one person in one hundred square miles. Apparently there has been no great change since the revolution 260 years ago when the Hudson's Bay Company entered the region and changed production from a subsistence to a commercial activity. At the end of the hunting season each family brings its product of furs to a trading post and settles down for the summer. The Hudson's Bay Company has eleven posts around James Bay, focal points on major streams.

The most important of these points is at the mouth of the Moose River where the outlet of a major stream system enters the bay at the best available ship's anchorage on the southern shore--the best of a bad lot of anchorages. Here was the natural objective of the railway reaching the bay from the south.

This focal point is the subject of another unit study. The anchorage is at the mouth of the Moose near Ship Sands. The Hudson's Bay post of Moose Factory is on an island upstream where the bank is high enough to give freedom from flood destruction. The new rival trading post of Moosonee (Fig. 33), is on the mainland on a site which would have been less satisfactory in the days when defense was important and all transportation was by water, but is now better than the island location of Moose Factory, since the railway has arrived at the river bank.

A pretentious city plan and real estate subdivision of the mainland site reflects a popular dream of Moosonee as the only tidewater seaport of Ontario, a major outlet for the leading Canadian province. The actual village on this site of empty spaces and slight activity reflects the present reality of Moosonee as merely commanding a new outlet for James Bay, the railway replacing the old connection of one ship a year between Moose River and the sea. This elimination of ocean shipping is an opposite effect from that conceived in the seaport dream.

Let us leave this place without for the moment trying to correlate the various overlapping regional concepts of the James Bay area.[1] Continuing along the traverse south of the James Bay lowland there is a change in the landscape. Within a few miles are the first hills, the first exposures of rock and sand, the first jack pine, the first village settlements, and finally the first farms. The next 174 miles of traverse may be looked upon from a generalized viewpoint as one unit.

This is the drift covered northern slope of the Laurentian upland, known as the Great Clay Belt. (Fig. 32). In certain ways the area is not very different from the coastal plain--in general dominance of spruce forest, prevalence of low relief, poor drainage and heavy soil, and scarcity of rock. But slight differences appear in undulations and outcrops on the plain, and major differences in land occupance.

Cutover land along the traverse gives evidence of forest exploitation, illustrated by one of the unit studies, a logging camp where a good stand of spruce is being cut by a gang of twelve men. The product is pulpwood.

In similar spots scattered in the Clay Belt a thousand men are cutting wood for the Abitibi Power and Paper Company. The central focus of their activities is the mill, at the best power site

---

1. "These regional concepts include the James Bay plain, the Great Muskeg, the Hudson Bay area of Paleozoic rocks, the northern spruce forest, the land of the Swamp Cree Indians, the fur trade district of Moose Factory, the territory of the Temiskaming & Northern Ontario Railway, and a number of other territorial units, such as the missionary diocese of Moosonee, and the Moose Factory district of the Royal Canadian Mounted Police."

on the largest stream of the vicinity, flowing out of the largest lake, near the first railway built into the spruce forest of the Hudson Bay slope. Three power plants develop 113,000 horsepower from the river below Lake Abitibi. From the watershed above pulpwood is rafted down to the mill and from the nearby area downstream it is brought in by rail and truck. The product-- newsprint--is shipped to the United States.

The location of this plant in relation to others indicates a regional pattern in which two mills in the spruce forest of the James Bay slope are far removed from older mills on the Great Lakes watershed.

Probably the Clay Belt is better known for its farming possibilities. Along the traverse agricultural occupance is scattered through the spruce woods in two districts (Fig. 32). In a distance of 77 miles there are 33 miles of cleared land. Homogeneity of land occupance here does not consist of continuous uniformity but of detailed variety in which items are oft repeated.

A functional unit study supplements the static pattern recorded in the traverse. A government agent selected what he called a representative selfsupporting farm (Fig. 34), yet this farm with its thirty acres cleared and its two cows and four pigs yields only food, shelter and firewood, the farmer eking out a living by working on the railway. Pulpwood is said to be the chief money crop of farms in the district.

There has been no recent drought, and this year, as usual, there has been too much late summer rain for satisfactory maturing of spring wheat. On the only night that we camped in the vicinity, August 13th, there was frost heavy enough to wilt potato plants.

Leaving the northern Clay Belt, the traverse enters a zone characterized by low rock hills, boulders and sand, broken streams and lakes, and trees other than spruce. In general this Rock Slope of the Laurentian Upland extends for 196 miles. In particular it breaks into four subdivisions within this distance (Fig. 32).

Near the northern margin the traverse crosses an inconspicuous ridge marking the divide between the Hudson Bay and St. Lawrence drainage basins, the Height of Land. In this vicinity human occupance is slight except at isolated points. The more widely scattered of these are prospecting camps. The more exceptional spots of concentrated activity are gold mines. One of these spots is the Kirkland Lake district.

Here are seven gold mines along a line of fracture near a contact between Pre-Cambrian sedimentary and igneous rocks in which veins occur. In the Lake Shore Mine operations have reached a depth of 4250 feet, and last year gold production was more than that of any other mine in America. The absence of placer deposits and surface ore bodies confines development to large scale, highly capitalized companies. Kirkland Lake is a rapidly growing town of fourteen thousand people, one of the few boom towns in the world at the present time.

Regional distribution of gold mining districts is less regular than are the distributions of phenomena more directly associated with surface conditions. Promoters have called attention to the proximity of mining districts to the Height of Land and have theorized on a causal relation. But a more fundamental clue is furnished by the underlying structure. Within the Laurentian Upland is a geosynclinal belt containing old sedimentary-igneous contacts favorable for ore occurence, its northern edge near the Height of Land, its southern edge one hundred miles farther south where the traverse passes another mining district, Cobalt.

Here is a cluster of about forty silver mines, all but one of them closed down. The underlying structure, like that at Kirkland Lake, includes a sedimentary igneous contact and veins in lines of fracture. But in this case the contact is a nearly horizontal one at shallow depth and there are several lines of fracture and scattered veins not carrying ore below a few hundred feet. Accordingly many small shallow mines had early success and a short life.

The one mine still in operation has survived by expanding its operations horizontally. From one shaft now in use ore is carried by a truck to an old mill on another part of the property. Thus is furnished the meagre total production of the district which was the world's greatest silver mining center a few years ago. The dilapidated town of Cobalt is mentioned with scorn by people in the bright new town of Kirkland Lake. These facts are consistent with the shallowness of the Cobalt deposits, the location of Cobalt on the southern threshold and not on the northern frontier of Laurentian mining districts, and depression in the value of silver.

Between Kirkland Lake and Cobalt the traverse passes through a district which is not typical of the Rock Slope--an undulating upland, cleared of forest so that here for the first time we had uninterrupted vistas across open farm land to distant hills. This area is known as the southern Clay Belt of Northern Ontario or as the older part of the Great Clay Belt. One farm selected as typical has 85% of its land cleared, and is self supporting with a cash income from the sale of meat, vegetables, milk and eggs carried by truck to a mining town.

The crops and animals along the traverse are the same as in the more northerly clay belt area. But this district which was accessible much earlier gives a different impression, not only in the better development of its farms and compactness of its farm area, but also in the character of the land itself, as a well drained and fertile upland underlain by Paleozoic limestone. ...

The traverse continues southward through a section of the Rock Slope where white pine is seen for the first time, distinguishing the forest from that farther north. Here a unit of focal significance is a sawmill located to receive pine logs from a watershed extending to the Height of Land and thus representing the last frontier of pine lumbering in the northern forest.

The district of lumbering is succeeded by 60 miles of forest, with hardly a clearing, where the highway crosses an area not

touched by the older water and rail routes to the north. The land
is typical of the Rock Slope. The forest is dominated by white
pine and most of it is virgin, preserved formerly by inaccessibility and now by inclusion in the Timagami Forest Preserve. Along
the traverse Martin River is one of the few inhabited spots. Here
are a forest ranger's and a game warden's cabin, a filling station,
and a tourist camp. The cars which stop are mainly from southern Ontario and the United States. Few of them go much farther.
For vacation campers from American cities the Timagami district is the northern frontier of the North Woods, a suitable arrangement in view of the fact that those who travel farther to the north
reach less picturesque and less wild country, in the clay belts,
the muskegs, and the pineless woods.

Emerging from the virgin forest the traverse enters a different major division, the Laurentian Borderland, an area of
stable and long established occupance. There are still rocky
hills and woods. But there are mature farms among the hills
and the woods are dominated by hardwood trees, particularly
maple (Fig. 32). One of the characteristic units is a hardwood
sawmill to which farmers bring logs from their wood lots. Another functional unit is a maple sugar camp accessory to a farm.

The southern escarpment of the Laurentian upland on the
traverse route is less marked than the northern. The rocky
wooded hills slip away in a transition to the fertile farmlands of
the Ontario lowlands, through which the traverse passes for 109
miles.

Functional units of the lowlands include a dairy farm in which
corn is prominent, a farm village, a small town factory importing its raw materials, and a summer resort hotel for people who
do not want to rough it. In the last 18 miles the traverse passes
through the metropolitan area of Toronto to the shore of Lake
Ontario. ...

The kind of field work represented in this traverse seems to
apply as well to major regions as to minor divisions--in fact, it
may be said to apply better, since all its findings are qualitative
and deal with the more conspicuous rather than with the finer
shades of regional characterization.

The importance of including functional unit studies with the
running traverse may be questioned. Justification of this inclusion lies in the fact that the traverse alone shows items of the
landscape only in the static aspects of their distribtuion. This is
sufficient for many basic landscape features. But human occupance of the land is a dynamic phenomenon and the items which
belong to it have a dynamic relationship to each other, in functional units of significant areal pattern. ...

Mention has been made along the traverse of many items
having a bearing on recognition of regions. Apart from the evident difference between natural and cultural features, these items
may be said to appear under two general concepts: that of static
areal homogeneity, such as in the pulpwood forest region or the

Pre-Cambrian rock region; and that of areal functional unity, such as in the James Bay fur trading region or the Province of Ontario. Confusion may result from mixing these two different points of view in a geographic discussion. But they are mixed in nature: human occupance of the land has to do with both areal homogeneity and areal functional organization. Therefore it seems important to distinguish them clearly in our thinking and to use one or the other or both as best serves our purpose.

The kaleidoscope of landscape features and the maze of overlapping regional boundaries suggested in this traverse may be reduced in mind to generalized average regional characterizations and a few fixed boundaries. The traverse divisions as presented represent steps toward simplification by generalization and we may even return to my elementary idea of monotonous uniformity in the direction of Hudson Bay. But advance in regional geography seems to lie rather in the direction of more complex interpretation involving the color and form of an areal pattern challenging mature and penetrating powers of thought.

AN URBAN FIELD STUDY: MARQUETTE, MICHIGAN[1]

by R. S. Platt

This study of Marquette is a sequel to a previous study of Republic, Michigan.[2] Passing from the rural community of Republic to the urban center of Marquette is taken to be a logical sequence; not a jump from the country to the city as a totally different subject, but a normal transition to the city as another part of the same subject, viz., the city as another item in the regional pattern of terrene occupancy, related to the country in development and similar to the country in basic features, even though vastly different in the relative intensity and complexity of those features.

Marquette has a population of 15,000 and property assessed at $11,000,000. Yearly it receives 4,000,000 tons of commodities and sends out a similar amount; and has an annual influx of 100,000 passengers and a similar outflow. This concentration of dense population, valuable buildings and restless movement, in

1. _Annals AAG_, vol. 21 (1931), pp. 52-73.
2. " 'Field Study of Republic, Michigan: A Community in the Marquette Iron Range,' _Scottish Geographical Magazine_, XLIV (1928), 193-204."

its external relations and its internal structure offers a subject for geographic interpretation. This paper is to consider, first, the city's existence and functions in the Upper Lakes region, and, secondly, its configuration in the immediate site.

RELATIONS TO IRON RANGE AND FOREST

The primary fact of the city's existence pertains to the location of Marquette Bay with reference to the Marquette Iron Range. The area from Sault Ste. Marie to the Keweenaw Peninsula was still an Indian hunting ground when the first discovery of iron ore in the Lake Superior region was made in the Marquette Range eighty years ago. At the harbor nearest to the iron deposit a clearing was made in the forest and a settlement established (Fig. 35).

Probably Father Marquette had never seen the spot, but his name was given to a mining company organized to operate in the region, then to the landing place where the company established a base, and to the iron range back of it.

The original relationship of Marquette to the iron range is still maintained, though modified in various ways. Once sledges brought a few barrels of ore to the water's edge to be transported by sailing vessel; now railways (Fig. 35) bring annually 3,000,000 tons to the Marquette Docks to be carried on by a fleet of specialized steamships. Once Marquette was the only ore port in the Lake Superior region and for years it was the greatest; now it is the least of the six major ports and ships only 5 per cent of the total ore.

Perhaps the most significant change for Marquette has been the relative decline of ore shipment among the activities of the community from first place to a rather small place in the modern life of the city. There would be no city of Marquette if the only urban activity were the ore shipment, for which the site of the city was selected. Ore shipment is still conspicuous--more so than formerly--but the very greatness of the equipment installed to handle ore denotes an overcoming of the break in transportation from land to water. The stream of ore flows through the city with a minimum of effort. The docks seem almost deserted as trains of ore arrive, cars are emptied by gravity into storage pockets and thence vessels are filled by gravity during a short stay in port. Marquette has become hardly more than a way station in the ore movement.

Indirectly, however, ore shipment has been a large factor in the development of the city, not only in the original selection of the site but also in later growth. From the two ore railways have grown two railway systems to serve a greater area than the iron district alone. For both of these Marquette has not only a terminal position, with reference to ore traffic, but also a central position with reference to the system as a whole. It has been a logical choice for the offices and shops of each. Both railways have become important connecting lines for the Upper Peninsula

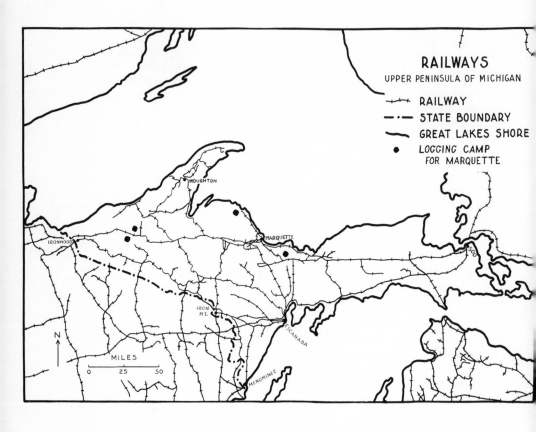

Fig. 35. "Marquette, the Upper Peninsula of Michigan, and Surroundings", points of focus and lines of movement in a pattern of organization.

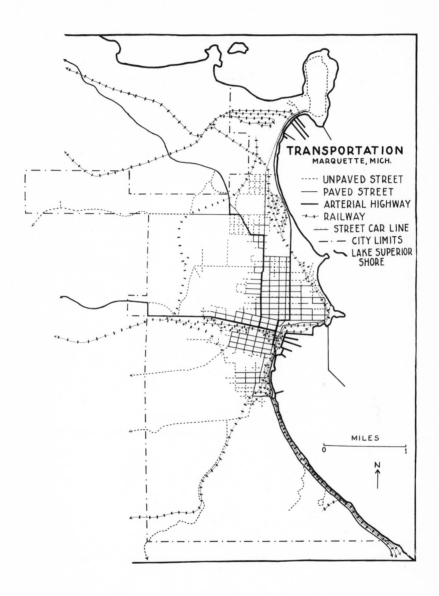

Fig. 36. "The Transportation Pattern in the Municipality of Marquette".

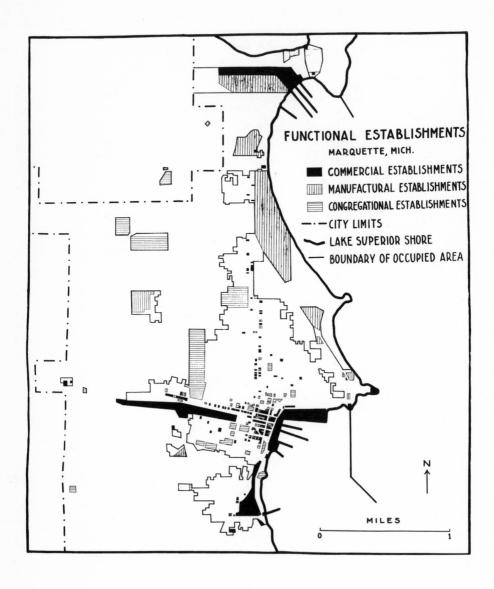

FUNCTIONAL ESTABLISHMENTS
MARQUETTE, MICH.

■ COMMERCIAL ESTABLISHMENTS
▦ MANUFACTURAL ESTABLISHMENTS
▤ CONGREGATIONAL ESTABLISHMENTS
–·– CITY LIMITS
⌇ LAKE SUPERIOR SHORE
— BOUNDARY OF OCCUPIED AREA

N

MILES
0   1

Fig. 37. "The Distribution of Non-residential Establishments within Marquette, according to Function".

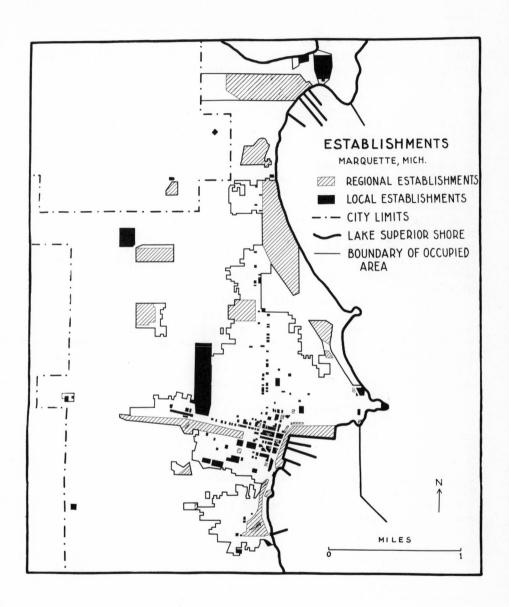

ESTABLISHMENTS
MARQUETTE, MICH.

REGIONAL ESTABLISHMENTS
LOCAL ESTABLISHMENTS
CITY LIMITS
LAKE SUPERIOR SHORE
BOUNDARY OF OCCUPIED AREA

N

MILES
0   1

Fig. 38. "The Distribution of Regional versus Local Establishments within Marquette".

and also serve timber lands as well as iron mines in the region.

In the days when logs were being driven down the streams of Michigan, most of the forest areas were tributary to points other than Marquette, at the mouths of the larger rivers. But in the recent period of hardwood logging by railway, forest interests have increased in the city. Marquette is not the only lumber center even for the railways which focus upon it, there being more convenient outlets for various parts of the forest lands. But it is one of the cities having access to a wide extent of forest lands and therefore within easy reach of timber supplies likely to last many years. The forest tracts from which timber is now being brought to Marquette (Fig. 35) will presently become exhausted and other tracts within reach of the city will take their places in supplying the demand.

Of the several wood-working plants in Marquette the most important are relatively permanent establishments manufacturing well fabricated products, in accordance with the fact that the city is a center of stable supply from scattered forest tracts. It is noticeable that the ore port of Marquette has become a wood-working rather than an iron-working center. With its position in the forest regions, the city is attractive to wood products industries which eliminate much waste material and provide their own fuel.

The smelting of iron ore likewise eliminates much waste material, but only by burning an even greater amount of fuel from other sources. Since the very beginning of iron mining in the Marquette range there have been various attempts to establish a local smelting industry, but these have had little success and the bulk of the ore has continued to pass unchanged through the port toward the coal fields and markets of the East.

An apparent exception which supports this generalization is a so-called iron furnace, employing more men than any other factory in the city. This plant utilizes Marquette ore, and solves the fuel problem by means of charcoal from the local wood supply. Nevertheless the higher value of charcoal iron is not sufficient to compensate for higher costs of manufacture, particularly since improvement in the quality of coke iron has reduced the price differential to a very small figure. Under these circumstances the continued operation and growth of the plant is accounted for by another line of activity--the utilization of chemical by-products incidental to the making of charcoal. These by-products have, in fact, become the main products, and iron has been relegated to the position of a by-product hardly justifying its manufacture.

Although this plant is thus seen to be a wood-products rather than an iron establishment, there are other factories which might be thought to owe their existence to iron ore. Two, in particular, use iron from the charcoal furnace as raw material, and are metal-working plants. Yet the nearby iron district is important to these establishments not as a source of raw material but as a market for their products. One factory manufactures machinery and the other diamond drills, for use in the mining industry. Their products are highly fabricated, developed in close contact with the market and made not merely of iron but of various assembled materials. The importance of proximity to the market is emphasized by the fact that part of the work has to do with repair or alteration of equipment. Yet the products being of a type in which special ingenuity is important, both plants have gained the advantage of producing specialties in which they have a monopoly. The market for such specialties is not confined to the Marquette Range but extends to other districts, in Michigan and beyond.

There are several other metal-working establishments in Marquette, but these have no products of unusual design. Therefore they depend entirely on the immediate demands of the local market, doing the small order and repair work of machine shops. The scale of such establishments is so small and their relations to the market so close, that they do not even cover the Marquette Range with their service, but work chiefly for customers in Marquette city.

COMMERCIAL AND MANUFACTURAL
FOCUS FOR A LOCAL MARKET

The function of the various metal-working plants with reference to market brings into view a great variety of other interests in Marquette, some of them manufactural and some commercial.

The city itself is a market for small scale establishments, such as the machine shops, which are duplicated in all the other population centers of the region. Most of the manufactural establishments of Marquette not already discussed are of this kind, making various products but all of a sort that benefits production close to market. Among these are bottling plants, printing presses, bakeries, and repair shops. These grade into commercial services, and there is a multitude of commercial establishments distributing to the same local market.

Obviously the small scale establishments, both manufactural and commercial, which serve only the city itself have little or nothing to do with Marquette's existence and functions in the region. From what has been said thus far Marquette might be thought of regionally only as an ore port and manufacturing city. But as a matter of fact, it is conspicuously a commercial center. The railways of the Upper Peninsula of Michigan (Fig. 35) serve their districts not only as areas producing ore and lumber, but also as communities consuming miscellaneous commodities. Marquette is distinctly the commercial center for the Marquette Range and the smaller nearby communities for which it is the transportation center. This cluster of communities is a market of only about 60,000 people, but large enough to be served by several wholesale establishments, particularly grocery and other food distributors requiring regional subdivision on a relatively small scale. Even retail establishments in Marquette perform some services for the same district, particularly those dealing

in commodities distributed with less regional subdivison than
groceries. Also Marquette banks do business beyond the city
and the Marquette daily paper circulates throughout the district.

It is the railways supplemented by the highway system,
and not the water connections of Marquette, which form the background of its commercial activity, except in respect to the one
commodity, coal. Boats coming to receive Marquette ore bring
enough coal from Lake Erie ports to supply the district and this
is accordingly distributed from Marquette. Occasionally a ship-
load is received of some other bulky commodity, such as cement,
but generally other merchandise is received and distributed by
rail or truck.

The territory thus tributary commercially to Marquette is
fairly distinct, comprising a cluster of communities, hedged in
by almost unoccupied woodlands. The boundary of the district
is drawn through the woodlands about halfway to the nearest commercial centers similar to Marquette--Sault Ste. Marie to the
east, Houghton to the west, and Escanaba to the south (Fig. 35).

The main part of the Marquette district forms a county,
the largest in Michigan, for which Marquette is logically the
county seat. The boundaries of Marquette County are for the
most part in the zone of unoccupied land around the Marquette
cluster of communities. ...

FOCUS OF MICHIGAN'S UPPER PENINSULA

Aside from the commercial status of Marquette in Marquette County, the place possesses significance for the Upper
Peninsula as a whole. There, among the several clusters of
communities, it is seen to have a central position. It is, to be
sure, on one of the shore boundaries, but most of the other
communities on which transporation lines focus also are on
boundaries, and the interior is mostly empty land. Marquette is
on a large reëntrant of the shore and is approximately halfway
between the Soo gateway to the east and the Gogebic Range to the
west, between the Copper Country to the north and the Menominee
Range to the south. Therefore certain interests that need central
headquarters with reference to these scattered communities find
Marquette an attractive place.

Lines of transportation and communication support this
choice; and yet Marquette is not the sole transportation focus for
the whole Peninsula, for each district has a separate focus and
separate outlet connections. Accordingly, the interests operating
from Marquette and covering the whole Penninsula deal with the
movement of people or intangibles rather than of commodities.
For example, many travelling salesmen who cover the Upper
Peninsula have their headquarters in Marquette, although the commodities which they sell are shipped directly to the various districts from some distributing point outside the Peninsula--Chicago
or some other major center greater than any of the more or less
equal small centers in the Peninsula.

The Upper Peninsula is not productive enough to support a great population center, yet, being a relatively large and detached area, it needs several services of the sort that can be located at a central point. Thus, in addition to travelling salesmen and sales agencies, there are head offices for the Upper Peninsula of telegraph and telephone companies and of the Post Office, several Michigan state offices having to do with the Upper Peninsula, the Northern State Normal College, the Upper Peninsula branch of the state prison, and the Peninsular cathedrals of three religious denominations.

Marquette cannot be said to have an exclusive tributary area belonging to it, because of the complexity of its relations and its regional establishments functioning diversely with reference to various areas--the Marquette Range, the logging camps, the county, the commercial district, the Upper Peninsula. Many of the interests are independent of each other in their functions and in the areas which they serve. Yet their concentration at Marquette shows interdependence, the ore traffic for the Marquette Range animating the development of railway systems for a larger area, and these in turn stimulating manufactural, commercial and political developments. The city is like a swarm of bees, in which the swarming place is chosen by a single one and the others follow.

THE CITY ON ITS SITE

Thus far Marquette has been discussed as if it were a point without areal extent. As a matter of fact this seems to be its fundamental aspect, a point where regional interests converge. In the swarm of bees the primary consideration of the individuals evidently is to be in the swarm rather than in any particular place or particular part of the swarm. The city interests are concerned primarily with reaching the focus of activity rather than in occupying land, and are even willing to lose contact with the ground altogether in attaining this end. Perhaps this fact may be considered fundamental in distinguishing urban from rural occupancy.

But in the city the established interests do have physical needs for mere space, some more than others. They are not all able to dance on the point of a needle, and are willing and able in varying degree to give up immediate proximity to the central point in exchange for space in which to operate. Accordingly the city is found to have areal extent with a definite arrangement fitting into the natural background of its site. In general, the city reflects development from a focal point about which the urban interests spread in accordance with their individual requirements and the exigencies of the site, this process being modified by the extension of some of the focal facilities from the major focal point to other points, making possible the development of secondary foci.

The major focal point of Marquette was fixed where the land route met the water route for ore shipment. The older (more southerly) of the two docks marks this point, on the shore of the bay at a place where one of the ore railroads reaches it through a small notch (Fig. 36).

With reference to this focus the nucleus of the city has developed, in characteristic form. The ore dock is flanked by the coal and merchandise docks and fisheries. The street and railway along the water's edge are faced by wholesale and storage houses and machine shops. The next street up from the waterfront is the base of the retail business district, on both sides of the railway approaching the ore dock. Farther inland along its tracks the railway has its stations, shops, and yards.

On the south side of the railway is the older part of town, early settlement having taken advantage of gently rolling land on that side and avoided a steep ridge 150 feet high which parallels the north side of the railway as it approaches the bay. On low hills of the south side are the county court house, the Roman Catholic Cathedral and associated establishments. But beyond the immediate vicinity of the railway the land on the south side is rough and broken, while the top of the Ridge on the north is smooth and slopes off to low level ground beyond, favoring the northward growth of the city. Moreover the modern highway from the interior enters the city along the lower slope of the Ridge paralleling the north side of the railway (Fig. 36). Accordingly, the modern heart of the business district is north of the railway at the junction of this highway and Front Street, where the four corners are occupied by three banks and a drug store with offices above (Fig. 37). From this place the business district extends inland for several blocks along the highway. Higher up the Ridge and beyond on its northern slopes are spread the newer sections of the city.

After the city nucleus had become fixed and adjacent land congested, modern extensions or duplications of some of the transportation facilities were added at several points to provide other places having at least some of the advantages of the city center. Such additions are represented by the newer (more northerly) railway and its ore dock (Fig. 36), where an equally good harbor is reached from the interior by a route of easier gradient but probably not chosen originally because longer than the other route and requiring a very high bridge across a gorge. The grouping of dock, yards, and shops is like that at the older center. A further extension of the line skirts the shore around the east end of the Ridge, to reach the older transportation focus, and thence the eastward extensions of both railways follow the shore, thus taking as short a course as possible and at the same time avoiding the hills in the southern part of the urban area (Fig. 36). At points in the city along the lines of both railways spurs provide facilities, and through a saddle in the western end of the Ridge a branch of the older railway extends northward to reach the flat land beyond.

This scattering of facilities has allowed a scattering of certain urban establishments, specifically, such establishments

-326-

as require considerable railway space and railway connections but
not other facilities which have accumulated in the heart of the city
(Fig. 37). These include not only the new ore dock but also the
larger factories, the county fair grounds and the state prison.
They are all on the low land north of the Ridge, except the prison,
which is also a factory, suitably situated by itself among wooded
hills near the south shore.

There are also some establishments needing considerable
space but not needing immediate contact with railway or other
focal facilities. Such are the normal college, parks, and cemeteries. These are located on sites with reference to residence
districts rather than other facilities.

The residence districts themselves are between and around
establishments of the primary nucleus and outlying secondary
focal points. Their primary function is to house the workers of
focal establishments, yet they do not need immediate contact
with focal facilities. They even tend to avoid immediate contact
with the railways and other establishments from which they receive directly injury rather than benefit--along the north shore,
for example, where there are fumes from the chemical plant together with other railway and factory phenomena. On the other
hand they cling to the transportation facilities which serve to
connect them with the focal establishments, avoiding land too
rugged for the convenient extension of the street system, and
extending north along the one practicable street car route (Fig. 36).

The development of motor traffic has made it practicable
for establishments to draw their workers from a wider radius
of residence districts than formerly. In fact the whole city is
now within the radius of every establishment. There is some
distribution of places of residence with reference to places of
employment. For example, a majority of the workers in the
older railway shops live on the south side, and a majority of
those in the newer shops on the far north side, i.e., each group
near the shop in which it is employed.

Nevertheless there are in every district employees of both
railways and also employees of central business establishments,
of all the larger factories, and even state prison guards. The
fundamental distinction between residence districts is not their
location with reference to places of employment but the attractiveness of their immediate sites and their development, as the
part of the Ridge overlooking the harbor in contrast with the
part overlooking the railway shops, or the vicinity of the normal
college in contrast with the vicinity of the chemical plant. A
classification of residence districts according to the financial and
social status of their inhabitants is the result.

More detailed analysis of individual districts, residential,
commercial and otherwise, would be possible but not now practicable. What has been said indicates that interpretation of the city
layout does not call for sharp distinctions between commercial,
manufactural, and congregational establishments (Fig. 37). In
locational requirements the small machine shops and boiler fac-

tories are less like the wood-products factories than like the whole-sale groceries.

Interpretation of the layout does not seem to call even for distinctions between establishments which are regional as compared with those that are local in their functions (Fig. 38). In locational specifications, the regional normal college is more like the local cemeteries than like the regional sales agencies. Commercial, manufactural, and congregational establishments have functions which are regional or local in accordance with the mobility of their service and the required intimacy of their contacts with the area served; and they occupy various sites in the city in accordance with their individual requirements for space and for connection with focal facilities.

Marquette has ample space for expansion, if distance from the facilities of the urban nucleus be disregarded. The city is still in a forest clearing and its political limits are out in the woods, like the limits of the county in the broader zone of woodland between groups of communities. The city limits might almost as well be halfway to the next city 12 miles distant in another forest clearing, in default of rural population between. A question might arise as to why there is another city so near. An answer from the Marquette point of view would involve the fact that the nearby city exists not in spite of the lack of rural population but instead of scattered rural population, being the nearest of the mining towns of the Marquette Range.

In view of the region which it serves, Marquette seems not to need the empty land around it for future expansion. On the other hand, the city seems less likely to shrink away in the near future than Republic or other communities in the region more richly endowed than Marquette in the resources of their immediate sites but less diversified in regional functions.

PROBLEMS OF OUR TIME [1]

by R. S. Platt

I must admit explicitly a fact which has always been implicit in microgeography: that the little spot of which I speak is included only because of its larger significance in relation to the world and as it contains the world--not merely as a simile but

1. Annals AAG, vol. 36 (1946), pp. 1-9.

as an epitome of the world and as a nerve cell in world order, like "the flower in the crannied wall" which holds the secret of life and is affiliated with the universe.

Problems of our time involve the interlocking of human life over the whole earth, and simultaneously the localization and even to some degree the isolation of life in every individual place on the earth. In one square mile there is evidence of these antithetical aspects of life--world unity and disunity, coherence and incoherence, attachment and detachment, conjunction and separation, interdependence and independence--opposite but coincidental aspects of life to be met and dealt with willy nilly by everyone who lives on the earth, and subject to understanding by geographers if understandable by anyone at all.

SECTION 16

Now look at the square mile in northern Illinois: Section 16 in Township 38 North, Range 13 East of the 3rd Principal Meridian. The checkerboard system of land subdivision in which this call number occurs was invented and adopted as the official system for carving up the lands of the Northwest Territory soon after the American Revolution. Northern Illinois was surveyed and the designation 16-38-13 was applied to a particular tract of land, on the ground, early in the Nineteenth Century. ...

Since that time Section 16 has become useful and valuable. Its present use is in contrast with that of surrounding sections in the lacustrine plain, apparently not because of any differences in the natural landscape but because of the number 16. The ordnances organizing the Northwest Territory contained a provision that all sections numbered 16 were to be dedicated to the support of education. ...

In striking contrast with the surrounding sections of other numbers, all of which have been subdivided and partly utilized for private homes or business, Section 16 has remained until recently largely unoccupied and available for the Chicago Municipal Airport, the most insistent new customer for such an unbroken tract of land. The Board of Education has leased 618 acres to the city for the airport. ...

CHICAGO MUNICIPAL AIRPORT

The airport has a suitable environmental setting. It is on a smooth plain, as it should be. Also it has runways for taking off in eight directions of the compass, which is in accordance with the fact that winds to be taken into account blow from all these directions at some time or other.

A preference for environmental causation in explaining the pattern may lead to a conclusion that the predominance of southwest and northeast winds has determined the construction of three runways oriented southwest-northeast, as compared with only two runways in any other direction. But a healthy impartiality toward

environmental and non-environmental interpretation leads to a
different conclusion. When the airport was enlarged from its
original half-mile square in the southeast quarter of Section 16,
the southwest-northeast runway was the only one which could not
be lengthened and therefore had to be lfet as it was, while two
new long runways were built, making a total of three of the same
orientation, one of them a short vestigial remnant of little utility
(Fig. 39).

Such historical accidents do not always coincide with the best
so-called "adjustments to the natural environment." For example,
the longest runway is the southeast-northwest, although the wind
rose shows less need of that orientation than of any other. It
happens that this is the longest because the only similar long diagonal, in the most important direction, is slightly shortened by
the location of the school yard in the southwest corner.

The pattern of runways is bordered by a string of closely
associated functional establishments (Fig. 39): a passenger terminal, mail and express terminals, offices and hangars of nine
air lines, the national headquarters and shops of one line, a traffic control tower, a Civil Aeronautics Administration control center, a Weather Bureau forecast center, immigration and customs
offices, an Army transient aircraft hangar, a National Guard hangar, air taxi offices, supply company stores; and various secondary
establishments within these: wire and radio communications,
lighting systems, cafes and newstands, ticket and information
offices.

These all operate in mutual accord in the coming and going
of aircraft. Some of them fulfill the immediate local needs of
people--the lunch rooms and ticket offices in the passenger terminal, for example; others the needs of cargo--the loading and
unloading devices, for example; others the immediate needs of
aircraft, such as the repair shops, and refueling equipment;
others the local arrangements of the landing field--the Weather
Bureau, the field lighting system and visual signals, the runways
themselves.

Some of the constituent establishments reach out farther to
operate as the focal center of a larger area: the traffic control
tower reaches out by radio supplemented by direct contact to a
distance of about ten miles; the Civil Aeronautics Administration
control center reaches out by radio to a distance of about two
hundred miles along nine air routes in northern Illinois and adjacent parts of Indiana, Michigan, Wisconsin, and Iowa (Fig. 40);
the Weather Bureau forecasts for an area about four hundred miles
in radius; the headquarters of the various airlines have jurisdiction
over part of a system for certain functions and over a whole system from coast to coast in the case of United Airlines with head
offices in Chicago. The Army headquarters for transient aircraft
has jurisdiction over an area in the North Central states.

The common objective of the whole group of establishments
is the orderly arrival and departure of air traffic to and from and
through Chicago. The traffic moves in and out along air routes

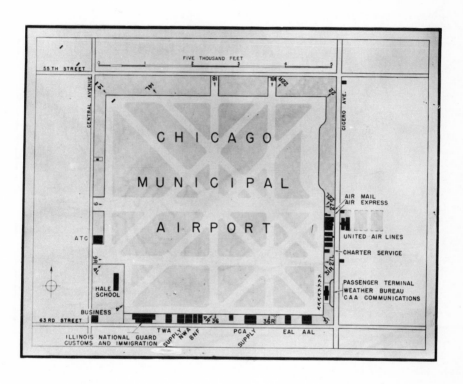

Fig. 39. "Section 16. Runways and buildings of the Chicago Municipal Airport".

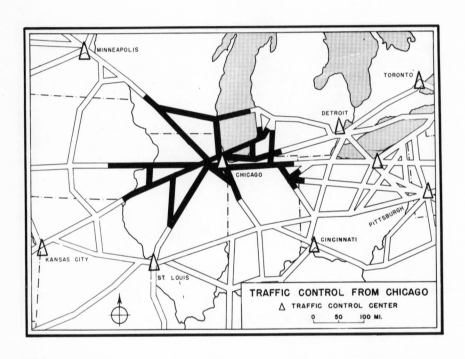

Fig. 40. "Extent of traffic control from Chicago center of Civil Aeronautics
Administration".

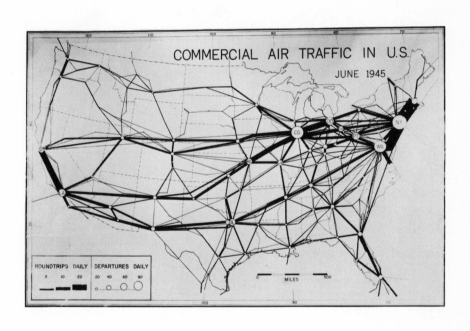

Fig. 41. "Traffic of domestic airlines in the United States".

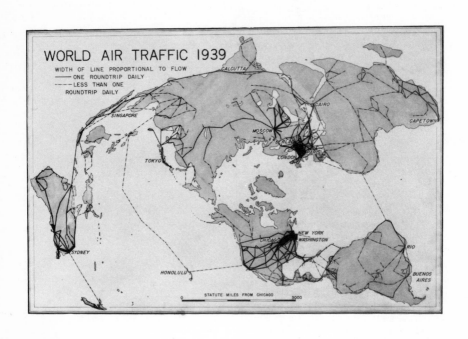

Fig. 42. "World air traffic before the war, on a projection equidistant from Chicago and for most of the world equidistant from Paris". Projection by James Wray, Chicago, 1945.

ramifying from Chicago east, west, north, and south over the United States. . . .

AMERICAN AIR TRAFFIC

From a Chicago point of view the airways of the nation have their center here. From another viewpoint based on the traffic pattern of the United States (Fig. 41) Chicago is seen to be one of the three major traffic centers of the country, in a class with New York and Washington. Chicago is the inland focus of heavy traffic, from which a crowd of lines extends eastward to the Atlantic Seaboard and divergent lines spread westward. Chicago is reached by nine airline companies, more than any other center, though it does not have a prominent place on every one of these lines.

Chicago is the main center for United Air Lines; a secondary center and northwestern terminal for American Airlines, with headquarters in New York; a secondary center for Transcontinental and Western Air, with headquarters in Kansas City; a primary eastern terminal for Northwest Airlines, with headquarters in Minneapolis; a western terminal for Pennsylvania Central Airlines, with headquarters in Washington; a secondary northern terminal for Eastern Airlines, with headquarters in New York; a northern terminal for Chicago and Southern Air Lines, with headquarters in Memphis; a northern terminal for Braniff Airways, with headquarters in Dallas; and a new northern terminal for Delta Air Lines, with headquarters in Atlanta.

Evidently Chicago is important but not preeminent with respect to airline connections. Of the airline traffic of the country 75 per cent is handled by these nine lines, and a third of this goes via Chicago, 25 per cent of the air traffic in the United States.

All the airline companies would be glad to serve all the large traffic centers, and although they are restrained by the Civil Aeronautics Board from flying wherever they please, there is nevertheless a tendency to allow all the major lines to reach the major centers, and to compete over the routes of heavy traffic. In general it is apparent that the pattern of air traffic corresponds with that of surface traffic: air traffic is heavy and closely spaced where surface traffic is heavy and closely spaced--particularly where first-class passenger and express traffic is heavy and dense.

WORLD AIR TRAFFIC

As the air traffic of Chicago is only part of a larger national pattern of traffic, so the national pattern is only part of a world pattern. The air traffic of the world just before the war is shown in Fig. 42 on an equidistant projection with Chicago as a center. Obviously this does not make Chicago the air transport center of the world. In the total pattern the area of heavy traffic in the United States appears as one of the two great regions of heavy traffic in the world. Eastern United States and Western Europe stand out as twin nuclei of air traffic, on opposite sides of the North Atlantic.

These two nuclei are fairly similar in form, size, and density. In spite of the fact that in one case the transport organization is based on private companies operating on overlapping airline systems and that in the other case organization is based on governmental monopolies operating from separate political centers, no great contrast appears in the resulting patterns. Chicago, New York, and Washington have counterparts in Berlin, London, and Paris as major focal points; intervening and outlying lines and secondary points are also comparable.

From the two nuclei of the North Atlantic, airlines extend to outlying regions of the world. In this extension of lines the two great focal areas have shared with a fair degree of equality, and without a division into hemispheres or continental spheres of influence. The great powers participate as world powers, not hemispherical powers. The name "Pan American Airways" indicates a first objective of American foreign effort, to link the United States with Latin America, but the name did not prevent a quick and natural transition to the rest of the world, reflecting both the lack of hemispherical division for air transport and the positive place of the United States as a world center rather than merely a Western Hemisphere center. So lines from the United States have extended not only to South America, but also across the Atlantic to Europe and Africa and across the Pacific to Asia and Australasia. Simultaneously lines from Europe have reached to the same outlying continents--South America, Africa, Asia, and Australasia--from different directions.

There have been differences in detail among the North Atlantic powers but general similarities in objectives, as further indicated in cases in which plans have not been fully carried out. For example, British plans to reach South America did not materialize before the war, but are proceeding now. German and Italian lines, not shown on the accompanying maps, did reach South America.

In general, lines from both of the North Atlantic nuclei have extended to all of the outlying continental areas. In general also the airlines have followed the main routes of surface traffic in the world, just as airline traffic in the United States and Europe has corresponded with surface traffic. So overseas airlines have paralleled the great sea routes and penetrated inland along railway and river routes, taking short cuts across land masses and making detours to refueling stations but really heading for the same ports and inland centers as those reached by modern surface transportation.

The war broke the world pattern of air transport, as well as that of surface transport, into three pieces: the two Axis spots and the United Nations over the rest of the world. Apart from the sharp break, a noticeable characteristic is the relatively slight amount of change in most parts of the pattern, in spite of the fact that Germany controlled all but a particle of the European nucleus and that accordingly worldwide air transport sprang mostly from the American center instead of from both sides of the North Atlantic.

Of course the redistributions of war produced many specific changes within the general pattern. One of these was a conspicuous concentration across the Hump from India to China--an abnormality in world air transport, where the airline did not parallel modern surface transportation but extended beyond the end of an ocean shipping route into an area not accessible by modern surface transportation. The fact that there are not many similar places in the air traffic pattern, either in war or in peace, suggests that areas with much freight to be handled are generally provided with cheap modern surface transportation and need depend only temporarily in special cases on the air to carry ordinary freight cargoes as well as first-class passengers and express. Freight traffic across the Hump has ceased with the end of the war. . . .

Now the postwar pattern has begun to form. Prewar ways are being resumed, with the retention of some wartime modifications and the abandonment of others. The United Nations have reached into the Axis spots. The European nucleus again has become a center of overseas lines to match those of the United States. Some overseas routes of the American Air Transport Command have been given to American domestic airlines. Once a week an airliner leaves Chicago for a roundtrip flight to London via Newfoundland and Eire.

WORLD UNITY

The increasingly irresistable unity of the world is disclosed in the pattern of airways--a pattern in which every part bears a clear relation to every other part. Aviation over the world is all cut from one piece of cloth; it is of one cultural variety. Even more than is usual in elements belonging to one type of culture the features of aviation are nearly identical over the world, the parts interchangeable: the fields, the planes, the pilots, the routine of operations, the ritual of service, the etiquette of crew and passenger behavior.

Other big city airports resemble that of Chicago, each with a criss-cross pattern of concrete runways according to the present style, and each conforming in specific details to local limitations of site. Even little airports in out-of-the-way corners of the world belong to the same species and resemble the Chicago airport of less than twenty years ago.

Why should not aviation be alike all over the world? There are no culture regions more closely bound together than the pattern of airways by actual passage of people and things and ideas, freely back and forth, in periods of time shorter than a phase of human life, or a change of season, or even than a passing mood or a current disposition. . . .

Our system of airlines is not necessarily permanent. The airway pattern is a fragile feature of the current unstable Occidental organization of the world. The wartime fracture into three parts indicates what can happen, not locally and temporarily, but completely and irrevocably, as a result of international discord and disintegration.

But even though this particular pattern may disappear, the problem of interrelations on a world scale is with us to stay and probably to increase, under conditions in which one place has contacts with other places, more and closer contacts with any or all places, for better or worse.

PRINCIPLES OF AREAL FUNCTIONAL ORGANIZATION
IN REGIONAL HUMAN GEOGRAPHY [1]

by A. K. Philbrick

Nodal Organization and Parallel Relationship

Interconnections between establishments may be thought of in two ways -- as parallel and as nodal. Fig. 43 shows a number of farm establishments in a uniformly agricultural area. All the farms are mutually connected by a pattern of section-line roads. Other connections analogous to the road network are not shown on the map. All the farms are reached by radio and television. They are all interconnected by the phone. They are all part of the same township, are served by the same school, belong to the same farm organization, etc. Each farm is connected in an analogous manner with establishments not shown on the map to which they all possess common linkage. Connections between farms do not appear to have a common focus anywhere within the area shown on the map. If there is such a focus, outside the map, its unspecified establishments are just as well connected with one farm as with another. The areal relationship of the farms in the map is that between establishments of corresponding or parallel functions. As the establishments are corresponding or parallel so their interconnections may be described as parallel, typical of areas of homogeneous occupance.

The same pattern of uniformity can be displayed for other types of establishments. Individual residences organized in blocks are connected by streets, sidewalks, alleys, telephones, water mains, and sewers. Interconnection of the houses by these means within the block is parallel. Interconnections lead away to establishments outside the blocks. Stores are in parallel relationship along the street frontage devoted to business.

In Fig. 44, however, these three areas of parallel uniform relationships are shown together as they are actually distributed in Boswell, Indiana. From the whole pattern, it appears that there

1. *Econ. Geog., vol. 33 (1957), pp. 306-336.*

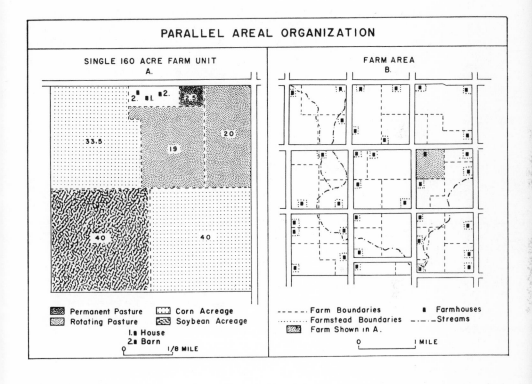

*Fig. 43. (A) a basic or first-order unit of organization, and
(B) an area of uniformity in such units.*

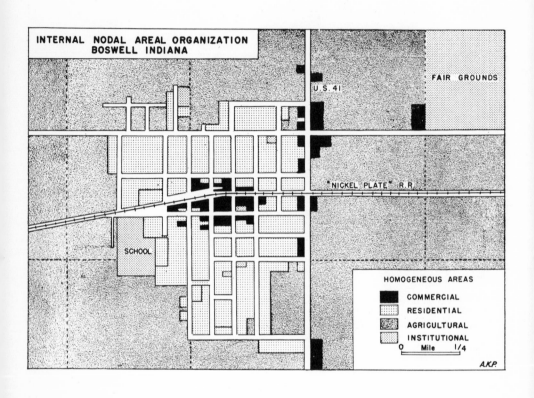

Fig. 44. *Functional establishments of areal organization in Boswell, Indiana.*

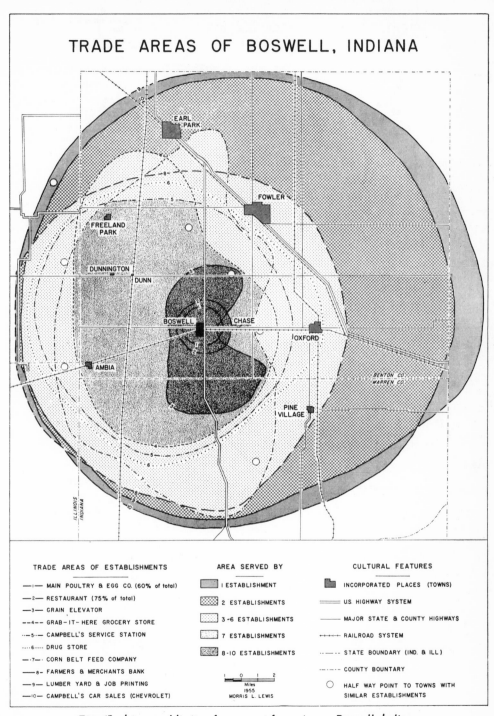

TRADE AREAS OF BOSWELL, INDIANA

TRADE AREAS OF ESTABLISHMENTS

— 1 — MAIN POULTRY & EGG CO. (60% of total)
— 2 — RESTAURANT (75% of total)
— 3 — GRAIN ELEVATOR
— 4 — GRAB-IT-HERE GROCERY STORE
— 5 — CAMPBELL'S SERVICE STATION
— 6 — DRUG STORE
— 7 — CORN BELT FEED COMPANY
— 8 — FARMERS & MERCHANTS BANK
— 9 — LUMBER YARD & JOB PRINTING
— 10 — CAMPBELL'S CAR SALES (CHEVROLET)

AREA SERVED BY

1 ESTABLISHMENT
2 ESTABLISHMENTS
3-6 ESTABLISHMENTS
7 ESTABLISHMENTS
8-10 ESTABLISHMENTS

Miles
1 0 1 2
1955
MORRIS L. LEWIS

CULTURAL FEATURES

INCORPORATED PLACES (TOWNS)
U.S. HIGHWAY SYSTEM
MAJOR STATE & COUNTY HIGHWAYS
RAILROAD SYSTEM
STATE BOUNDARY (IND. & ILL)
COUNTY BOUNTARY
HALF WAY POINT TO TOWNS WITH SIMILAR ESTABLISHMENTS

Fig. 45. Lines and limits of movement focussing on Boswell, Indiana.

-341-

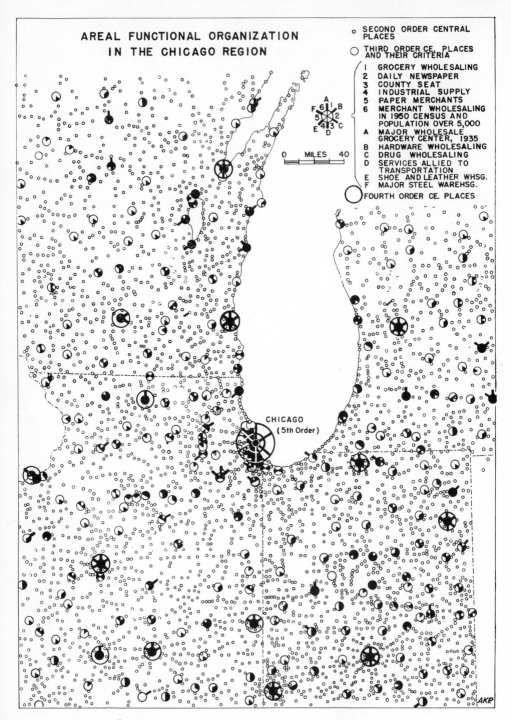

Fig. 46. Points of focus in a hierarchy of central places in the Chicago region.

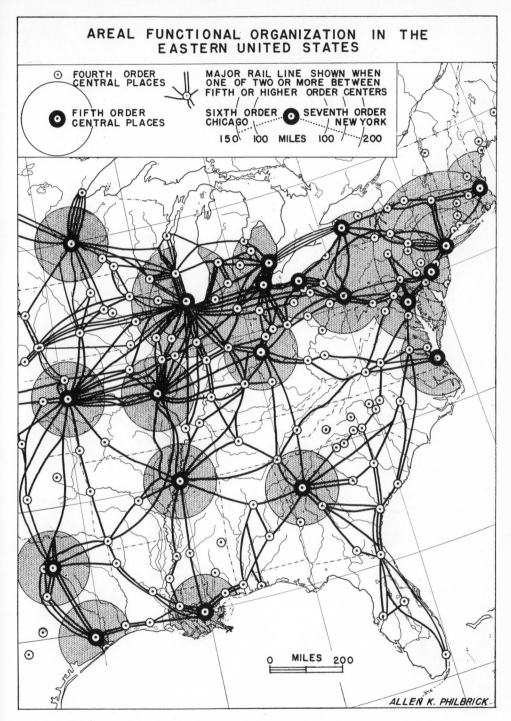

AREAL FUNCTIONAL ORGANIZATION IN THE EASTERN UNITED STATES

⊙ FOURTH ORDER CENTRAL PLACES

◉ FIFTH ORDER CENTRAL PLACES

MAJOR RAIL LINE SHOWN WHEN ONE OF TWO OR MORE BETWEEN FIFTH OR HIGHER ORDER CENTERS

SIXTH ORDER CHICAGO

SEVENTH ORDER NEW YORK

150 100 MILES 100 200

0 MILES 200

ALLEN K. PHILBRICK

Fig. 47: *Lines of movement and points of focus in a hierarchy of higher order central places in the Eastern United States.*

is a second concentration of business establishments along US
highway 41 on the outskirts of town. Land devoted to business is
thus intermittently mingled with residential land illustrative again
of the idea of discontinuity. A concentric pattern of different types
of uniformity is evident, however. Concentric zones of residential
and then agricultural establishments surround a dual commercial
core. In addition to parallel organization in areas of homogeneity,
interconnections between establishments of different type and
function constitute nodal areal organization.

Some of the farmers sell grain to the Elevator and buy feed
and fertilizer from the same sources. Others sell chickens to the
Main Hatchery and purchase feed from the Corn Belt Feed Store.
Still others bring cattle to the Livestock Auction to sell, and purchase others for fattening, or farm machinery from any one of
three farm implement dealers. Most of the owners and employees
in these and other commercial establishments live in Boswell.
Both town and farm families trade at the retail stores in Boswell
for food and a wide variety of other goods and services. There
exists, then, a focality of functions concentrated in the village. It
is symbolized in this case by the pattern of the community including the surrounding farms. The focus upon the village makes
it the nerve center or node of a sizeable area. The agricultural,
commercial, and residential establishments of this area of organization are mutually interconnected by transportation and communication facilities and establishments. They extend beyond the
limits of the Boswell area of organization. They connect Boswell
with other units of areal organization of the same kind and of a
higher order also.

In summary, then, individual interconnected areal units of
occupance possess two kinds of areal relationship simultaneously.
In one case it is the parallel relationship of similar-type units.
In the other case it is a series of interconnections between unlike
establishments focusing upon the core of a nodal area of functional
organization.

Alternation of Homogeneity and Nodality with Scale Progression

It is now possible to note a certain order in the classification of areal organization discussed thus far--an order which
varies with the scale of the units of occupance and their successive nested combinations. The maps in Figs. 43 and 44 show a
scale progression from large to smaller. They are (1) the scale
of the individual parcel of land; (2) the scale of the individual es-
tablishment--farm, store, dwelling, etc.; (3) the scale of the
parallel areal relationship of a small arbitrary group of similar
establishments into areas of farming, residence, and business;
and (4) the scale of their combination as a settlement. Accompanying the scale progression from large to smaller an alterna-
tion of type of organization--homogeneous, nodal, homogeneous,
nodal--is apparent. The map of any given type of establishment,
such as that of the farm, shows first homogeneous fields, and

then the <u>nodality</u> of the farm unit as a whole. The maps of parallel areal relationship of like establishments show the <u>homogeneity</u> of farms in a farm area, of homes in a residential area, of stores in a commercial district. The map of the village and parts of its service area portrays a larger <u>nodal</u> community unit of areal functional organization.

Putting it another way, the nodal farm unit is composed of homogeneous fields; the homogeneous agricultural area is composed of nodal farm units; and the nodal town market area is composed of homogeneous agricultural-residential areas surrounding a homogeneous commercial core. . . .

<u>Society as a Multiple Series of Bi-Polar Interconnections</u>. . .

The recognition of the nested hierarchical nature of areal units of organization is the key to geographical analysis of this complex maze of interrelationships. How do we know where the boundaries are between such areal units? How can areal units of functional organization be recognized and classified? What is the principled basis for differentiating between orders in a cumulative or nested hierarchy of such functional units and for locating their areal limits?

<u>First-Order Areas of Functional Organization: Internal and External Sub-Areas</u>

The focus of each individual establishment is the core of a first-order area of functional organization. In the case of the farm shown in Fig. 43A, part of the farm is the nucleus; and the areal arrangement of dependent fields is the area for which the farmstead is the primary focus. The limits of the internal area of a unit of areal functional organization at the establishment level are drawn quite simply at the limits of ownership, control, or jurisdiction. The internal area is composed of two parts, core and periphery. . . .

<u>Second Order Areas of Functional Organization</u>

As a geographical entity, Boswell, Indiana, like thousands of its counterparts, is a cluster of commercial and residential establishments. It includes also the surrounding farms which are its economic base. The resulting roughly circular, not necessarily spatially-continuous area, is the functional unit for which the establishments of the core are the primary focus.

Fig. 45 shows the service areas of ten major establishments of Boswell. Each boundary is a generalization of part of a first-order area of functional organization for a particular establishment. All ten, in their overlapping, plus an additional finite number of other first-order functional areas not shown, define an area for which Boswell enterprise as a whole is the primary focus. This is the internal portion of a second-order area of functional organization. In this internal portion there are two parts, a core and a periphery. The core is the built-up area of the village proper. The periphery is the village agricultural hinterland. From this example it seems clear that retailing and service establishments characterize the function of the second order focal place.

What about the ramifications of Boswell establishments with connections beyond this locality--the suppliers scattered over the Middle West, the Chicago and eastern seaboard markets for meat and grain? They too are appropriately to be considered as spatially-discontinuous parts of the areal functional organization of Boswell; they constitute its external area of functional organization. . . .

Higher Order Areas of Functional Organization

The qualitative change from first to second-order takes place when a number of relatively homogeneous areas of similar type establishments develop nodally around a focus of establishments of one particular type of function, such as farms and village residences around a business district. They then possess in common the mutual benefits of a division of labor among a number of unlike types of establishments. This is the nodal functional principle upon which is based the development of nucleated settlement as a larger unit of organization than the individual establishment. As the size and complexity of second-order places increases by addition in both number and type of establishments, further qualitative changes may be expected to take place in the development of higher orders of more complex areal organization. . . .

Third Order Areas of Functional Organization--the Cluster of Focal Places

The qualitative change from second- to third-order areal organization takes place when communities are mutually connected in terms of some higher-ordered function into a cluster of focal places. In economic areal organization, for example, wholesaling (including the wholesaling by manufacturers) is the basis for the nodality of one focal place in a cluster of several such places. . . .

Kankakee: An Example of a Third-Order Central Place. . .

On the basis of its internal areal structure, Kankakee exhibits not only first order (establishment) and second order (focal place) areal organization, but third order as well. Its inner area (the built-up or urbanized area) is the sum and functional integration of a number of second-order areas, each with a separate focus. These are in turn focused upon the major core of the city as a whole. Kankakee is a clear example of a contiguous cluster of second-order focal places clustered around a single major business district. It is the inner portion of the internal area of an areal unit of third-order functional organization.

In addition, Kankakee has developed wholesale, retail, and labor market functions which reach out to interconnect Kankakee with a number of non-contiguous central places. Kankakee's wholesale and retail trade area extends generally 25 miles to the north, and 40 miles east, west, and south. Some 50 towns and villages are included within a radius of those distances from Kankakee. . . . Detailed data concerning wholesaling and labor force interconnections are not available. The local regional character of downtown Kankakee as a larger second-order retail trade center is shown by the percentages of people from outlying towns who patronize stores in Kankakee. The towns mentioned above together comprise, in the sum of their second-order areas of functional organization, the outer portion of the internal area of organization focused upon Kankakee, a non-contiguous cluster of central places focusing upon a major core.

Beyond the limits of this rather extensive internal area, Kankakee establishments, analogous to those of Boswell, undoubtedly have a great number of interconnections with establishments in other places. Their finite sum defines in principle the absolute limits of the external area of Kankakee's areal functional organization. . . .

The Hierarchy of Central Places in the Chicago Region. . .

Fig. 46 shows the distribution of third-order centers of the type represented by Kankakee. If agricultural collection and supply and retail establishments are the indices of second-order centers, wholesaling may be taken as one convenient and significant index of third-order focal places. Since wholesalers in practice distribute to retail outlets which in turn distribute to individual consumers, the three scales of marketing operation correspond logically to the three scales of a hierarchy of units of functional areal organization. These are, of course, the cluster of focal places (served by a wholesale center), the individual focal place (served by a retail trade center), and the individual consumer (the establishment)--third-, second-, and first-order units of areal organization respectively. The functions of wholesaler, retailer, and consumer are intended here as generalized symbols or indices of functional organization. They are not intended as all-inclusive analytical characterizations of total organization necessarily applicable universally. It seems probable that three separate systems of areal units are necessary to describe total areal organization--economic, political, and social. . . .

Centers of focus for contiguous and non-contiguous focal places of the third-order in Fig. 46 are defined on the basis of the variety and types of wholesale trade establishments reported in a wide range of sources. Additional criteria employed were the presence of a daily newspaper and the political-administrative cultural significance of the county seat.

Composite symbols were employed in the map in order to differentiate between the more complex centers possessing a greater diversity of the criteria employed. At the same time, they make possible identification of the association of criteria in each city. These cities are primary foci for clusters of focal places by virtue of the special focality of certain of their establishments which characterize them as wholesale centers. The wholesalers reach out to their retail store customers in an extensive over-lapping pattern of the smaller second-order places shown by the small hollow circles in Fig. 46. Such interconnections provide only one of the bases for the discontinuous overlapping of non-contiguous clusters of smaller towns around each third-order city. In many of them manufacturing enterprises attract significant portions of the labor force of near-by smaller places. Also, the larger number and greater variety of retail merchandise offered in the commercial districts of the larger third-order cities attract a wide circle of shoppers from surrounding communities. Such third-order centers are likely to be political, social, educational, medical, and recreational, as well as economic foci for the entire population within several hundred square miles of territory around them.

It is readily apparent, however, that the generally even dis-tribution of third-order centers (including all higher-ordered cities, of course) shown in Fig. 46 is characterized by consider-able unevenness in degree of centrality. There is room, there-fore, for further sub-classification of such centers on the basis of more detailed analysis in the future.

The repetition of nodal third-order centers shown in Fig. 46 is also capable of interpretation at still smaller scale as the par-allel homogeneity of third-order units of areal functional organi-zation. Again, each unit contains all the lower-ordered compo-nents. The much greater distance between centers of third order compared with those of second order may be taken as an index of the difference in the sizes of the corresponding areas of third- and second-order organization. . . .

Once again, at the same time that all third-order focal places, with their complexly interwoven inner and outer internal and external areas of functional organization, may be classified as parallel in areal relationship, certain of them are nodally or-ganized through the interconnections of their establishments into larger, higher-ordered units of areal organization.

Fourth-Order Areal Organization: The Cluster of Clusters of Focal Places. . .

Every establishment or focal place involves some transpor-tation and communication. It is, therefore, not the mere existence of this function, but rather its degree of development and service of other places which counts. When the handling and shipment of goods is developed beyond the needs of the locality to service the needs of several clusters of focal places, it enables one third-order center to become the focus of an area of fourth-order or-ganization--in a word, a specialized center of transshipment. . . .

The additional criteria are the number of trunk-line railroads, the number of tracks, and the number of routes radiating
outward from a given central place; the number of cities interconnected by two or more separate rail routes; and rail-freight-
yard car capacities of individual cities as measures of rail interconnection and centrality.

Others are the number of air line companies, the number of
air route directions radiating from a given central place, the number of cities mutually connected by two or more air line companies, and the number of air freight carriers serving the given
city as measures of air interconnection and centrality.

Still other criteria are the trucking industry's own estimate
of the gateway status of trucking centers, the number of highway
freight carriers listed as based in a given center, and the number of "common and joint trucking terminals" along with the number of individual carriers involved in each, as measures of highway interconnection and trucking centrality.

In the absence of detailed quantitative information tracing
the flow of goods between establishments and between central
places, such indices as these are substituted as a practical basis
for tentative classification of fourth-order centers within 150
miles of Chicago.

Fig. 46 shows 15 central places. Four of these, Chicago,
Milwaukee, Indianapolis, and Grand Rapids, exhibit a marked
development in all 12 of the transportational criteria of fourth-
order centrality. Four more--Fort Wayne, South Bend, Peoria,
and Rock Island-Moline--are lacking only a common and joint
trucking terminal. Two of the 15--Terre Haute and Springfield--
are missing two of the criteria. Springfield is served by only one
air freight carrier and has no common trucking terminal, while
Terre Haute, sharing the latter void, is connected to no other
cities by two or more airlines. The remaining five cities are
lacking in various criteria. In the case of Rockford three criteria
are missing, four each in the cases of Green Bay and Danville,
and five each in the cases of Decatur and Bloomington. . . .

Fifth-Order Centers of Areal Functional Organization: Major Urban Regions

As a transportation hub, Chicago is probably the world's
best-developed and clearest example of a transportation focus for
a quasi-centinental grouping of clusters of clusters of central
places. Chicago is either first or very close to the top in continental ranking as a center in the case of railroads, air transport, trucking, and as a port. This dominance of Chicago in the
field of transportation is even more striking in Fig. 47. Chicago
is the hinge at the right angle between the pre-industrial north-
south axis of the continental interior region along the Lake
Michigan-Mississippi valleys on the one hand, and the twentieth
century industrial axis eastward from Chicago to New York on
the other. As the major rail gateway of the continent, Chicago

can truly be described as the hub of a cluster of central places. In this function it serves as the nodal core of a fifth order region of areal functional organization. As a matter of fact, however, Chicago is undoubtedly also a center of higher than fifth-order organization. Before dealing only briefly with that phase of Chicago's position in the hierarchy of functional organization, however, something else should be noted. The fifth-order functions of Chicago are repeated by a number of other cities. Taking freight car capacity, number of rail interconnections, highway carrier gateway status, number of originating air carriers, and number of ocean shipping companies servicing the various centers of fourth or higher order centrality, the map, Fig. 47, shows for the eastern United States the pattern of nodal centers of fourth and fifth order, respectively.

The greater number of fourth-order central places within 150 miles of Chicago does not constitute a difference in principle from the patterns of other fifth-order centers with their smaller number of fourth-order places. Each of such centers as Detroit, Toledo, Columbus, Cincinnati, Buffalo, Pittsburgh, Boston, New York, Baltimore, Norfolk, and others possess nodal organization of parallel sub-units of all lower-ordered components in successive steps of nodality, uniformity, etc. Together, all fifth-order centers are, once again, in parallel relationship. In the American northeast the denser parallel organization of fifth-order centers coincides with a continuous region of relative uniformity familiar as the American Manufacturing Belt. . . .

Centers of Higher Orders of Functional Organization

Within nations certain cities possess nodality greater than that assigned to the fifth order as hubs of clusters of central places. This dominance of a few selected centers is akin to the phenomenon recorded by Mark Jefferson in his conception of the primate city.

Perhaps, in the United States, there are three regional primate cities. . . .

Applying, now, the concept of the primate city to each of these three great regions, Los Angeles and Chicago are each the center of a sixth-order region of functional organization, while in the case of the East, New York is a single sixth-order center for the eastern region and the single highest, seventh-order central place of the national organization of the country as a whole.

The question of the roles of Chicago and New York as special sixth- and seventh-order central places must be viewed within their national context. The national functioning of the urban northeast as the core region of a nodally-organized national or even continental unit of human occupance rests upon the actual division of labor between virtually the sum total of all establishments and the activity of their people. In such an areal organization of society with respect to both numbers and types of establishments, Chicago and New York play key roles in the organization of the economy and the culture of the country. . . .

World Nodal Organization

The repetition of nodal organization of the United States, of the nations of western Europe, and the Soviet Union at a scale on the order of 1/300,000,000, demonstrates the parallel relationship of national units of occupied surface into a single core region characterized as the industrially developed Northern Hemisphere, based upon modern technology and interconnection of a highly developed regional division of labor. At the same time as this huge industrialized region can be considered an area of uniformity, it is so in a setting of the rest of the world. . . .

The nodal organization of the world focuses upon the major industrial world-core region in the Northern Hemisphere. It is interconnected locally, regionally, nationally, internationally, and intercontinentally by all forms of land, water, and air transportation and communication. . . .

Conclusions. . .

Reliance has been almost exclusively upon examples from what could be called economic area organization. What are the problems involved in applying these principles to political and social establishments? Examples, furthermore, have been drawn almost exclusively from the western world, specifically the United States. What are the problems involved in applying these principles to subsistence societies, to the complex dual societies in colonial areas where both commercial and subsistence organization exist together?

C H A P T E R 16

Derivatives of
Type 8 (Culture Origin)

The concept of culture origin and dispersal has grown in importance in geography from that of a doubtful archeological tangent to that of a valuable and trustworthy line of thought not to be ignored in any study of human geography. Almost from the beginning (as the topography of art and under other names) it was pursued vigorously and variously as a separate and self-sufficient approach in geography. More recently it has been used in concert with other concepts, as already indicated, and now pervades and strengthens the work of geographers almost everywhere.

A first step from archeological beginnings[1] was immediate application to forms which to geographers were most familiar than potsherds: namely, settlements and houses of present occupance. "Some Rural Settlement Forms in Japan" by R. B. Hall, 1931, is an excellent early example of settlement study under this concept, an application of the idea of culture origin and dispersal to the areal layout of occupance. The field method is partly from cultural anthropology and partly from the geography of landscape uniformity and diversity, thus depending particularly on types 8 (Culture Origin) and 6 (Areal Uniformity).

1. *pp. 141-160 above.*

The excerpts included here from "Rural Settlement Forms in Japan" are devoted to settlement types, and the kindred topic of house types
is illustrated by a more recent study: "The
Log House in Georgia", by W. Zelinsky, 1953.

The field method is similarly based and follows
particularly types 8 (Culture Origin) and 6
(Areal Uniformity). A contrast in approach with
that of "The Anglo-Saxons of the Kentucky Mountains", by Miss Semple, 1901, (type 4, Explanatory Human) is to be expected, if progress from
stage to stage over a period of fifty years is
to mean anything. One difference is epitomized
in Miss Semple's reference to the log cabin home
as "the only type distinctly American"[1] in
contrast with Zelinsky's tracing of log cabins
back to European origins.

Another allied branch of study is that of man
as agent in producing the cultural landscape.
This is clearly rooted in study of the origin and
dispersal of culture and also has other roots.
A part of "Human Geography and Ecology in the
Sinú Country" by B. L. Gordon, 1957, is taken
as an example.

The author of this study quotes G. P. Marsh
in "The Earth as Modified by Human Action,"
1863, as a major source of inspiration, thus
looking back to Marsh along another line in addition to that of conservation of natural re-

1. p. 68 above.

sources.[1]   Also this study is connected with
"The Morphology of Landscape" by C. O. Sauer,
1925[2], more specifically than is the early work
on culture-from-an-anthropological-viewpoint
by Sauer himself.[3]

The title of the study, "Human Geography and
Ecology", does not refer, it may be assumed,
to human ecology as proposed by Barrows,[4]
but does refer to plant and animal ecology with
a human component or factor. The field method
involves observation and inquiry directed along
specific lines, with a background of plant ecology,
anthropology and history and with special reference to type 8 (Culture Origin).

The preceding studies in this chapter are concerned primarily if not exclusively with the
concept of the origin and dispersal of culture
in geography. The last item, "Reconnaissance
in Dynamic Regional Geography: Tierra del
Fuego" by R. S. Platt, 1949, is included to illustrate the application in field study of this
concept together with other useful concepts in
geography.

This is not a distinguished choice with which
to conclude, but it is taken as an available study
in which a conscious effort has been made to take
account of all eight of the types appearing in

1. p. 186 above.
2. *Univ. of Calif. Publ. in Geog.*, vol. 2, p. 53
3. pp. 141-160 above.
4. H. H. Barrows: "Geography as Human Ecology" in *Annals AAG*, vol. 13 (1923),
    pp. 1-14

this series, with emphasis on types 8, 7 and 6,
as providing consistent unification in associated
processes and expressive devices: culture origin
and dispersal, functional organization and its
areal pattern, and areal uniformity and diversity. And it harks back at least faintly to
ideas of the analytical study of occupance (type
5), environmental relations (type 4), physical
geography (type 3), areal description (type 2)
and exploratory traverse (type 1).

SOME RURAL SETTLEMENT FORMS IN JAPAN[1]

by R. B. Hall

THE YAMATO BASIN. . . .

The Yamato Basin may aptly be called the "cradle of Japanese civilization." Here, according to the Kojiki, the first emperor
of the Japanese led his people from Kyushu in the seventh century
before the Christian era. Here Buddhism was first introduced and
was soon followed by other elements of Chinese culture. On the
level floor of this graben, soil, climate, and drainage conditions
favored an intensive use of the land, and at an early date a dense
population was found.

SYSTEM OF LAND DIVISION

Among the material cultural forms that reached Yamato
from the Celestial Empire was a system of land division known as
the Han den, or Chinese land system. This involved a partition
and repartition of the land into squares. The smallest and basic
unit of division was a plat measuring about six by six feet. This
unit was presumed to produce enough rice to feed one adult male
for one day, and the plan was called the ku bun den, "mouth share
land", system. Three hundred and sixty such plats formed the
next largest square, enough on the basis of the lunar calendar to
maintain one man for one year. All dividing lines were oriented
north-south and east-west. The main roads left the four great
gates of the Heijo (Nara) capital, and the entire settlement pattern

---

1. *Geog. Rev.*, vol. 21 (1931), pp. 94-122.

was adjusted to them and to the system of land division. The original plan can be reconstructed by referring to ancient temple maps, the ruins of the Heijo capital, geographical place names, unusual surface and drainage forms, and certain historical documents. It will be found that elements of the landscape that antedate the introduction of the Han den do not fit the pattern. Such are the older imperial tombs and some ancient villages. Also, features which have been developed since the breakdown of the system do not conform. This is particularly true of recent village growth. The Han den is not a mere adoption of the ancient Sei den of China, or "well and field" system. It was altered and adapted to Japanese conditions and probably never was applied in full detail.

Furthermore, the same unit of measurement was not used throughout Japan. During the Asuka period, the Han den was applied to the Osaka Plain and possibly about the Asuka capital in the southeastern corner of the Yamato Basin. At that time the square cho measured forty ken; and on the Osaka Plain double this unit, or eighty ken, was used. However, after the Heijo capital was established and the Han den was prescribed for all of the Yamato Basin, the new square cho, or sixty-ken, unit was introduced. The later division of the paddy lands of Kinki seem to have all been on the sixty-ken measure. In dry lands a double unit, or 120 ken, was apparently used.

The smallest political division is the mura, which in turn is divided into economic entities called azas. For example, muras that lie on the border of the plain may contain an aza of dry crop upland. There may also be an aza containing only eta peoples, who in addition to farming prepare leather, glue, and other animal products. Villages of these outcast people are found at the foot of most of the imperial tombs. As the land of the Yamato Basin is quite uniform throughout, it frequently happens that all of the land of the mura is suitable for rice cultivation. In such cases, the detailed operation and maintenance of facilities for irrigation and flood control are the responsibilities of the aza. The normal aza contains one agglomeration of houses. As the size and productive quality of the aza domain is much the same everywhere on the basin floor, these agglomerations tend to be uniform in size and distribution. They also tend to conform to the pattern of the ancient Han den system (Fig. 48). About two hundred and fifty village agglomerations are found on the Yamato Basin floor, varying in size from a minimum of twenty houses to a maximum of eighty, with the majority having about sixty. These lie at an average distance of one kilometer from each other.

THE COMPACT VILLAGE: KAITO

The typical village is also an exotic form and was introduced from China. It is an exceedingly compact agglomeration of rectangular form surrounded by a hedge and a moat, so compact indeed as to appear a detached bit of urban landscape. These agglomerations may be described as of a checkerboard pattern and are

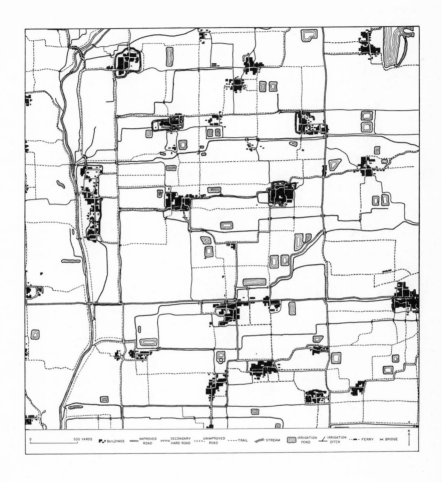

Fig. 48. "Map of an area including Heiwa Mura and vicinity, Yamato Basin, Nara
Prefecture. Note the rectangularity of all forms of the landscape. The
impress of the ancient Han den is everywhere evident on the basin floor.
Note also the dekaitos or detached houses and small agglomerations beyond
the moat. Scale 1: 35,000."

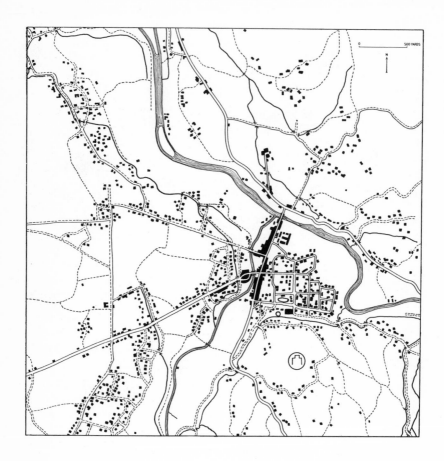

Fig. 49. "Map of an area about Izumi, Kagoshima Prefecture. Note the ancient
castle site (enclosed in a circle). The government offices (shown by an
oval) occupy part of the old fumoto, or walled village. Samurai families
still reside to the immediate north and east of the government offices.
The machi, commercial settlement, the elongated area of compact buildings
west of the government offices, occupies a characteristic position in regards
to the fumoto. For legend see Fig. 48. Scale 1: 35,000."

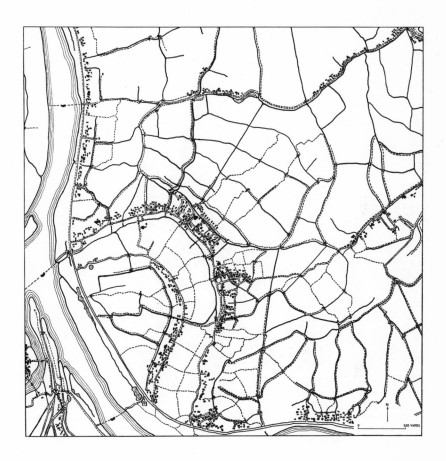

Fig. 50. "Map of an area, including Sonogi Mura and vicinity, Echigo Plain, Niigata
Prefecture. Note the road and settlement pattern marking the levees of an
abandoned meander in the southwestern portion of the map. For legend see
Fig. 48. Scale 1: 35,000."

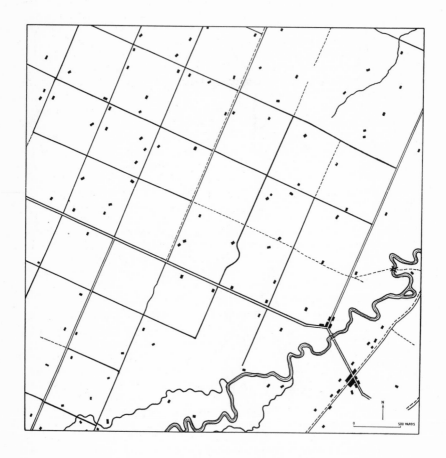

Fig. 51. "Map of part of Memuro Mura, Tokachi Plain, Hokkaido. Note the rectangular road pattern and the disseminated pattern of population distribution. Note also the small agglomerations near the crossing of the river. For legend see Fig. 48. Scale 1: 35,000."

called locally <u>kaitos</u>, as such villages are in the old Middle Kingdom. The term kaito has been translated as "inside the wall." The writer found two villages in Yamato where remnants of ancient walls are to be seen and documentary evidence in three others that such walls once existed. Another feature corresponding to the Chinese village is the four passages from the villages corresponding to the cardinal points of the compass. These are still referred to as the north, south, east, and west gates in spite of the fact that there have been no gates within the recollection of any living person. Two hundred and twenty-five kaitos can be identified within the Yamato Basin, or 90 per cent of all village agglomerations, lying below the 100-meter contour.

The moat, which may have followed Buddhism in its long journey from India, has lost its primary function, which was one of protection. Improved transportation and marketing facilities have lessened the need for the home cultivation of fish and so have decreased the value of the moat. The application in recent years of larger-scale and improved irrigation minimizes the dependence of the village upon a hand distribution of water from the moat during the dry season. Better flood protection, too, has been established, and hence the moats are not so necessary as drainage depressions. The breakdown of the village as a self-sufficient social and economic entity has done away with the desire for isolation. The advent of a money economy, replacing a purely land and rice economy, and the growth of larger-scale industrial and marketing establishments have destroyed many of the village industries and have forced contacts with the outside. The arbitrary establishment of political units, often enclosing several kaitos under one mura office, has helped to break down the village personality. The abolition of laws prohibiting individuals from moving away from their villages has had the same effect. New ideas have come with western science. A few years ago a young man was compelled to marry a girl of his own kaito. Now, the modern parent looks beyond the moat for a daughter-in-law, as he believes inbreeding to be undesirable. In every respect, then, the need for the moat has disappeared. On the other hand, the constantly increasing demand for more rice land takes a toll upon the ancient moat. In many cases the moats have completely disappeared and can be traced only in narrow, depressed paddies. Often, only the section on one side of a village has been reclaimed. In others the width has been reduced to a mere fraction of its former size.

The moat limits the number of houses which may be built within it. In Japan the eldest son inherits the property of the family, and the younger sons wishing to build their own home are soon forced to settle outside. This has been accomplished in two ways: first, by the development of new kaitos adjoining; secondly, by the formation of a <u>de</u> kaito (outside of "inside the wall") just beyond the moat and along one of the roads leading from the village. De kaitos are found on upland areas where cotton was grown a century ago and where now mulberry is the chief crop. Other de kaitos are of recent origin and have grown up where the road from the village crosses a railroad or interurban line. The secondary agglomerations can be traced to their place of origin by family names, shrines, and the detail of agricultural methods and house structure.

Another feature of settlement which can sometimes be recognized is the rough arrangement of houses into groups of five, six, ten, or twelve. This system is called the kumi or goningumi (company of five) and in China and Korea was a military expedient. In Japan it seems to have been purely for social control. The kumi had a contemporary introduction with the Han den and kaito and so became established in the Kinki district but apparently did not develop in central or northern Japen. Such an arrangement of houses into company groups is not an obvious feature and usually can only be recognized after attention has been called to it. . . .

THE SATSUMA TYPE

The Satsuma type embraces a number of relict culture forms dating from or in some cases antedating feudal days. The essential characteristics of this type dominate the settlement of Satsuma, Osumi, and adjacent areas in Hyuga.

The southern portion of Kyushu is an ash plateau through which protrude, in places, granite mountains and andesitic cones. Deep gorge-like valleys cut into the plateau, and small alluvial plains border the sea. The climate is subtropical, and the area lies near the center of the great typhoon path. Bamboo is abundant and often reaches seven inches in diameter. Evergreen broadleaf trees grow to great size. A soft, friable, ash-colored rock occurs near the surface in many places. It can be easily quarried and cut. The Kumakii mountain land crosses Kyushu from east to west and effectively separates Satsuma from the rest of Japan. To the south, however, easy communication is maintained with the Loo Choo Islands. These conditions have fostered political independence and southern cultural affiliations.

ISOLATION AND INDIVIDUALITY

Southern Kyushu is at least a quarter of a century behind the rest of Japan. Satsuma is at the same time the most difficult and most profitable place to study ancient Japan, at least in one phase, for its individuality has always been well marked. Satsuma remained as a semi-independent state even to the extent of making individual treaties with foreign nations and to waging war on the Imperial troops after the Restoration. Even today the standard dialect of Japan is called voso-no-kotoba, or the outside language; and the Satsuma dialect, which is unintelligible to other Japanese, is spoken in the home. Temples to the rice goddess, which are found in all other provinces, do not occur; and instead the paddy fields are graced by a small local rice god. Several important industries are common to and apparently had their origin in the Loo Choo Islands. The sweet potato, which serves as the chief food of the masses of southern Kyushu, is called the Satsuma imo, or potato, in Tokyo. In Satsuma it is called the Loo Choo imo. In Loo Choo it is called the kara, or Chinese potato; and in south China it is referred to as the foreign potato. There are historical data also to prove the introduction of the sweet potato by this path. The exterior appearance of the Satsuma rural house is more like the houses of the northern Loo Choos than like other parts of Japan.

CASTLES AND WALLED VILLAGES

In the early feudal days each lord maintained a castle and ruled his domain with little interference from the outside. Satsuma is still known in legend and ballad as "the land of a hundred-and-twenty castles." After the rise of the Shimazu family and a conquest of Satsuma by the forces of the Shogunate, these castles were destroyed and the power of the Shimazu became complete. Upon the ancient sites were constructed walled villages, fumotos, which were occupied by a new people especially set into the social system for the purpose (Fig. 49). These were the Go-samurai, or farmer-warriors, who owed allegiance directly to the house of Shimazu and were controlled by it in the same fashion as other parts of Japan were ruled by the Shogun.

The castle had doubtless drawn the country folk to it, and the new fumoto tended to have the same attraction. As a result, we find the present huts built in a series of roughly concentric circles about the fumoto site, which, as the name implies, lies at the foot of the mountains. It is interesting to note that the number of fumotos so far identified, 102, corresponds closely with the present number of muras, 140. Another element, too, is found. This is the so-called machi, or commercial agglomeration. Normally it approximates a strassendorf at some central location near to and on the main road from the fumoto. Today but few fumotos maintain their original structure. In most cases the sites are now used for schools, village offices, military barracks, and other public buildings; but the name and the great walls still persist, as does the center of local government. It is interesting to note that the mura boundaries have undergone but little change through the centuries. They are essentially the same as they were in the thirteenth century when the Shimazu family arrived from Kamakura. This is well shown on the interesting and valuable map collection of the Shimazu Museum in Kagoshima. It is highly possible that the lines represent much earlier tribal division. . . .

THE ECHIGO TYPE

The Echigo type involves a dry point settlement which is serpentine in form owing to location upon ancient dunes and active and abandoned levees, a particular distribution of landownership, and a house form well adapted to the local conditions. It is characteristic of the complex delta plains bordering the Sea of Japan, particularly the Echigo, Takata, and Shonai plains.

The Echigo plain, which constituted the datum area for this study, is the largest delta plain in Japan. It is formed by the deposits of the longest of the Japanese rivers, the Shinano, and other streams. The chief utilization and settlement problem here is the superabundance of water. The shallow, meandering rivers that cross the flat, poorly drained plains are not able to handle the floods that accompany the thaw of late April and early May or occasionally occur with heavy August rains. The coasts of the Sea of Japan receive a heavy winter precipitation, and the heaviest snowfall of Japan occurs in this general area. Everywhere on the Echigo Plain the average annual snow accumulation is between one and two feet. On the adjacent Takata Plain it is three to four feet. The entire mountain area of the prefecture, constituting the chief drainage area, has an accumulation of over three feet, with considerable areas having eight feet and limited areas having slightly more than ten feet. Maximum accumulations of as much as twenty-three and a half feet were recorded in the winter of 1926-27.

Seven parallel dune ridges are found on the Echigo Plain, lying approximately equidistant from one another and parallel to the coast. In addition, many levees marking present stream channels or abandoned meanders and ancient lake strand lines occur, which, in general, trend at an angle to the shore. These serpentine elevations afford flood protection for roads and settlements (Fig. 50). They also afford land for vegetables and other dry crops that cannot be grown on the rice land, for here the paddies are wet at all seasons. Bordering areas with rugged coasts afford elongated village sites between cliff and sea. These are settled chiefly by fisher folk.

Historically, this general area has been isolated from the central government in eastern Japan by the mountain masses intervening. The elaborate system of land laws which in other parts tended to discourage the growth of great landlords were not enforced here. Furthermore, the large scale and costly reclamation by drainage which was so often necessary could best be borne by wealthy individuals. It is said that here the farmer landlords controlled the military lords in the feudal days. Today, the largest and wealthiest landowners of Japan as well as the most serious agrarian problems are found in this area.

SHOESTRING SETTLEMENT PATTERN

The general pattern of settlement, as we have noticed, is of shoestring form. The greatest development of strassendorf settlements in Japan occurs here. Frequently, such settlements extend unbroken for more than a mile. Disregarding slight interruptions, a few exceed five miles. Over ninety per cent of all agglomerations on the Echigo Plain are either well developed strassendorfs or approximate that form. The overwhelming majority are on elevated sites as well. About 55 per cent of such sites are levee tops, 8 per cent are lagoon strand lines, and the remainder are on ancient dune ridges. In many cases such forms constitute the nucleus for present-day expanded towns and cities. The completion of the Ozu cut, a flood canal from the inner plain portion of the Shinano River to the sea, has reduced the flood hazard in certain areas, and a departure from the old settlement form may be expected in the future...

SOME LARGE ESTATES

An analysis of the individual village shows a central focal point occupied by the great enclosed estate of the local landlord or by the public buildings of local administration. Near by resides the commercial population. From this locus the peasant homes extend in either direction along the road. The largest landowners of Japan proper, as has been noted, are found on the delta plains of the western shores of Honshu. Most of these families date back about three centuries, i.e. from early Tokugawa times. The acquisition of land took place chiefly through money lending, although a considerable amount of reclamation must also be credited to these families. The greatest landowning family of all is found on the Shonai Plain. The second greatest arose in Suibara mura on the Echigo Plain. More than 4000 acres of land are owned by this family, of which 3500 acres are in crop; and the land is tenanted by 2486 families, or about 14,000 persons. The owner is an absentee landlord, residing in Tokyo; but the great estate house is still kept open. Before 1919 the tenant paid 60 per cent of all crops as rent; but by constant opposition, legal and otherwise, the tenants now pay but 40 per cent. The value of the estate has consequently decreased from 6,841,000 yen to 4,044,000 yen. At the same time the land tax has been considerably increased. The lot of the big landowner thus has its difficulties, yet there seems to be no increase in the number of small landowners. The northern part of the Echigo Plain is almost completely occupied by tenant families, and the central and southern parts more than half so. Suibara village proved to have 83 per cent tenants and the remainder shopkeepers, artisans, and a few freeholders. Several adjacent settlements are under the control of the same family estate.

The Sea of Japan periphery of Honshu has been one of the chief areas of emigration. Thousands of Echigo families have settled in Hokkaido. At present there is a rapidly increasing migration to Brazil. Another result of the existing lack of opportunity and uneven distribution of wealth is seasonal migration. In the summer, agriculture and fishing afford some occupation; but during the cold winters many laborers move to the industrial parts of Japan. The professional fishermen, in large numbers, ply the waters about Karafuto and Kamchatka in summer but return to Niigata harbor and the Shinano River in winter....

THE TOKACHI TYPE

The Tokachi type is of recent development and is adjusted to the extensive agricultural system and severe winters of the Hokkaido frontier. It is more or less characteristic of all settled areas of low relief in Hokkaido.

The Tokachi Plain is a complex coastal and elevated delta plain whose floor is overlain with thin deposits of volcanic ash. Entrenched below this ash level are found the wide alluvial valleys of the Tokachi River and its tributary streams. Climatically, the area is characterized by short, hot summers and long, severe winters. Precipitation is low for Japan, and the maximum occurs in winter as snow.

A half-century ago the Tokachi Plain was inhabited only by Ainu tribes except for a few Japanese fishing villages along the seashore. The Ainus were a fishing and hunting people settled along the banks of the rivers. Agricultural settlement by the Japanese proceeded inland along the same rivers until the construction of a railroad from Sapporo two decades ago. The lands nearest the rivers contain the densest populations, and the important agglomerations are with few exceptions located on the river banks.

NORTH AMERICAN INFLUENCE

In the agricultural settlement of Hokkaido the Japanese Government secured the assistance of American agricultural experts, who were responsible for the introduction of a small-scale likeness of our range and township system (Fig. 51).

A base and a range line were first established, at right angles, in each unit of low relief. These lines conformed to the lay of the land and not to compass direction. From them, parallel lines were established dividing the land into rectangular areas of 270 square cho, or 661.5 acres. These in turn were divided into nine divisions of thirty square cho, or seventy-three and a half acres. The third, or basic, division was an oblong area of five square cho, or twelve and one-quarter acres, i.e. one sixth of the second-ary unit. The system was much less regularly applied than its counterpart in the United States. The area of five square cho was presumed to support one family, and settlement was made on this basis. In 1875 and subsequent years militiamen were settled in different parts of Hokkaido to serve as an outpost against Russian advance. Each man was given five square cho, and when this was reclaimed he could petition for a further grant. Many of these families can still be identified. The grants to ordinary agricul-turists, who began to arrive somewhat later, were in five-cho lots. This is still the average holding except where rice lands have been established.

Along the rectangular road pattern thus established, isolated individual farmsteads have been constructed. As the density of population is low and as large areas of land are involved in the present system of dry and extensive agriculture, the population pattern is a disseminated one (Fig. 51). Some rather large voids occur where big tracts of land have been granted for horse and sheep pastures. Small areas of high density are found where paddy cultivation is established. Minor agglomerations occur in the form of the Greek cross, and T-shaped towns at the intersection of main roads; they are comparable in structure and function to similar features found in the western United States.

LACK OF HOMOGENEITY IN HOUSE TYPES

The house types of Tokachi show little homogeneity. Settlers from all parts of Japan have migrated here and have introduced elements of their own culture. The Echigo house is well adapted to the heavy winter snows and, as the Sea of Japan area has contributed more settlers than any other part of the country, many such houses are found. Ainu houses of marsh reed and grass with protecting split-log palisades are frequently adopted by the newcomers for temporary occupation. There are still a few Ainu families in Tokachi, as well. American log cabins and frame houses characterize areas of earlier settlement. The house structure of Old Japan cannot be used in Hokkaido without difficulty. Both cedar and pine are lacking; and native woods, especially the firs, are not strong. Most of the better houses of Hokkaido are now being built of imported American woods. The heavy winter snows tend to crush flimsy structures, the great temperature changes cause warping, and the freezing and thawing of the ground pulls the framework out of line. Japanese tile is not used, as the marked temperature changes soon break it up. In most cases a large shed accompanies the dwelling unit to afford shelter for the work animals and storage for the bulky products of general agriculture. A variety of modified western and Russian stoves are found. However, settlement in Tokachi is still in its infancy, and the rural house is still in the experimental stage aiming to preserve the chief elements of Japanese culture and still afford comfort during the rigors of the long winter.

THE LOG HOUSE IN GEORGIA [1]

by W. Zelinsky

Few traits in the older material culture of the United States have captured as prominent a place in its folk mythology as the log cabin. An even stronger incentive for the study of this frontier phenomenon is the fact that it has much to tell us of our culture history, and even of contemporary human geography, in Anglo-America. For these reasons, and because time is running out for the American log house, special attention was devoted to the recording and interpreting of the log culture complex of Georgia during a general study of the settlement characteristics of that state.

1. Geog. Rev., vol. 43 (1953), pp. 173-193.

The lack of detailed regional studies on log architecture in other parts of the continent seriously reduces our insight into the Georgia data and prevents generalization. Consider this less an apology than an invitation for other students of Americana to join in the collection of material wherever log dwellings or memories of them persist.

CONSTRUCTION OF LOG HOUSES

The log house can be defined by its material, method of construction, and function. The walls are made of round, undressed logs or of logs hewn with ax or adz (but never sawed) to rectangular shape. The logs are laid one above the other and are mortised at the corners of the building by some form of notching that eliminates the need for hardware. These buildings are lacking in affectation, a condition that excludes an increasingly large number of hunting and vacation lodges and also boy-scout cabins and the like.

The details of log-house architecture and construction have been dealt with so well previously that only a short summary is necessary here. In Georgia the material is generally oak or pine, according to the local silva. The diameter of the logs ranges from about 6 inches to 15 inches, or even 18 inches or more; in general, it decreases in the more recent houses. In a climate where frame, stucco, and even brick structures deteriorate with distressing rapidity, the well-seasoned logs of a good log house are practically ageless as long as they are under a tight roof and away from the ground.

Although a great number of notching techniques, some rather elaborate, are practiced in Europe, only one is numerically strong in Georgia--saddle notching. A semicylindrical groove is cut across the underside of a log to half or less of its diameter near its end so that it will fit snugly over the log it joins at a right angle. The technique is so strongly dominant that its areal occurrence was not recorded for this study. Dovetail notching--the carving out of angular tenons at the very end of the log--occurs sporadically along with various kinds of square notching, but the distribution of these almost extinct techniques has little meaning in Georgia at present, though this is not to imply that study of them throughout Anglo-America is not strenuously advocated while sufficient evidence remains.

The major technical problem confronting the log-house builder is the finishing of the walls, for even the straightest and roundest logs cannot be superimposed without leaving wide chinks. During the ruder days of the frontier, many log-house dwellers in the Deep South were content with the simple log wall that admitted air freely--tolerable enough for most of the year under a relatively genial climate. Frederick Law Olmsted was only one of several travelers to comment on this kind of house:

> The logs are usually hewn but little; and, of course, as they are laid up, there will be wide interstices between them-- which are increased by subsequent shrinking. These, very

commonly, are not "chinked" or filled up in any way; nor is the wall lined on the inside. Through the chinks, as you pass along the road, you may often see all that is going on in the house; and, at night, the light of the fire shines brightly out on all sides.

This practice has now vanished: not a single inhabited log house without weatherproofed walls has been noted in present-day Georgia. Most often, the gaps between logs have been chinked with twigs, plus clay, lime, or some other variety of cement, according to the locality. As sawed lumber became more abundant and as log-building skills declined, weatherboarding the outside of the walls, lining the inside with thin planks, or both, grew increasingly common. The crudest expedient, nailing short lengths of narrow board (often scrap lumber) over the interstices, is apparently a rather recent innovation.

The plan of the Georgia log house has always been simple. In its most elementary form it is a rectangular pen, the length (generally 15 to 20 feet) governed by the size of available logs. Until recent years the roof ridge has always been parallel to the front of the house, with the gable ends facing sideward. Log houses with frontward-facing gables are a modern idea, nowhere dominant. The one-room log house, which soon proved inadequate even on the frontier, was frequently enlarged, either by the addition of a frame wing or by the attachment of another log pen. The double log pen may be differentiated into two subtypes, one with a corridor extending all the way through the house between the two pens, the other with the two sections adjoining. The former is called the "dog trot" house, after the popular term for the central breezeway or porch; it is indigenous to the South, where the climate can be readily invoked to explain its wide acceptance. Two-story log houses are almost nonexistent in Georgia: expansion of the log house, as of other types in the South, was virtually never vertical.

Changes in the architecture of the log house have been slow and gradual (a fact, incidentally, that makes the dating of these otherwise recordless structures risky), but within this century another type has emerged. It borrows the floor plan of its predecessors, but in every detail of carpentry, door and window frames, chimney, roof, floors, and foundation—in everything except the wall material—it resembles its modern frame neighbors. And even the finishing of the walls has changed: commercial cement is often used and covered with whitewash or paint; the logs themselves may be given a coat of varnish or dark stain.

The log houses of Georgia, like many other dwellings in the state, are erected on piers that keep them a good distance above the ground. In the northern half of the state either rocks or short sections of log may be used, but in the relatively stoneless Coastal Plain the piers are almost exclusively log or brick. The rationale of this practice is obscure, but it is essentially Southern in distribution and may be accounted for partly as an economy measure and partly as a method for dealing with the ventilation of the house and its protection from moist soil and vermin.

The traditional roof was composed of thin slabs of wood—shingles or "shakes"—laid over a framework of poles. If, as often happened, a porch was added along the front of the house, the roof was continued over it at a somewhat lower pitch. During the earliest years, and particularly in the Coastal Plain, the gable-end chimney was built of mud wattled with twigs. Stone construction came later, and the use of brick for the chimney postdates the frontier era. The stick-and-mud chimney is only a memory in Georgia now, but its past importance is attested by the still common practice of extending the roof past and around the gable-end chimney, in a sort of hood; the reason, of course, is the sheltering of the easily weathered chimney from the elements. Windows were accorded slight consideration in the old log houses. Some were windowless; in others the few apertures were rarely covered, and then usually with a crude board shutter.

NUMBER AND DISTRIBUTION OF LOG HOUSES

The log house was only a single element in the log culture complex that characterized the Southern frontier and has persisted strongly in many sections to this day. It may be safely stated that almost the whole of the gross material culture of the Georgia pioneer was based on the log. He lived in a log house and kept his livestock in log barns (if they were penned at all) and stored his implements and crops in log bins and cribs. If he took the trouble to build a fence around his fields, he split logs lengthwise and arranged them zigzag in a worm fence, again without the benefit of any metal except his ax blade. If he had a well, its superstructure was most likely a pair of logs, one with the bucket fastened to its end pivoted on a vertical log and operating almost effortlessly with the aid of gravity—the now almost extict sweep well. This frontiersman worshiped in roughly built log churches; he sent his children to equally primitive log schoolhouses. Tidings of an impending Indian raid would send him scurrying to the protection of one of the log forts. When a town was founded, many of the first dwellings and inns were log, and the chances were that the county courthouse was fashioned from logs; the neighboring log jail frequently outlasted the other urban log structures.

The documentary evidence is emphatic concerning the dominance of log construction in most parts of Georgia from the latter half of the eighteenth century until the eve of the Civil War. But since we have only the casual accounts of travelers, there is no way of determining the relative number of log and non-log dwellings for any particular locality during most of the state's history. The general pattern was probably an almost completely log architecture during the pioneering period, then the steady decline of log building as the well to do took to using frame or even brick construction, and finally its reduction to an archaism as the multiplication of sawmills made frame construction feasible even for the poorest classes. The last phase began in earnest after the Civil War and has continued steadily up to the present. Although the decennial censuses of housing do not include any data on the use of logs, the Bureau of Home Economics of the United States Department of Agriculture fortunately conducted a survey in 1934 of farm housing in sample counties throughout the country that did tally log structures. Sixteen of Georgia's 159 counties were included, and although the inventory was not quite complete, a door-to-door questionnaire was used. Of the 33,139 dwellings recorded, 3.2 per cent, or 1060, were reported as being of log; the percentage ranged from 0.4 in Hancock County to 9.2 in Rabun and Habersham Counties together. By applying the figure of 3.2 per cent to the estimated total of rural dwellings in Georgia in 1934, the probable total number of log houses in the state in that year was found to be 15,000.

From 1950 through 1952 a total of 274 log dwellings were recorded during field work in Georgia. Of this total, 154 were discovered on four methodical cross-state traverses during which every rural dwelling was tabulated on nine intensive local surveys, each covering one or more Georgia militia districts (the equivalent of a township). The remainder were noted during the many reconnaissance and incidental trips made during the period. Precautions were taken to make the sample as random and representative as possible. Since all the counties of Georgia were visited, it is probably safe to apply conclusions to the entire state. The total number of dwellings observed in local surveys and on traverses was 6792, or roughly 1.5 per cent of the total number of rural dwellings in Georgia in 1951. Log houses constituted 2.3 per cent of the observed structures; but since observation was, in the majority of cases, a simple roadside inspection and did not include questioning the householder, a significant number of clapboarded log houses must have escaped notice. By allowing for this underenumeration and repeating the extrapolation, we find that there were probably 10,000 to 12,000 log houses left in Georgia about 1951. The decrease from the estimated 15,000 of 1934 and a current 36.7 per cent incidence of abandonment among observed log dwellings show how rapid the present decline must be. If the trend continues, the virtual extinction of the log house by the end of this century seems probable.

Although the median point of contemporary Georgia log houses falls near the areal center of the state, their distribution is markedly uneven (Fig. 52). They occur with greatest frequency in the Blue Ridge, the rough inner edge of the Piedmont, and the small corner of the Cumberland Plateau falling within Georgia, and next most frequently in parts of the Valley and Ridge country, the intermountain basins of extreme north-central Georgia, and a broad belt of territory running northeastward from the Florida line through the central Coastal Plain. They are rare at the present time in most of the Piedmont and Fall Zone, and they do not seem to be indigenous to the lower Coastal Plain and Sea Island areas. Although the areas of intensive field work in 1950-1952 do not coincide with the territory covered by the 1934 sample survey, except accidentally, a similar distribution might be derived from

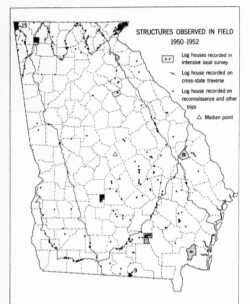

STRUCTURES OBSERVED IN FIELD
1950-1952

⬚ Log houses recorded in intensive local survey

↘ Log house recorded on cross-state traverse

• Log house recorded on reconnaissance and other trips

△ Median point

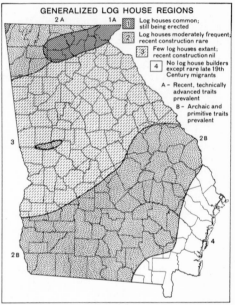

GENERALIZED LOG HOUSE REGIONS

2 A   1 A

▨ Log houses common; still being erected

▧ Log houses moderately frequent; recent construction rare

▨ Few log houses extant; recent construction nil

4 No log house builders except rare late 19th Century migrants

A – Recent, technically advanced traits prevalent

B – Archaic and primitive traits prevalent

Fig. 52. *Log house distribution shown by dots and by regions of uniformity.*

-372-

the earlier data, a fact that bolsters the credibility of both sets of evidence. It is to be regretted that the writer's total itinerary could not be given in Figure 52, to afford a better idea of the relative frequency of log houses in various parts of the state, but it proved difficult to keep the detailed and elaborate notes during field work that would have permitted this. It should be realized, however, that superior coverage is the reason, for instance, for the several log examples near Athens, an area no richer in log houses than most other parts of the Piedmont.

Of the other elements in the log culture complex, only the rapidly disappearing split-rail or worm fence has been systematically recorded in the field, and its distribution correlates reasonably well with that of log dwellings. The occurrence of log barns and sheds, which are both more numerous and more widespread than log houses, has proved to be much more difficult to chart in the field than that of log houses, and quantitative evidence cannot be offered; they seem to vary in frequency in much the same way as log dwellings and worm fences. The log churches described in the earlier literature appear to be gone, and only a single log schoolhouse has been recorded. Log courthouses, jails, and forts are now one with Nineveh and Tyre.

SIGNIFICANCE OF THE LOG HOUSE
IN THE CULTURAL LANDSCAPE

The distributional facts of log culture in contemporary Georgia have been presented by means of word and map, but there still remains the task of accounting for these facts and interpreting their significance in the total cultural landscape of Georgia. A major question raised is the dichotomy between an apparently logless tidewater Georgia and a much larger inland area where log culture was for a long while supreme. The absence of log dwellings along the Georgia coast during colonial times (except for the few cases noted below) is strongly established by negative documentary evidence; and their extreme rarity and peculiar nature in this area at the present time have been proved by field work and by consultation with local scholars. The bulky early records of the state have been sifted several times by students of various topics, including architecture, without the discovery of a single valid reference to a bona fide log dwelling built by a colonial Georgian of British origin, and it is unlikely that any future researches will alter this statement. This writer has looked into every known post-Revolutionary travel account of Georgia; references abound to log houses in the interior of the state, but there is not a single mention of them along the coast. Log jails and forts, and probably log palisades, did occur, but the only authenticated log dwellings before the late nineteenth century include two in the now dead town of Frederica on St. Simons Island built by Henry Michel and Henry Myers, who were _German_ immigrants, and the early dwellings of the Salzburger settlers at Ebenezer (founded 1734), some 25 miles up the Savannah River from the city of Savannah.

For an understanding of these exceptions, the distribution of the log-house trait in the Old World must be briefly described. The practice reaches across Eurasia in two broad bands: the first extends through the sub-Arctic forests of Sweden, Finland, and central and northern Russia, and, since the seventeenth century, across Siberia to the Pacific, then, later, to Russian America; the second--and the more relevant here--begins in the French Savoy, with a possible minor outlier in northern Spain, and reaches through the mountainous spine of Eurasia at least as far eastward as Iran and possibly Kashmir. Included within it are the rugged areas of southern Germany, Switzerland, Austria, Bohemia, the Carpathians, Transylvania, and perhaps Turkey. Log construction is completely alien to the British Isles, the Low Countries, and the parts of France from which migrants to America were drawn. The log-building technique is apparently of such slight moment in Spain that it was never effectively transferred to Hispanic America; thus, even if there had been much cultural contact between the English in the Carolinas and the Spanish missions in Georgia in the seventeenth century, nothing would have come of it as far as the log house was concerned. A few log houses were known in Spanish Florida, but mutual hostility prevented the English in Georgia from learning of them. There is no evidence that any aborigines in the United States were familiar with log construction (except, possibly, in corncribs), and a spontaneous invention in America, even under the most beneficent environment, is hardly likely. The general answer to the problem of how the log house arrived in the New World and eventually migrated to inland Georgia but not to its coast has been supplied by Shurtleff's brilliant researches and can best be summarized in his own words:

> 1. Log dwellings were never built by the English or Dutch in their earliest colonial settlements. English and Dutch alike proceeded directly from various temporary types inspired by English or Indian models to framed houses. 2. Log-dwelling technique was brought to the Delaware by the Swedes in 1938 but did not spread beyond that place until the last quarter of the seventeenth century at the very earliest.

Then further:

> Delaware Bay was the principal center from which log-wall dwelling construction spread. There the Swedish log-house craft was reinforced in the eighteenth century by immigrants from the forested regions of Germany and Switzerland where log houses were common. The Scotch-Irish who came hard on the heels of the Germans adopted the log house and helped to spread it along the frontier.

After having learned the craft from the Pennsylvania Germans, English-speaking frontiersmen carried it rapidly westward and southwestward. The log-building trait entered Georgia at the eastern edge of the Piedmont and quickly advanced with the frontier all over the state except the fraction of the Coastal Plain previously occupied by migrants direct from the British Isles. Even though the Oglethorpe colony came some 30 years after the introduction of the log house into Pennsylvania and Maryland, its members had had no opportunity to acquire the skills needed for log-house construction. A further consideration, as Shurtleff suggests, is the fact that the presence of an artisan class along the coast made sawed lumber relatively cheap and abundant, whereas the primitive structure and material poverty of pioneer back-country society made the log house a practical expedient.

The problem is complicated by the presence of the several hundred Protestant Salzburgers at Ebenezer and a small colony of Swiss at Purrysburg, below Ebenezer and across the Savannah in South Carolina. These people had certainly practiced log construction in the Old World and during their first years in America. For reasons that are not at all plain, they not only failed to transmit their architecture to the English but abandoned it for the frame house. The final complication is the fact that log culture had probably arrived in tidewater South Carolina by 1700 (by what route?). Its failure to migrate farther down the coast may be attributed to Georgia's terminal position in British America, the general sluggishness of coastwise traffic, and the late institution of slavery in Georgia (in South Carolina log building found its principal use in slave housing).

The line between the Inland Log Culture Area and the early-settled sections of Georgia where the log complex never took root separates two cultures that differ in many nonmaterial, as well as in material, respects. This line, or rather zone, in the lower Coastal Plain represents the high-water mark of an inland culture spilling out from the interior but dammed by an inhospitable and hard-to-penetrate wilderness of pine and swamp that is densest about 50 miles from the coast. Coastward of this line, certain framehouse traits derived from log culture are lacking or rare; for example, the dog trot, multiple front doors, "hooded" chimneys. In addition, certain subtle carpentry traits, more easily discerned than described, that are indicative of the temporal or spatial proximity of log houses do not occur in the coastal area. The logless character of Georgia coastal culture is essentially unmodified by late-nineteenth-century instrusions of a very few log houses from the interior. The log barns and sheds of the coast, also probably of late-nineteenth-century introduction, have held on, possibly because of a cost differential favoring them over frame structures. Worm fences were not unknown in the past, but the date of their entry is uncertain.

Within the Inland Log Culture Area variations in the frequency of log houses are a matter of the date of settlement and of differential isolation. In Wilkes County, an east-central Piedmont area settled in the last quarter of the eighteenth century, the log houses that were once dominant seem to have vanished, but they are still

numerous in Echols County, at the edge of the Okefenokee region
and opened to settlement just before the Civil War. The incidence
of log houses in a given locality seems to be inversely proportion-
ate to the tempo of traffic in men, goods, and ideas. Good roads
are the bane of log houses, and cities the harshest possible environment. (In spite of constant vigilance, not a single log house has
been found on a site that could be termed urban.) The mechanism
of isolation may be the forbidding topography of the Appalachian
chain and its foothills or the swamps and dense forests of parts of
south Georgia; and there are many subtle forms of economic in-
ertia and isolation that perpetuate the log house in odd corners of
the state. It is quite possible that, as a result of the rapid economic progress of south Georgia in recent years, the log house will
quickly lose ground there, as it has already done in the Piedmont,
with its relatively dense web of roads and rails and its earlier
urbanization and industrialization. Besides being a sensitive gauge
of cultural isolation and a clue to culture areas, the log house remains to testify to the paramount fact that the human geography of
the South is one of an arrested frontier.

The plotting of various log-house traits in inland Georgia re-
inforces our speculations on the historical geography of the log
complex in the state. The single log pen appears to be universally
and rather evenly present in the log areas, but the double log pen
is concentrated within the southern half of the state. The fact that
the double pen is an early form that is no longer being built accen-
tuates the peripheral character of south Georgia culture. The
modern log-house types, in contradistinction, are most strongly
represented in north Georgia, as is shown by the centrographic
analysis used throughout the accompanying series of distributional
maps.

Although the preparation of round logs is capable of considerable refinement in expert hands, the preparation of square-
hewn logs generally indicates a higher degree of skill and produces
a superior house. The dominance of a round-log tradition in south
Georgia and the popularity of square-log architecture in the north
are further clues to the relative cultural complexity of the two
areas.

The walls of a log house need special treatment if they are
to repel wind and rain. The skilled woodsman carefully selects
and shapes his logs and then daubs the spaces in between with
some sort of cement. Where a log house has been partly or wholly
covered with siding inside or out--a relatively inelegant solution--
that fact has been noted and mapped. The median points of boarded
log houses fall well south of the center of the state; the crudest de-
vice--boarding over the chinks with narrow planks--shows the
greatest displacement.

Incidental to our purpose but of some intrinsic interest is
log-house occupance. The high rate of abandonment has already
been noted, but even more striking is the low frequency of Negro
occupance, some 9.2 per cent of occupied log houses, though
Negroes constitute roughly one-third of the state's rural population.

The explanation is historical. Many observers remarked on the abundance of Negro log cabins on ante bellum plantations, but during the havoc of the Civil War and its aftermath the old slave quarters were destroyed, and the freedmen moved to new homesites, where they usually built frame houses instead of the obsolescent log cabins. The continuity of log-cabin occupance and construction was maintained largely by white yeoman farmers left comparatively undisturbed by the social upheavals of the nineteenth century, and the log houses now occupied by Negroes have often been acquired from whites by default. Although too few aborigines remain in Georgia to affect the contemporary cultural geography of the state, by the early nineteenth century the Indians had borrowed the log-house technique from the whites.

All these distributional facts point to a major conclusion concerning the cultural evolution of that preponderant part of Georgia in which the log house has appeared. North Georgia, with its more recent house types, its square-hewn timbers, and the dominance of relatively skilled techniques for sealing walls, would seem to lie closer in time and space to the center of dispersion for log-house traits (and presumably others) than south Georgia, with its greater proportion of archaic or degenerate house types, round logs, and cruder treatment of walls.

Other lines of evidence also suggest an early flow of population and ideas from northeast and north to southwest and south. In the case of the log house, Georgia is decidedly colonial to Pennsylvania and certain parts of the Upper South through which the practice of building in logs was introduced by German and Swiss immigrants at the beginning of the eighteenth century and from which it spread outward to vast sections of North America. In the Deep South, as in other frontier regions, logs in the form of houses, churches, barns, sheds, and fences became a mainstay of the economy and profoundly modified the subsequent development of the region's material culture.

HUMAN GEOGRAPHY AND ECOLOGY IN
THE SINÚ COUNTRY OF COLOMBIA[1]
by B. L. Gordon

My intention has been to describe a South American landscape and to outline the history of the peoples who have used it. It is hoped that this study of one area and its inhabitants, past and

1. Ibero-Americana: 39, Univ. of Calif. 1957.

living, will contribute toward the understanding of the total and time-based ecology. The landscape is part of the northwest of Colombia, called the Sinú. To better mark its place and characterize its contents, we shall refer occasionally to other folk and other country at its margins. Our central interest will be the area drained by the northward-flowing Río Sinú which empties into the Caribbean Sea.

In 1863 an American scholar, George P. Marsh, in The Earth as Modified by Human Action, endeavored "to indicate the character and, approximately, the extent of the changes produced by human action on the physical conditions of the globe we inhabit." Among the topics which he discussed were the removal of forests, "the transfer, modification, and extirpation of vegetable and animal species," and the physiographic consequences of human occupancy. Though Marsh's was not the first exposition of this theme, it is masterful and still stimulating.

From personal observation in the Sinú Valley and study of its history, I have come to regard Marsh's viewpoint as significant and applicable to that area. A number of prominent geographic and ecologic circumstances are understandable only when man's presence is taken into account. Furthermore, in Sinú country, peoples of different cultures, in putting similar territories to traditional uses, have created distinctive landscapes. That there has existed such an interrelationship between man and nature, between culture and landscape, is the underlying theme of the ensuing discussion.

To contend that differing cultures influenced the physical environment in different ways is possible only if persistent differences in culture can be found. The forested and mountainous headwaters of the Sinú and San Jorge rivers are now occupied by Chocó Indians. In the sixteenth century the lower Sinú, then apparently deforested, was occupied by the Zenú. In the second, third, and fourth chapters these two aboriginal peoples are described and compared. Several sample topics are discussed: personal apparel, houses, fields, and so on--homely things that were recorded by the early Spaniards, whereas other aspects of culture were described vaguely if at all.

Several sources indicate that reforestation of the lower Sinú followed the destruction of the Zenú nation. Within the past century the Sinú has again been deforested and settled by Spanish-speaking citizens of the Colombian nation (Fig. 53). The invasion of the Sinú Valley by the Cuna Indians, surviving cultural relatives of the Zenú, is also discussed. The Cuna have been driven out, the Zenú, absorbed; Colombiano and Chocó are now neighbors. Attention is directed in the fifth chapter to the ecologic significance of deforestation, both that of the modern Colombiano and that of the sixteenth-century Zenú. . . .

THE RÍO SINÚ AND ITS FLOODPLAIN

Between the eastern and the middle prong of the Cordillera Occidental, the Río Sinú flows through a wide and irregular basin

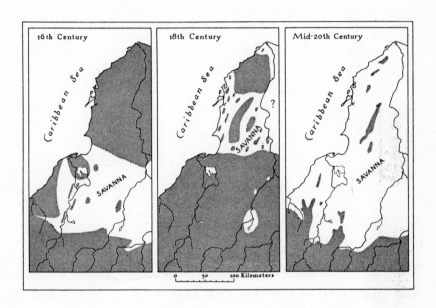

Fig. 53. "Changing extent of savannas".

into the Gulf of Morrosquillo. Only its headwaters drain from igneous mountains; the greater part of its 300-mile course is flanked by beds of sedimentary rock, upwarped as noted in the last diminished Andean spurs. The present floodplain and earlier alluvium of the Sinú basin begins about halfway between Tai and Frasquillo. Below Frasquillo the river runs narrowly for some miles through low hills; this stretch is known as the Angostura de Urrá, after a small tributary entering near Frasquillo. Another narrows with rapids, locally called the Angostura del Sinú, lies upstream, just above the junction of the Río Verde.

The only flood land above the Angostura de Urrá is a few square miles between Frasquillo and Nain, but below Tai, which is about 100 miles from the coast, the floodplain is extensive and continuous.

Scattered over the floodplain are a great number of ciénagas, shallow depressions seasonally covered with water, or permanent backwater lakes; many of these are partly filled oxbows. Such abandoned segments of the river, caños, serve as supplementary channels of local transport. On the Sinú, as on neighboring rivers, the lower junction of such a channel with the main stream is often called boca falsa, probably so named by the boatmen who pole their dugouts laboriously upriver.

The river has built low levees along its meanders, especially in the lower half of the valley (i.e., from Montería northward). Since it changes course continually, a patchwork of swells and ridges, old levee remnants, are scattered over the floodplain. When inundated, the cut-off former channels catch flood and rain waters that are fed slowly back to the river as it falls. The deeper and more persistently swampy of these are likewise called ciénagas. . . .

THE PEOPLE OF THE SINÚ FORESTS -- The Chocó Indians

A great rain forest, mainly mountainous, stretches east from the Gulf of Urabá across the upper drainage of the Sinú and San Jorge rivers to the Río Cauca and beyond. Within the watersheds of the Sinú and the San Jorge it is the domain, and nearly exclusively so, of the Chocó Indians, who form an active and harmonious part of the forest ecology.

"Emberá" is the name by which the Chocó Indians distinguish themselves from others. They say of themselves that they are river people. A large number of the place names of northwestern Colombia derived from their language can be readily identified; most have the suffix do, their name for "river": Chigoradó, bamboo river; Pegadó, the river of the clearings. Furthermore, among men's given names those which are considered most attractive commonly include that syllable, as in Do-chamá, river hawk.

The northern limit of the Chocó at present corresponds roughly to a physiographic boundary which is close to the northern limit of the forest. It is at the lower edge of the rougher country, out of which small rapid streams run over basement rocks to form the slow, muddy Sinú and San Jorge rivers.

This association of present Indian territory with relief reflects the preferences and pressures of the Colombiano neighbors in the lowlands. The agricultural demands and customs of the local Colombiano fit the plains country downriver and exclude the Indian. Elsewhere (as on the Pacific coast, where they have not yet been crowded out) Chocó and other Indians still inhabit lowland as well as upland. Evidence will later be presented of the southward push of Colombiano colonization and of a northward extension of the Chocó with at least a temporary balance maintained, along the edge of mountain and forest, against lowland savanna.

There appears to have been scarcely any mixing of blood between the Chocó and their neighbors, but the racial background of the adjacent Colombianos is very confused. They may be pure Negro, as at Uré and Boca de Uré, or mulatto over the rest of the San Jorge drainage; pure Indian (but non-Chocó) or mestizo around Ituango; Spanish or mestizo in the direction of Medellín; or, in the Sinuano downriver, an indefinite fusion. . . .

CLEARINGS AND FIELD CROPS

Within a short distance of each Chocó house are several small clearings, usually of an acre or so. In felling heavy forest, all lianas, the sparse understory of young plants and shade plants, and the small trees are cut at the beginning of the dry season (January) and left until dry. It is difficult to accumulate enough dry litter to destroy the larger trees. Branches and leaves are occasionally carried in from the surrounding area and especially from the regrowth of abandoned clearings, for growth in these is low, dense, and easily cut. There is no danger of forest fire; the forest will not burn without such preparation. Even so, the prepared tract is not entirely cleared, as the dead trunks of the larger trees stand for a while before toppling. The whole procedure is finished in time to plant the corn before the beginning of the oncoming wet season.

All seed crops, especially corn and beans, grow best if planted by men, the Indians say. However, some people have "good hands" for planting, and should a woman be so endowed, she too may plant, though the crop will not be as good as if a man had planted it. If a woman's hands are "good," her name will often include the syllable be, their word for "maize."

Plants which are vegetatively reproduced (grown from cuttings or ratoons) may be planted by anyone; these include the plants locally introduced from the Negroes downriver: yuca, ñame, batatas.

Maize is the principal crop. It is indeed the only field crop, except for groves of plantains and bananas. A period of comparatively dry weather in August or September is the main season for planting. April and May, at the beginning of the long rainy season, constitute a secondary planting season. Of the two maize crops, the larger is harvested in December and January; the smaller, in July and August. Beans are an associated crop in some places.

A digging stick is used to loosen the ground for the seeds. The seed grain is carried in a small basket, slung by a bark strap around the planter's neck and resting on his chest.

The fields are productive but unkempt. They are not kept clean of other growth, and several shrubby species of Piper commonly grow to a height of several feet among the cornstalks. Undecayed tree branches lie scattered about the field, and there is little or no working of the soil between the corn plants. Bare soil is exposed only at planting time.

Fields away from the stream bank are used for a few years, then given up for four or five years, sometimes for dozens of years, before they are used again. . . .

ABANDONED FIELDS AND REGROWTH

An abandoned field that has been reoccupied by wild woody growth is called a rastrojo. The plants in the Indian rastrojo fall into two main classes: those which are not found in the surrounding forest, and those which occur in the surrounding monte but are strikingly more plentiful in the rastrojo.

Among the plants of the first group is a high proportion of useful plants, such as may be planted about the house. A kind of wild fig (Ficus sp.) from which bark cloth is made, and a tree yielding blue dye (Genipa caruto), are typical of the Indian rastrojo. They are frequently planted near Indian houses and are seen occasionally along open forest trails or sunny streamsides. . . .

For many forest plants, the relationship to human activities is uncertain. That part of the heavy forest which covers the narrow valley bottoms and the gentler hillsides represents varying stages of man-induced plant successions through repeated clearing, as well as survivals of plants he set out. A maze of scarcely noticeable pathways extends over the area; along them the Indian continues to disturb natural conditions. Wayside plants indicate that he acts as a disseminator well beyond the formerly cleared ground. Considerable doubt arises whether certain plants were a part of the pre-human forest flora.

The natural balance in the complex rain-forest environment which assures a livelihood to its components did not provide place for an animal with the habits of man; this forest is poor in human food. To be left in the forest without food is a serious matter, even to the Indian. If people are to take a permanent livelihood from the forest they must change it.

The least-disturbed forest is a meager source of foodstuffs not only for man but also for a number of animals. The Indians carry on an endless fight against animals which raid corn and plátano fields. . . .

The Indians do not speak of new or old rastrojo but of high or low rastrojo, since, aside from trees left sanding, the abandoned pega is occupied by progressively taller species which attain within several decades the height of the surrounding forest.

Our concept of a pristine forest applies to little of this Indian country. Flora and fauna are not unaltered. The Indian, however, by varying the habitat and accommodating additional species, has enriched the ecological setting. . . .

The Indians' tendency is to use the existing landscape, the varied forest environment; the Colombianos' is to simplify it, to encroach upon the edge of the forest near his village and change it into fields for his crops. The individual who makes his living from the forest has at his command an impressively greater number of skills than are needed or prossessed by the village dweller. . . .

THE ZENÚ -- THE OLD SAVANNA PEOPLE

The Zenú Indians formerly inhabited plain and valley beyond and below the northern limit of the Chocó to the Caribbean Sea. Their name is preserved in the name of the Río Sínú; other evidence of their existence and character persists in the landscape. Kindred Zenú peoples lived from the Gulf of Urabá eastward to the lower Cauca Valley. They spoke, it seems, the same language; aside from a few small differences in custom, they were distinguished only by allegiance to different rulers. . . .

The Spanish were surprised to find the two cities Finzenú and Ayapel with plazas at their centers and arranged in streets. Houses at Finzenú were of two sorts. Some twenty were extremely large (communal or multi-family), and each had three or four smaller buildings nearby, smaller but still spacious, which served as lodgings for servants and storehouses for harvests. These, too, caught the eye of the Spaniards as they "were made almost according to the plan and form" of those of their homeland, neatly kept and swept clean with brooms of long canes. The houses had dirt floors; the inmates slept in hammocks. . . .

THE LOCATION OF FINZENÚ AND OTHER ZENÚ CITIES

Since Finzenú lay in a "treeless savanna plain stretching beyond the horizon and of more than fifteen leagues circuit," historians have sought to find its site in such a savanna existing today-- at Tacasuán (now San Benito Abad) on the Río San Jorge, for example. The locating of Cenú (Finzenú) at Tacasuán is, however, unsatisfactory. Tacasuán is a pre-Conquest name. Could it also have had the name Finzenú?

Savannas are transient features; they are not natural grasslands. The savannas of the time of the Conquest were a consequence of Zenú occupancy. That there was no natural condition which prevented local forest growth we may say with confidence. Trees can and do grow there; the Zenú kept sacred groves in their plazas and graveyards, and eventually forests have repossessed their fields and cities. . . .

The outer ciénaga shore was a favored location for Indian cities. Where the forest was removed behind such ciénagas to accommodate tillage, to provide fuel for hearths and ceramic industries, grasses spread outward as sunny ground became available, invading fields and occupying fallow land.

When trees are cleared away (desmonte), their seeds and roots remain. Few tree seeds, however, germinate in the altered surroundings; in a short time the supply is spent. The roots are exterminated as a result of the continuous hewing back (in Zenú time probably burning back) of shoots. Unless excluded by the cultivation of crops, grasses become dominant. Once established, these grasses may have been maintained selectively as against woody growth by fires that spread readily across them, fires originating perhaps both in the desmonte and the game drive. Grass would itself have discouraged tillage, and grassland thus become persistent savanna, stocked with the animals that seek such vegetation.

The farmers who supplied Finzenú and Ayapel would, rather than crop the cleared upland continuously, move farther out where easier tillage and better yields were provided by recently cleared forest soil. Cities of persistent occupation, associated with monumental cemeteries, would be as the Spanish depicted them, in spacious savannas. At the outer margins of the savannas, marking the more recent clearing for provision crops, lay small villages. . . .

Root crops, however, were the basis of Indian food supply over the whole area, as we may surmise from the number mentioned at Ayapel, the shortage of maize there, and the stress on root culture among the Urabá. Furthermore, there are at present few varieties of maize in this country. The emphasis is now on roots, of which there are at least a dozen yuca varieties, several sweet potato varieties (yellow-skinned and lavender-skinned; smooth and rough), and occasional arrowroots (Maranta sp.). The arrowroots are now called sagú or yucca sagú. . . .

Zenú descendants survive by the thousands, but they have lost their identity as a people; with the exception of a few place names, scarcely a word of their language can be recovered. Thus, if the Zenú were not exterminated, aside from a few fragments their culture was; it included qualities which made their coercion easier than that of the forest-dwelling Chocó. Spanish cavalry was particularly effective in the extensive tracts of cleared land, and the compact Zenú towns were easily burned.

Defeats in warfare do not, however, wholly explain their downfall. Their urban character, likewise, rendered them especially susceptible to the European diseases which ran ahead of the Spanish. Finzenú was already severely reduced and weakened by one of these when, in 1534, the expedition of Heredia reached it. There the Spanish noted: "el consumo de aquel pueblo, por las grandes ruinas que descubrian en el y otros señales de haber vivido gran numero de vecinos." When asked the cause of this depopulation, the Indians replied that since the time, a few years previously, when they had killed a group of Spaniards, "les habian venido tales y tantas enfermedades de las inumerables que habia, los habian reducido a los pocos que estaban." . . .

The inference is made here that the Chocó lived scattered through forests of a large territory, then as now occupying the Department of Chocó; that if they were spreading northward, they had reached these districts before the sixteenth century; that their presence was as dependent at that time as it now is on forest cover; that as the cities of neighboring savanna-making and-dwelling Zenú were destroyed, the forest and the Chocó came down over the formerly open country. . . .

MONTE AND DESMONTE

The desmonte (deforestation) is the activity of man which has had the greatest ecologic consequence; thus the subject is central in a discussion of either Zenú or Colombiano landscape.

FOREST AND SAVANNA

The words sabana, monte, and desmonte have meanings which may vary locally. In speaking of vegetation, the major distinction is made between sabana and monte. Country sown to pasture grasses, in garden, or covered with rastrojo -- a collective term for nonarborescent secondary vegetation -- is called sabana. A sixteenth-century account of Castilla del Oro, Panamá, defines the term as it is most commonly used today throughout Colombia and Central America: "Sabana se llaman los llanos y vegas, y cerros que estan sin Arboles, y toda tierra rasa, con yerba o sin ella." However, in areas in which a distinctive terrain has such plant cover, the word has occasionally acquired meaning as a physiographic term. When tree species appear in it, rastrojo is in some places called monte, but the name monte, or monte firme, is more commonly applied to dense formations of tall, thick-trunked trees growing on land that supposedly has never been cleared. In the older savanna country, in the vicinity of Sincelejo and northward, the verb desmontar describes the cutting by machetes of shrubs and sprouts which appear in the pastures, there being few mature trees left. Nowadays fire is little used because it damages valuable introduced forage grasses.

The question whether grasslands in the area are natural or a consequence of human occupancy has already been raised. As we have seen, in attempting to locate the site of Finzenú, this question is fundamental in interpreting the data of historical geography. It is equally important in a consideration of local natural history.

At the forest edge an abrupt change takes place in plant cover: grasses and shrubs replace great trees and lianas. Forest and savanna (whether the latter is grassland or scrub) present obviously different aggregates of species. Since the forest assemblage is markedly the richer, its retreating boundary represents a line of local extinction; if there were strictly endemic elements, they have been totally removed. An upper story of the forest has epiphytes, besides a considerable animal life of mammals, snails, and insects which do not live at ground level; the removal of several stories, each representing a special environment, attends the reduction in species number. Beyond firing and cutting the forest for tillage, man has compounded his influence over the cleared land through the introduction of grazing animals and forage plants.

Thus the abrupt and irregular line which today marks the junction of forest and savanna is not the result of contrasting climatic circumstances. Nor is there an association of forests and a special topography (except for an association between really rough country and forest, such land being never cleared, or last to be cleared). A great deal of hill country is at present grassy.

In support of the foregoing statements, some more detailed evidence will be presented on the location of the forest border from Zenú time to the present.

THE SIXTEENTH AND SEVENTEENTH CENTURIES

The Zenú depended even more upon fire to clear land than do modern Sinuanos. Only so could the machete-less Indian have opened new fields, later to become grassland. Savanna, following on tillage, provided hunting grounds. . . .

THE EIGHTEENTH AND NINETEENTH CENTUIRES

Pertinent for this period are comments by Alexander von Humboldt. Of Turbaco he said, "This small Indian village stands on a hill at the entrance of a majestic forest which extends toward the south as far as the canal of Mahates (El Dique) and the river Magdalena." Stopping at the mouth of the Sinú, his ship

> . . . sought shelter in the Río Sinú or rather near the
> Punta del Zapote situated on the eastern bank of the
> Ensenada de Cispata into which flows the Río Sinú. . .
> A few scattered houses form the village of Zapote. . .
> we went to herborize in the forest . . . quitting the
> coast of Zapote, covered with mangroves, we entered
> a forest remarkable for a great variety of palm trees. . .
> After an hour's walk we found a cleared spot . . . the
> great humidity and the thickness of the forest forced us
> to retrace our steps. . . .

THE TWENTIETH CENTURY

The road from Cartagena to the Sinú runs southwest across rounded ridges and shallow, broad valleys and, beyond Ciénaga de Oro, out onto the Sinú floodplain, through shrubby regrowth, through extensive pastures planted to tall bunch grass and infested with such cosmopolitan tropical weeds as Lantana, Stachytarpheta, and spiny amaranths, past fields of yuca and rice, and between rows of the fence-tree mataratón; but it never enters or approaches a forest. A branch leaves the raod near Corozal for Magangué, passing through the same vegetation with scattered groves of fire-scarred palma de vino (Scheelia butyracea) as it nears the Magdalena. . . .

GEOGRAPHIC AND PHYSIOGRAPHIC DIFFERENTIATION IN SINÚ FORESTS

The continuous forest of the upper Sinú is composed mainly of large, straight-trunked trees. Trees with gnarled twisted trunks or of spreading habit are scarcely to be seen. Small elliptical leaves predominate; the broad-leaved forms typical of regrowth in clearings are scarce. The flowers are mostly in the tree crowns. Epiphytes and lianas are numerous; in places so many of the latter trail from the branches--their stems often flattened, their ramifications confused and reticulate--that passage even on foot is difficult. Shrubs are scarce. Such understory as there is consists mostly of thorny palms and stilt palms. The stilt palms are among the more conspicuous and beautiful plants; the stilted habit gives them the appearance of being adapted to floodwater, but they grow upon the rougher terrain. Like the stilt palms, the milpeso is restricted to forest tracts which preserve little indication of having ever been cleared. This palm, the tallest in the forest, I was unable to identify. Oil from its fruit is a minor commercial item.

To the north are a few forests, left behind in the Colombiano deforestation. Between Tai and Montería are a few patches on the riverbank, the only floodplain forest extant. A fairly extensive block has been preserved on the finca Marta Magdalena south of Montería, a short distance west of the river. According to old settlers the large Ciénagas Babilla, Grande, and Hoya de León below Montería once had forest between them; of this forest very little remains. Some residents remember when the country from Montería upriver was mostly monte firme. Between Cerro Las Mujeres southeast of Betancí and Toluviejo are several forested tracts on hilltops. Beginning at Toluviejo, forest or heavy woods extend northward along the crest of the Serranía de Maria. . . .

The last remnants of forest which are being cleared near Betancí contain such an abundance of archaeological materials that we do not need historical evidence to prove their secondary nature. Whether the forest in this condition could, in time, duplicate its prehuman prototype is an interesting question.

Some naturalists regard the virgin rain forest as having existed in a sort of sylvan equipoise which could be reconstituted only through an impossible reenactment of the event which first produced it. It has even been maintained that at its periphery man's sustitution of grasses for certain tropical forest growth is irreversible. Others think in terms of extrasylvan environment (particularly climate) and consider that any human disruption of such forests can never be more than temporary.

It is clear that heavy forests have been reestablished in the Sinú country. Dense forest grew up on Zenú savannas, to be removed during recent Colombiano colonization. Only in limited areas does such regrowth forest persist; where it does, it contains several indications of its secondary nature (about which more will be said).

Where clearing is limited and brief, as among the Chocó, replacement by heavy vegetation is swift. In spots which have been kept cleared since an unknown prehistoric time, where cattle have grazed, and the soils have been greatly modified or eroded until coarse sandstones protrude (which would never be seen in a Chocó clearing), reconstitution of the primeval cover is unlikely.

SUMMARY HISTORY OF FOREST DISTRIBUTION

Several conclusions may be drawn from the foregoing evidence. In aboriginal times, forests were more conspicuous in northern than in southern Bolívar (Fig. 53). The annual rainfall decreases and the length of the dry season increases from southwest to northeast; such a distribution of forests is just the reverse of what we would expect from these climatic conditions.

In early historic times the savannas of southern Bolívar became reforested except near settlements which have survived from the time of the Spanish Conquest. These were, with the possible exceptions of Nain and Tucurá in the Alto Sinú, all on the San Jorge side of the interfluve at Ayapel, San Benito Abad, and Morroa (near modern Sincelejo).

The coast of northern Bolívar, with its center at Cartagena, was continuously, perhaps increasingly, populated after the Conquest. Dense forests were gradually removed to provide grazing land for the expanding cattle industry; nevertheless, they were still conspicuous there two centuries later, and in the Department of Atlántico sizable remnants still exist.

The cattle industry spread south from Cartagena, encountering only limited savannas about a few scattered population centers. A century ago the interriver country south of a line running from Montería to the north of Sahagún to San Marcos, was, save for a few localized clearings, densely forested; heavily forested tracts still existed north of that line. Only within the last thirty to forty years have the southern limits of former Zenú savannas, around Monte Líbano, Planeta Rica, and Tierra Alta, been reached. The first Colombiano desmonte at the site of Monte Líbano was undertaken in 1913.

The historical accounts cited do not refer to the gallery forests that are common in dry country, or to forests restricted to hill crests where they receive additional rainfall. Thus it is plain that forest was not limited to either. The edge of continuous forest can now be found less than 250 feet above sea level in the upper Sinú and San Jorge valleys.

DEFORESTATION AND ANIMAL LIFE

In general, deforestation has impoverished the native fauna. Some animals depart when the selva is only beginning to be destroyed. The black spider monkey, marimonda, leaves at the first disturbance. In spite of its shyness, when captured it makes the most affectionate pet of any of the monkeys. The capuchin, mico maicero, and the marmoset, titi, soon follow. The red howler, <u>mono tramador</u>, persists, thriving even where there is only tall rastrojo or stream-side trees. Bands of howlers travel from one wooded area to a-nother if there remain connecting avenues of vegetation tall enough so they need not descend to the ground. In some restricted wood-land areas they are surrounded by extensive grasslands and com-pletely cut off from the great forest. This monkey is seen in tall rastrojo even more commonly than in forest country. A partial explanation may be that, while it is game to the Chóco Indian, the Colombianos will not eat it. Thus bands are encountered even in country near the large towns. On the wharves at Magangué, in the early morning, one can frequently hear the howling of these monkeys coming from thickets across the Río Magdalena. In the course of a day's walk I have seen several bands near San Andres and also on the Quebrade Betancí where the pastures extend to the tree-fringed banks.

Sloths and the prehensile-tailed porcupine (<u>Coendou</u> sp.) tend to stay within the rim of deep forest; they are found mainly to the south of Tierra Alta except for some in a tract of selva preserved at the <u>finca</u> Marta Magdalena, a few miles southwest of Montería....

LIMITING FACTORS

With deforestation, obviously, the forest shade is gone; air, water, and soil temperatures are changed. The magnitude of these changes is apparent to anyone who carries a light meter and a thermometer from a potrero into a Sinú forest. However, in as-sessing the influence of all this on motile forest life, it is futile to record such measurements. To single out one aspect of the change, evaluate it, and label it as the major cause is seldom possible. It can only be said that such changes, along with many others, occur. Certain forest inhabitants survive the changes, but the majority do not, and are replaced by migrants. The reasons for their dis-appearance are included among the numerous physical alterations attending deforestation. Finally, the forest gives way before the labors of man; fire and the machete effect these displacements. . . .

PHYSIOGRAPHIC ALTERATIONS

Lake and delta sedimentation was presumably influenced by the Zenú. Deofrestation, the transport of masses of sand and the general disturbance of terrain in the construction of the great tumuli and <u>ciegas</u>, agricultural activities, and the traffic of large numbers of people could hardly have continued without increased erosion and silting of ciénagas.

Old people at Guasimal, a small settlement a little below the mouth of the Quebrada Jaraguay, speak of numerous ciénagas sur-rounded by forest at the time of their childhood, in which fifteen-foot canoe poles did not touch bottom. The forest is gone and the ciénagas have been either filled or reduced to shallow ponds. Ciénaga Tuminá, which existed in the eighteenth century close to the site of Montería, has totally disappeared.

Erosion has exposed archaeological materials at several spots on deforested slopes around Toluviejo. Among them are burial urns; unlike those of the Zenú, they were not placed in the loose earth of artificial mounds.

In hilly country the dirt floors of houses are commonly left elevated, platform-like, above the dooryards; and in the villages these in turn stand above gullied streetways. Many examples are found in and around the town of Corozal.

The forest margin has separated two cultures, and continues to do so, and therewith the biologic and physical circumstances peculiar to each. In their deforesting activities both Zenú and Sinuano have transformed the landscape. In other ways, however, than in the common practice of desmonte, the Sinuano culture also recalls that of the Zenú. . . .

The culture of the Zenú, as we have seen, left imprints that are still discernible in the landscape; and the modern Sinuano has habits which can be assigned in part to the Indian side of his ancestry.

Local mestizo culture owes to Spanish sources such obvious things as language, religion, modes of dress, and cattle. A lesser number of traits arrived with the numerous Negroes, still others have been introduced from non-Hispanic Europe, and recently an increasing number have come from North American sources. . . .

CONCLUSION

Man has modified the natural landscape by occupancy; the character of the change is determined by his culture. Pronounced and persistent cultural differences are evidenced in the Sinú country. These represent, in part, decisions and preferences established in custom. Proceeding in accordance with different traditions, the inhabitants of the Sinú have varied the physical conditions. They have created new habitats for plants and animals. They have introduced domesticated and commensal species. They have practiced direct selection on native species and preserved selected forms; an even larger number of plant and animal species has been exposed to unplanned selective actions.

Contrasting landscapes have developed in association with the territories of peoples of differing cultures. Such sustained selective influences of culture upon biota and ecology presumably affect the course of evolution, introducing into that process an element of human choice.

RECONNAISSANCE IN DYNAMIC REGIONAL GEOGRAPHY:

TIERRA DEL FUEGO[1]

by R. S. Platt

Tierra del Fuego is at the southern tip of South America, about 6,000 miles south of Chicago, and 600 miles north of Antarctica. The Andes come to an end in Tierra del Fuego; and also the Atlantic coastal plain of South America.

So the main island, of about 20,000 square miles, is commonly divided into two regional areas: a mountainous region in the south, and a plains region in the north, with a transitional zone of foothills between. The mountains are forested on their lower slopes and snow capped above. The plains are grass-covered. The transitional zone is partly wooded and partly grassy.

Areas of human use correspond in general with these divisions of the natural environment. A few hundred sheepherders with a million sheep live in the plains. A few woodsmen live in the mountains. And a few shepherd-woodsmen live in the transitional zone.

Thus far, this description of Tierra del Fuego follows the conventional concept of regional divisions as homogeneous areas.... This concept of generalized static homogeneous regions is a useful device in geographic thinking, but not the only device....Regional geography has advanced in practice by...working systematically,... viewing the pattern of human occupance, in every aspect, as an historical functional phenomenon in a regional setting. . . .

Tierra del Fuego is an area of dynamic occupance, reflected in a pattern of organization, composed of lines and points. The dots and other symbols on a map of rural and urban establishments make it not merely a dot map of static distribution, but a dynamic map of points of focus in a pattern of organization: ranches, towns, packing plants, sawmills (Fig. 54). The lines are not boundaries of static homogeneity, but limits of activity (ranch boundaries and international boundaries), or lines of movement (such as roads). This pattern is dynamic, in being formed by people moving in coordination and occupying the area.

Sheep ranches are a functional feature of an economic structure. . . . The managers in most cases are Scotch, the shepherds Chilean, the sheep of a New Zealand crossbreed. These establishments have a distinctive place, in a geography and a history extending far beyond Tierra del Fuego and the present time. This involves an overseas movement of enterprising Scotchmen, the first of them reaching Tierra del Fuego about 50 years ago, some coming via the Falkland Islands, and others directly from the British Isles; and also involves a migration of settlers from densely

1. *Revista Geográfica do Instituto Pan Americano de Geografía e História,* Rio de Janeiro, vols. 5-8 (1949), pp. 3-22.

populated middle Chile, to the ends of their country, and a little beyond; but involves little or no migration from the not-yet-over-populated central part of Argentina. Scotchmen and Chileans have joined forces in Tierra del Fuego, in both Argentina and Chilean parts of the island, on both sides of the international boundary (Fig. 54). Geography and history here involve also continuing connections with the farms and markets of the Occidental commercial world.

Any individual ranch is like others in general characteristics, and different in particular. La Sara has an area of 250 square miles, and contains 80,000 sheep, 1,000 horses, 1,000 cattle, 1,000 dogs, and 100 men (Fig. 55). The sheep are divided into 30 flocks, and the land into 30 pastures, fenced with 1,000 miles of wire. Each pasture is laid out with reference to a convenient source of water; shepherds posts are grouped for access to pastures; central head-quarters are located for general accessibility, and in the lea of a hill for some slight shelter from wind and snow.

Meat packing plants and ports are points of major focus for the ranches. These have the general characteristics of such establishments in the commercial world, as well as individuality peculiar to each site.

The ranches are distributed in both Chile and Argentina, regardless of the international boundary. But the boundary is not to be disregarded....It is no mere line separating static regional divisions, even though it is often taken to be so.

Whereas the sheep ranches appear as a product of British enterprise from the Atlantic, meeting and absorbing an influx of Chilean labor from the Pacific, the international boundary appears as the meeting place of political activity, from Buenos Aires on the Atlantic and Santiago on the Pacific side (Fig. 56). . . .

Argentina and Chile, through most of their extent, meet along the crest of the Andes, but not so in the far south. There the boundary leaves the mountains and extends eastward in the plains, across the continent, to the point where the Straits of Magellan meet the Atlantic (Fig. 54). In Tierra del Fuego the boundary continues southward, across the plains and across the mountains, to the south coast.

Thus Chile holds the Straits of Magellan from end to end, and Argentina has the whole Atlantic coast, In this alignment is reflected a major interest of Chile in the Straits, as Chile's primary connection with the North Atlantic, practically the only connnection before the Panama Canal; and the primary concern of Argentina as a country of the Atlantic coast, facing Europe and having a minor interest toward the south, diminishing with distance, at least until recently (Fig. 56).

Originally the boundary bisecting the plains and mountains of Tierra del Fuego was of little or no importance. The sheep ranches developed indiscriminately in both countries, belonging to world economy rather than to the national economy of either country.

Then, with the worldwide rise of nationalism after the First World War, government activities spread to the limits of their

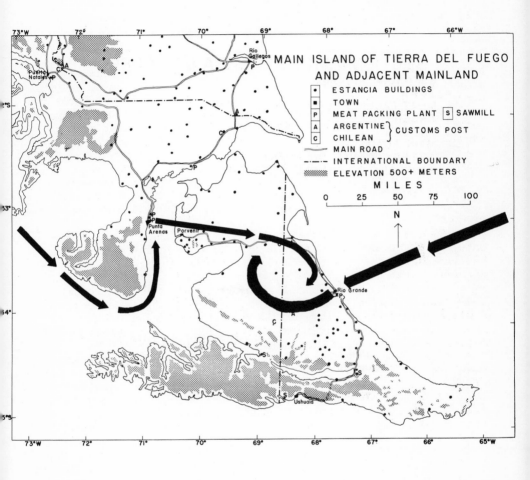

Fig. 54. "The arrows represent diagrammatically British ranchers from the Atlantic
side joining forces with Chilean sheepherders and laborers from the Pacific
in Tierra del Fuego".

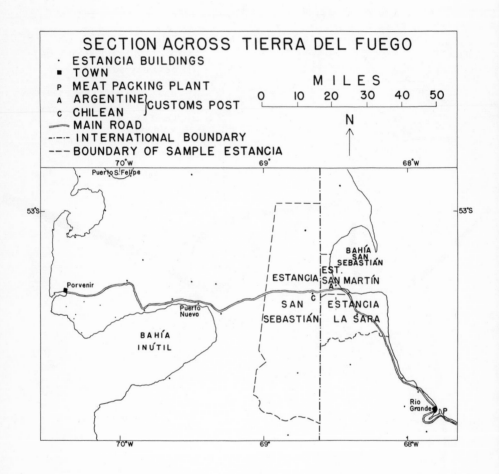

SECTION ACROSS TIERRA DEL FUEGO

· ESTANCIA BUILDINGS
■ TOWN
P MEAT PACKING PLANT
A ARGENTINE ⎫ CUSTOMS POST
C CHILEAN ⎭
~ MAIN ROAD
—··— INTERNATIONAL BOUNDARY
——— BOUNDARY OF SAMPLE ESTANCIA

MILES
0   10   20   30   40   50

N

70°W   69°   68°W

Puerto S. Felipe

53°S   53°S

BAHÍA
SAN
SEBASTIÁN

ESTANCIA ᴱˢᵀ· SAN MARTÍN

Porvenir

SAN   C   ESTANCIA
SEBASTIÁN   LA SARA
Puerto
Nuevo

BAHÍA
INÚTIL

Rio
Grande   P

70°W   69°   68°W

Fig. 55. *"Neighboring ranches in Argentina and Chile and the main road across Tierra del Fuego".*

Fig. 56. "The arrows represent diagrammatically the political influence of Argentina reaching south from Buenos Aires along the Atlantic coast, diminishing with distance, and that of Chile reaching south from Santiago through the Straits of Magellan".

territory, and barrier functions were begun. The boundary was fenced. Customs posts were established, and passage was brought under control.

Up to the time of national self-consciousness, ranch operations had not been limited by the boundary. For instance, the Estancias San Sebastián, Chile, and San Martín, Argentina, were operated as a unit, and all their sheep, most of them from Chile, were driven to an Argentine port on Bahía San Sebastián for shipment (Fig. 55). After boundary regulation began, passage was hampered by inspections and official permits, and red tape increased, until the Chilean owners abandoned the effort, disposed of their Argentine ranch, and established a new Chilean port on Bahía Inútil.

Recently many of the sheep marketed from San Sebastián have been driven northwestward to Puerto Natales, almost a month's journey, including a boat trip across the Straits (Fig. 54). This is in view of the separation of Chilean ranches from the nearby packing plant at Rio Grande, Argentina, and the separation of Argentine ranches from nearby Puerto Natales. In general the Chilean packing plants, built earlier to handle both Chilean and Argentine sheep, have suffered from boundary restrictions and the establishment of Argentine plants on the Atlantic coast.

Thus an area, formerly participating freely in international economy, has been divided into partly closed segments of two national economies. Now, after the Second World War, Tierra del Fuego shows signs of totalitarian and imperialistic nationalism, particularly on the Argentine side of the boundary.

The Argentine government has announced a plan to expropriate all the estancias in Tierra del Fuego fronting on the Atlantic coast, and to subdivide much of their land into small farms for new settlers. Rio Grande has grown suddenly into a town of soldiers and government employees, and conspicuous government buildings. A federal highway is being pushed from Rio Grande over the Andes, to the old territorial capital of Ushuaia on the south coast (Fig. 54).

Ushuaia in turn takes on new importance, as a key point or territorial capital, in the extension of Argentine activity into Antarctica. Argentina and Chile, having learned the game of nationalism and imperialism from the North Atlantic powers, now find themselves in a strategic position to claim slices of the only land left open to them for imperialistic expansion. By associating their southern settlements in Tierra del Fuego with Antarctica, as part of the same region, and carrying on operations across Drake Strait, coupled with public demonstrations at home, they seem able to make a case no less plausible than that of Britain, and other faraway claimants, in the same sector. In Tierra del Fuego they have the settlements farthest south in the world, even though these are as far from the South Pole as Scotland is from the North Pole. So here, in these overlapping claims to the Antarctic mince pie, we seem to have a reductio ad absurdum...of territorial sovereignty and imperialism.

This paper on Tierra del Fuego may properly be called a
reconnaissance report. . . . It adopts the viewpoint of dynamic organization. . . . and from this viewpoint looks beyond the mosaic
blocks of static generalization to the areal layout of functional
activity, of the people who occupy the area and who make the
phenomenon we are trying to interpret: the cultural pattern in
its earthly setting.

CONCLUSION

Continuing Field Geography

The end of this series is only a way station, not a terminus, of field study. Geography continues as a subject of field research, and theory and method continue to evolve.

The selections in this volume are in most cases early examples of the types and their derivatives. This is by intention in the search for turning points in theory and method. Even now it would be possible to classify some later work differently into additional types. But at this point such procedure would seem less consistent than final mention of recent field study in terms of the types already described. Along each of these lines the earlier studies have in fact been followed by later ones up to the present.

A survey of recent geographic literature shows a continuation of the various lines of study, sometimes separately and in their original form, more commonly as derivatives and in combination. There is change too as well as continuity, but this is less easily classified and so can only be taken for granted while continuity is given specific reference in the following pages.

In the past five years (1954–1959) approximately a hundred articles involving field study, more or less, have been published in three American geographical periodicals: the Annals of the Association of American Geographers, the Geographical Review and Economic Geography. Most of these depend on more than one of the types of study, but they can all be assigned to one or another type according to a primary emphasis.

In these articles of the past five years the first four types and their derivatives are represented by only a quarter of the studies: 4% in type 1 (Exploratory Traverse); 7% in type 2 (Area Survey); 7% in type 3 (Explanatory Physical); 7% in type 4 (Explanatory Human).

An example of the few studies assigned to type 1 (Exploratory Traverse) is O. J. De Laubenfels' "Where Sherman Passed By."[1] Naturally fewer exploratory traverses of unknown lands are made now by geographers, and the recent examples are all derivatives of this type, retraversing old routes and gathering specialized data, continuing to use the traverse as an available method of sampling.[2]

An example of type 2 (Area Survey) is C. R. Hitchcock's "Sierra de Perija, Venezuela."[3] This type is represented by very few if any other examples as good as the one cited to il-

1. Geog. Rev., vol. 47 (1957), pp. 381-395.
2. For example also, E. C. Mather and J. F. Hart: "Fences and Barns", in Geog. Rev., vol. 44 (1954), pp. 200-223.
3. Geog. Rev., vol. 44 (1954), pp. 1-28.

lustrate generalized description in a survey
report. There are more examples of derivatives for special purposes, but the number of
these is not large unless the great body of studies
distinguishing types of land use be included here,
in view of their sequential relation to the western surveys of Wheeler[1] and his colleagues.

An example of type 3 (Explanatory physical) is R. J. Russell's "Alluvial Morphology
of Anatolian Rivers."[2] In the work of geographers derivatives are more numerous in this
case also, particularly in dealing with natural
resources and other features of natural environment.[3]

A recent example of type 4 (Explanatory
Human) is S. S. Visher's "Changing Significance
of Environmental Factors at Bloomington, Indiana."[4] Here also derivatives are more numerous, especially in studies of sequent occupance, and these are progressing even further
from the original idea.[5]

In contrast with the first four types represented in relatively few recent articles, the last

1. p. 28 above.
2. *Annals AAG*, vol. 44 (1954), pp. 363-391.
3. An excellent example slightly earlier than the others under discussion is W. C. Calef:
   "The Winter of 1948-49 in the Great Plains", in *Annals AAG*, vol. 40 (1950),
   pp. 267-292.
4. *Annals AAG*, vol. 46 (1956), pp. 411-416.
5. For example, A. H. Meyer: "The Kankakee 'Marsh' of Northern Indiana and Illinois,"
   included as a selection in this volume, chap. 12, pp. 202-216, has been followed by
   Meyer's later contributions depending less on the original meaning of sequent occupance and adjustment: "Circulation and Settlement Patterns of the Calumet Region
   of Northwest Indiana and Northeast Illinois", in *Annals AAG*, vol. 44 (1954),
   pp. 245-274, and vol. 46 (1956), pp. 312-356.

four types and their derivatives are represented by three quarters of the articles: 29% in type 5 (Analytical Economic), 21% in type 6 (Areal Uniformity), 18% in type 7 (Areal Organization) and 5% in type 8 (Culture Origin).

A good example of the large number of articles in type 5 (Analytical Economic) is W. M. Kollmorgen and G. F. Jenks'"Suitcase Farming in Sully County, South Dakota," and "Sidewalk Farming in Toole County, Montana and Traill County, North Dakota."[1]

Of the 21% of recent studies in type 6 (Areal Uniformity) a good example is L. E. Klimm's "Empty Areas of the Northeastern United States."[2] This type and its derivatives deal not only with large uniform regions but also with the small uniform areas of landscape and land use studies, especially in urban geography.[3]

1. _Annals AAG_, vol. 48 (1958), pp. 27-40, 209-231. _Among examples of the same type in the geography of mining there is C. F. Kohn and R. E. Specht: "Mining of Taconite, Lake Superior Iron Mining District", in Geog. Rev., vol. 48 (1958), pp. 528-539. In the geography of manufacturing there is M. D. Thomas: "Manufacturing Industry in Belfast, Northern Ireland", in Annals AAG, vol. 46 (1956), pp. 175-196. A fair proportion of recent studies in the geography of planning may be considered derivatives of this type and an example of these is C. L. Dozier: "Establishing a Framework for Development in Sardinia: The Campidano", in Geog. Rev., vol. 47 (1957), pp. 490-506. Finally in a derivative line of political geography an example is J. P. Augelli: "The British Virgin Islands: A West Indian Anomaly" in Geog. Rev., vol. 46 (1956), pp. 43-58._
2. _Geog. Rev._, vol. 44 (1954), pp. 325-345).
3. _An example of the latter is R. E. Murphy and J. E. Vance, Jr.: "Delimiting the C. B. D." and "Internal Structure of the C. B. D." in Econ. Geog., vol. 30 (1954) pp. 189-222, and vol. 31 (1955), pp. 21-46. Good earlier examples are: N. S. Ginsburg: "Ching Tao: Development and Land Utilization", in Econ. Geog., vol. 24 (1948), pp. 181-200; C. D. Harris: "Ipswich, England", in Econ. Geog., vol. 18 (1942), pp. 1-12; and H. M. Mayer: "Railway Terminal Problem of Central Chicago", in Econ. Geog., vol. 21 (1945) pp. 62-76. Some studies in statistical or mathematical geography include field work facilitated by systematic sampling and some of these are in type 6 (Areal Uniformity), as for example W. F. Wood: "Use of Stratified Random Samples in a Land Use Study", in Annals AAG, vol. 45 (1955), pp. 350-367._

Of the 18% of recent studies in type 7 (Areal Organization) one has been included in this volume, A. K. Philbrick's "Principles of Areal Functional Organization in Regional Human Geography."[1]

Of the 5% of recent studies in the last type, 8 (Culture Origin) and its derivatives, a good example is M. W. Mikesell's "Role of Tribal Markets in Morocco."[2] The relatively low percentage of studies of this type in the periodicals under consideration is in contrast with that in another current series, the University of California Publications in Geography (Berkeley), in which a majority of the recent studies are in type 8 (Culture Origin),[3] and the rest in type 3 (Explanatory Physical). An example of type 8 from this series is P. L. Wagner's "Nicoya: A

1. Chap. 15, pp. 338-351 above. An example in urban geography is A. L. Rodgers: "The Port of Genova: External and Internal Relations", in Annals AAG, vol. 48 (1958), pp. 315-354; and this is sequentially related to the earlier study by E. L. Ullman: Mobile: Industrial Seaport and Trade Center, (Dept. of Geog., Univ. of Chicago, 1943), forerunner of "spatial interaction." Some advanced statistical field studies with sampling technique depend on type 7 (Areal Organization) rather than type 6 (Areal Uniformity), as for example B. J. L. Berry and W. L. Garrison: "The Functional Bases of the Central Place Heirarchy" in Econ. Geog., vol. 34, (1958), pp. 145-154.
2. Geog. Rev., vol. 48 (1958), pp. 494-511. A more complex example based not only on type 8 (Culture Origin) but also on type 7 (Areal Organization) for small units of study and type 6 (Areal Uniformity) for encompassing regions, with statistical technique for sampling, is J. M. Blaut: "Microgeographic Sampling, A Quantitative Approach to Regional Agricultural Geography", in Econ. Geog., vol. 35 (1959), pp. 79-88. This theoretical statement is linked with two substantive studies by the same author published separately: "Study of Cultural Determinants of Soil Erosion and Conservation in the Blue Mountains of Jamaica", in Social and Economic Studies, Univ. College of the West Indies, Jamaica, Vol. 8 (1959), and "Economic Geography of a One-Acre Farm on Singapore Island," in Malayan Jour. of Tropical Agriculture, Vol. 1 (1953), pp. 37-48.
3. Five out of nine, in the period 1948-1958.

Cultural Geography;"[1] and an example of type 3 is E. H. Hammond's "Geomorphologic Study of the Cape Region of Baja California."[2]

Obviously the University of California series differs from the three periodicals previously surveyed in representing a group of younger contributors and a more limited editorial policy under supervision of a small staff. Similar limitations apply to another series with which comparisons may be made, the Research Series of the Department of Geography, University of Chicago, 1948-1958, which likewise represents a younger group of contributors and an editorial policy under a small staff.

In the University of Chicago series of 60 titles, among which 54 studies seem to have involved field work, no one type has a majority. But the first four types are represented by only 10% of the field studies. There are none in type 1 (Exploratory Traverse); none in type 2 (Area Survey); 4% in type 3 (Explanatory Physical); and 6% in type 4 (Explanatory Human). Even the few studies in types 3 and 4 are not clear cases of derivatives of these types.[3]

---

1. _Univ. of Calif. Publ. in Geog._, vol. 12 (1958), pp. 195-250.
2. _Univ. of Calif. Publ. in Geog._, vol. 10 (1954), pp. 45-112.
3. For example, as a derivative of type 3 (Explanatory Physical) there is G. F. White _et al_: "Changes in Urban Occupance of Flood Plains in the U. S." No. 57, 1958, dealing with natural conditions in the physical environment. As a derivative of type 4 (Explanatory Human) there is J. S. Matthews: "Expressions of Urbanism in the Sequent Occupance of Northeastern Ohio" No. 5, 1949, dealing with sequent occupance but not in the original environmental sense.

Ninety percent of the studies are in the last four types and their derivatives: 16% in type 5 (Analytical Economic); 45% in type 6 (Areal Uniformity); 20% in type 7 (Areal Organization) and 8% in type 8 (Culture Origin). This is a lower percentage of type 5 than in the three periodicals previously discussed and a higher percentage of each of the last three types than in the periodicals. Geographic concern with planning projects appears in some of the studies in each of the types.

An example of type 5 (Analytical Economic) is P. G. Phillips' "Hashemite Kingdom of Jordan: Prologomena to a Technical Assistance Program."[1] An example of type 6 (Areal Uniformity) is M. M. Colby's "Geographic Structure of Southeastern North Carolina."[2] An example of type 7 (Areal Organization) is E. M. Bjorklund's "Focus on Adelaide - Functional Organization of the Adelaide Region, Australia."[3] Finally an example of type 8 (Culture Origin) is A. E. Larimore's "The Alien Town: Patterns of Settlement in Busoga, Uganda."[4]

So much for recent studies following lines of thought already well established but gaining

1. No. 34, 1954.
2. No. 58, 1958.
3. No. 41, 1955. *Another example by a senior geographer is H. M. Mayer: "The Port of Chicago and the St. Lawrence Seaway" No. 49, 1957. A derivative of this type in political geography is R. H. Brown: "Political Areal Functional Organization: With Special Reference to St. Cloud, Minnesota," No. 51, 1957. A derivative of the same type in social geography is W. A. Hotchkiss: "Areal Pattern of Religious Institutions in Cincinnati" No. 13, 1950.*
4. No. 55, 1958.

better integration and equipment as time goes on, progressing by degrees toward better understanding of human occupance on the Earth, taking into account the vital choices of people trying to make themselves at home by calling on their cultural experience to aid them in meeting the environmental problems of which they have become aware.

Future work may involve not only better integration of the types already developed but also distinct new types supplementing or supplanting the old in reaching toward the same general objective. In the progress of our voyage the next turn may be in a new direction as yet uncharted.

THE UNIVERSITY OF CHICAGO
DEPARTMENT OF GEOGRAPHY
RESEARCH PAPERS (Planographed, 6 × 9 Inches)

(Available from Department of Geography, Rosenwald Hall 24, University of Chicago, Chicago 37, Illinois. Price: four dollars each; by series subscription, three dollars each.)

1. GROSS, HERBERT HENRY. *Educational Land Use in the River Forest–Oak Park Community (Illinois)*
   September, 1948. 173 pp. 7 maps in pocket.

2. EISEN, EDNA E. *Educational Land Use in Lake County, Ohio*
   December, 1948. 161 pp. 2 maps in pocket.

3. WEIGEND, GUIDO GUSTAV. *The Cultural Pattern of South Tyrol (Italy)*
   June, 1949. 198 pp. (out of print)

4. NELSON, HOWARD JOSEPH. *The Livelihood Structure of Des Moines, Iowa*
   September, 1949. 140 pp. 3 folded maps.

5. MATTHEWS, JAMES SWINTON. *Expressions of Urbanism in the Sequent Occupance of Northeastern Ohio*
   September, 1949. 179 pp.

6. GINSBURG, NORTON SYDNEY. *Japanese Prewar Trade and Shipping in the Oriental Triangle*
   September, 1949. 308 pp. (out of print)

7. KEMLER, JOHN H. *The Struggle for Wolfram in the Iberian Peninsula, June, 1942—June, 1944: A Study in Political and Economic Geography in Wartime*
   September, 1949. 151 pp.

8. PHILBRICK, ALLEN K. *The Geography of Education in the Winnetka and Bridgeport Communities of Metropolitan Chicago*
   September, 1949. 165 pp. 1 folded map.

9. BRADLEY, VIRGINIA. *Functional Patterns in the Guadalupe Counties of the Edwards Plateau*
   December, 1949. 153 pp.

10. HARRIS, CHAUNCY D., and FELLMANN, JEROME DONALD. *A Union List of Geographical Serials*
    June, 1950. 144 pp. (out of print)

11. DE MEIRLEIR, MARCEL J. *Manufactural Occupance in the West Central Area of Chicago*
    June, 1950. 264 pp. (out of print)

12. FELLMANN, JEROME DONALD. *Truck Transportation Patterns of Chicago*
    September, 1950. 120 pp. 6 folded maps. (out of print)

13. HOTCHKISS, WESLEY AKIN. *Areal Pattern of Religious Institutions in Cincinnati*
    September, 1950. 114 pp.

14. HARPER, ROBERT ALEXANDER. *Recreational Occupance of the Moraine Lake Region of Northeastern Illinois and Southeastern Wisconsin*
    September, 1950. 184 pp. 3 folded maps.

15. WHEELER, JESSE HARRISON, JR. *Land Use in Greenbrier County, West Virginia*
    September, 1950. 192 pp.

16. McGAUGH, MAURICE EDRON. *The Settlement of the Saginaw Basin*
    December, 1950. 432 pp.

17. WATTERSON, ARTHUR WELDON. *Economy and Land Use Patterns of McLean County, Illinois*
    December, 1950. 164 pp. (out of print)

18. HORBALY, WILLIAM. *Agricultural Conditions in Czechoslovakia, 1950*
    June, 1951. 120 pp. 1 map in pocket.

19. GUEST, BUDDY ROSS. *Resource Use and Associated Problems in the Upper Cimarron Area*
    June, 1951. 148 pp. 2 maps in pocket.

20. SORENSEN, CLARENCE WOODROW. *The Internal Structure of the Springfield, Illinois, Urbanized Area*
    June, 1951. 204 pp. 5 maps in pocket.

21. MUNGER, EDWIN S. *Relational Patterns of Kampala, Uganda*
    September, 1951. 178 pp. 3 folded maps. (out of print)

22. KHALAF, JASSIM M. *The Water Resources of the Lower Colorado River Basin*
    December, 1951. Volume I, 248 pp.; Volume II, 15 maps in pocket.

23. GULICK, LUTHER H. *Rural Occupance in Utuado and Jayuya Municipios, Puerto Rico*
    June, 1952. 268 pp.

24. TAAFFE, EDWARD JAMES. *The Air Passenger Hinterland of Chicago*
    August, 1952. 176 pp. 1 folded map

25. KRAUSE, ANNEMARIE ELISABETH. *Mennonite Settlement in the Paraguayan Chaco*
    December, 1952. 160 pp. 4 maps in pocket.

26. HAMMING, EDWARD. *The Port of Milwaukee*
    December, 1952. 172 pp. 1 folded map.

27. CRAMER, ROBERT ELI. *Manufacturing Structure of the Cicero District, Metropolitan Chicago*
    December, 1952. 192 pp. 2 maps in pocket.

28. PIERSON, WILLIAM H. *The Geography of the Bellingham Lowland, Washington*
    March, 1953. 172 pp. 3 maps in pocket.

29. WHITE, GILBERT F. *Human Adjustment to Floods: A Geographical Approach to the Flood Problem in the United States*
    June, 1942. 236 pp.

30. OSBORN, DAVID G. *Geographical Features of the Automation of Industry*
August, 1953. 120 pp.

31. THOMAN, RICHARD S. *The Changing Occupance Pattern of the Tri-State Area, Missouri, Kansas, and Oklahoma*
August, 1953. 152 pp. 1 folded chart.

32. ERICKSEN, SHELDON D. *Occupance in the Upper Deschutes Basin, Oregon*
December, 1953. 152 pp.

33. KENYON, JAMES B. *The Industrialization of the Skokie Area*
July, 1954. 144 pp.

34. PHILLIPS, PAUL GROUNDS. *The Hashemite Kingdom of Jordan: Prolegomena to a Technical Assistance Program*
March, 1954. 208 pp.

35. CARMIN, ROBERT LEIGHTON. *Anápolis, Brazil: Regional Capital of Agricultural Frontier*
December, 1953. 184 pp.

36. GOLD, ROBERT N. *Manufacturing Structure and Pattern of the South Bend–Mishawaka Area*
June, 1954. 224 pp. 6 folded inserts. 2 maps in pocket. (out of print)

37. SISCO, PAUL HARDEMAN. *The Retail Function of Memphis*
August, 1954. 176 pp. 2 folded inserts.

38. VAN DONGEN, IRENE S. *The British East African Transport Complex*
December, 1954. 184 pp. 3 maps in pocket.

39. FRIEDMANN, JOHN R. P. *The Spatial Structure of Economic Development in the Tennessee Valley*
March, 1955. 204 pp.
(Published jointly as Research Paper No. 1, Program of Education and Research in Planning, The University of Chicago.)

40. GROTEWOLD, ANDREAS. *Regional Changes in Corn Production in the United States from 1909 to 1949*
June, 1955. 88 pp.

41. BJORKLUND, E. M. *Focus on Adelaide—Functional Organization of the Adelaide Region, Australia*
December, 1955. 144 pp. 2 folded inserts. 1 map in pocket.

42. FORD, ROBERT N. *A Resource Use Analysis and Evaluation of the Everglades Agricultural Area*
June, 1956. 128 pp. 1 folded insert.

43. CHRISTENSEN, DAVID E. *Rural Occupance in Transition: Sumter and Lee Counties, Georgia*
June, 1956. 172 pp.

44. GUZMÁN, LOUIS E. *Farming and Farmlands in Panama*
December, 1956. 148 pp.

45. ZADROZNY, MITCHELL G. *Water Utilization in the Middle Mississippi Valley*
December, 1956. 132 pp.

46. AHMED, G. MUNIR. *Manufacturing Structure and Pattern of Waukegan–North Chicago*
February, 1957. 132 pp.

47. RANDALL, DARRELL. *Factors of Economic Development and the Okovango Delta*
December, 1956. 282 pp.
(Published jointly as Research Paper No. 3, Program of Education and Research in Planning, The University of Chicago.)

48. BOXER, BARUCH. *Israeli Shipping and Foreign Trade*
April, 1957. 176 pp.

49. MAYER, HAROLD M. *The Port of Chicago and the St. Lawrence Seaway*
May, 1957. 304 pp. 2 folded maps. Cloth $5.00. University of Chicago Press

50. PATTISON, WILLIAM D. *Beginnings of the American Rectangular Land Survey System, 1784-1800*
December, 1957. 260 pp.

51. BROWN, ROBERT HAROLD. *Political Areal-Functional Organization: With Special Reference to St. Cloud, Minnesota*
December, 1957. 130 pp.

52. BEYER, JACQUELYN. *Integration of Grazing and Crop Agriculture: Resources Management Problems in the Uncompahgre Valley Irrigation Project*
December, 1957. 131 pp.

53. ACKERMAN, EDWARD A. *Geography as a Fundamental Research Discipline*
July, 1958. 40 pp. $1.00

54. AL-KHASHAB, WAFIQ HUSSAIN. *The Water Budget of the Tigris and Euphrates Basin*
December, 1958. 113 pp.

55. LARIMORE, ANN EVANS. *The Alien Town: Patterns of Settlement in Busoga, Uganda*
August, 1958. 210 pp.

56. MURPHY, FRANCIS C. *Regulating Flood-Plain Development*
November, 1958. 216 pp.

57. WHITE, GILBERT F., *et al*. *Changes in Urban Occupance of Flood Plains in the United States*
November, 1958. 256 pp.

58. COLBY, MARY MC RAE. *The Geographic Structure of Southeastern North Carolina*
December, 1958. 242 pp.

59. MEGEE, MARY CATHERINE. *Monterrey, Mexico: Internal Patterns and External Relations*
December, 1958. 122 pp.

60. WEBER, DICKINSON. *A Comparison of Two Oil City Business Centers (Odessa-Midland, Texas)*
November, 1958. 256 pp.

61. PLATT, ROBERT S. *Field Study in American Geography*
July, 1959. 408 pp.

30-103

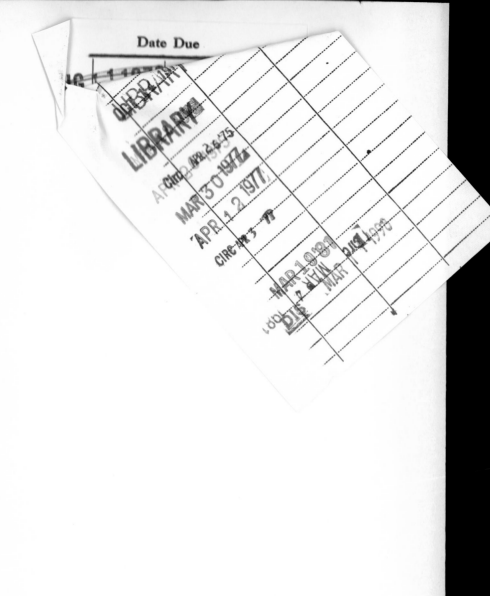